STORM
IN A
TEA CUP

DIARY OF AN INPATIENT

EMMA DAVID

The Book Guild Ltd

First published in Great Britain in 2020 by
The Book Guild Ltd
9 Priory Business Park
Wistow Road, Kibworth
Leicestershire, LE8 0RX
Freephone: 0800 999 2982
www.bookguild.co.uk
Email: info@bookguild.co.uk
Twitter: @bookguild

Typeset in Garamond Premier Pro

Printed and bound in Great Britain by 4edge Limited

ISBN 978 1913551 056

British Library Cataloguing in Publication Data.
A catalogue record for this book is available from the British Library.

For everyone who didn't make it.

"At the going down of the sun and in the morning,
We will remember them."

LAURENCE BINYON, FOR THE FALLEN

Author's Note

This book contains my truth,
my version of things,
as they happened and as I felt them.
Names have been changed to protect those who couldn't consent,
and those who woudn't want to.

It's important you remember it is subjective.

We are all the villain in someone's story.

Contents

1

WELCOME TO THE NUTHOUSE

'You need a rest.'
'Well, I'll go home, take a nap.'
'No. You need to go somewhere where you can get a genuine
rest. And you're very lucky. The best place for someone like
you… is less than half an hour from here.'
'You don't mean Claymore?'

Girl, Interrupted

'Welcome to the Henshaw hospital.' I dated a guy once, Ian,
who was six foot three. He used to have to bend down to kiss
me and equally I'd have to go up on my tiptoes to reach his lips,
but the man who was standing in front of me now would have
towered over even Ian; he was a giant. Plus he was big, really
big, maybe thirty or forty stone. He extended his hand for me
to shake it.

'I'm Lyle.' His palm was hot and sticky against my cold skin.

'Hi, I'm Emma.' I pulled my hand away and subtly wiped
it on my jeans. A door a few feet away that had the words
'9/15' written on it squeaked open and an attractive man with
shoulder-length black hair stepped out.

'Emma?' I nodded. 'Hello, I'm Grant – the lead therapist here. Has Lyle explained the situation to you?' I shook my head and caught what I thought was a disapproving look at Lyle from Grant. 'Ah. Okay, well come in and we can go through it.'

I assumed the 9/15 must be Grant's office and followed him in behind Lyle. Oh, how wrong I was. The small office that I had envisioned walking into was a huge hall. Chairs lined the walls, maybe sixty or seventy altogether, and in them sat dozens of people, all quiet, all staring at me. I immediately noticed Susie who had been in my initial meeting a couple of weeks ago and quickly sat next to her. I darted my eyes around; were these patients? Therapists? They were all dressed in regular clothes, no badges, no notebooks. Why were they all staring at me? What was this? Panic started to course through my body, my chest getting tight. Grant had taken a seat in the middle of them all; he cleared his throat purposefully.

'So welcome, Emma,' he paused. 'We have a problem this morning because you're late joining us, we were expecting you at nine.' I glanced up at the round clock that was sitting on the wall behind him which read 9:36.

'I'm really sorry, the bus didn't show up so I got a cab, I got here as fast as I could.' Grant smiled but clearly didn't care what my excuse was.

'Well, unfortunately being late for meetings is a rule break here. And considering this is your first day, the question of whether your being late is actually a larger statement about your attitude to therapy has been brought up and discussed in your absence.' He paused. 'And what we do at the Henshaw in the event of a serious decision having to be made is take a vote. So that's what we're going to have to do to see if you can stay with us today.'

I was dumbstruck. Stay with you? *Stay with you?* This is a nuthouse, yes? I was here because I had to be! I was sent here! It's not like I was out for an inner-city hike in this white-trash shit hole of a town in south London and thought, *Oh, I know, I'll wander into that decrepit-looking psychiatric hospital and see if I can't bed down for the night.* And what was that little comment about my attitude to therapy? This was already way too overwhelming. I shrugged my shoulders, the irritation starting to show.

'Sure, whatever.'

Grant smiled again. 'Okay, all those in favour of Emma being able to stay raise your hands.' The majority of people in the room raised their hands and to my surprise I felt a little flutter of something resembling relief.

'Good. Those in favour of her not being able to stay?'

Two people shot up their hands. I couldn't tell if they were staff or patients but I made a note of their faces.

'And undecided.'

Someone who seemed to be a therapist put up his hand, followed by a teary-eyed girl. As she raised her arm I saw one of her hands was missing. I looked away quickly, but again, faces noted. Grant turned back to me.

'Well then! It looks like you're staying, Emma.'

*

'I'll carry that.' A twenty-something man with dark hair winked at me from behind his glasses as he took my small suitcase out of my hands. 'I'm Irfan, one of the patients. I'm going to be showing you around, well, you and the others,' he motioned with his head to a group of women walking towards us. Susie was one of them; she threw her arms around me.

'Em! I'm so glad to see you!' She lowered her voice. 'And glad that you got through that stupid vote.' She squeezed my shoulder as she let me go – I wasn't really a fan of the impromptu touching from an almost-stranger, but Susie seemed so sweet and Christ knows I needed an ally in this place. Behind her appeared a short black woman with a purple mohican, bright red poncho and a huge grin.

'Hey, I'm Candace! I'm new too!' I smiled back at her but before I could answer the third woman spoke.

'And I am *not* new. My name is Augusta. I'll be taking you on the tour with Irfan. Right, let's go.' She turned around, her black mane of hair whipping behind her. I looked at Irfan who chuckled and started after her like an obedient dog. Augusta spoke with a thick Russian accent and in short, sharp, robotic sentences. 'So you have the visitors' room first; if someone comes and you want to spend time with them you go in there; they are not allowed to wander around the hospital.' She pointed to a staircase. 'Up there is the art room, strictly out of bounds for patients unattended.'

'What if I just want to sit and listen to music, can I go in then?' asked Candace.

Augusta snorted. 'No, of course not. There are sharps in there, they don't want us chopping our limbs off when no one's looking.' I stifled a laugh. 'Nine fifteen you already saw – that's for meetings or socialising.' She motioned to a set of wooden doors on our left. 'Gardening and maintenance over there, the pool room is back there also.' She walked over to a dimly lit hallway leading to a conservatory. 'Kitchen and dining room. There's a payphone through there if you actually have anyone you need to call.'

We climbed another flight of stairs and walked through a long hallway of doors with numbers on them. 'My room, Irfan's room, Chrissie's room, Mike's room, Lyle's room, Megan's room.' She reeled off several more names without pausing for breath. 'This is the meds room and over there is the staffroom – obviously strictly no access to patients. Candace and Susie, these are your rooms.' She pointed to two doors side by side numbered nine and ten. 'Irfan can go through the rest. Emma, your room is upstairs, come with me.'

WELCOME TO THE NUTHOUSE

I thanked Irfan and took my case from him, quickly padding down the hall after her – now who was the obedient dog? – but she had that about her: when she spoke I felt like I had to jump to attention.

Augusta pushed open door number twenty-six, right next to the art room. I walked in and put down my bag. 'Okay, so I need to check your suitcase.' I knelt down and opened it. Augusta rather coyly looked through a few items of clothes. She glimpsed into my toiletry bag and then stood up and headed for the door. 'Fine. Only bin the mouthwash or hide it.' I looked down at the bottle of blue liquid.

'Why?'

Augusta had already started to walk away but called back over her shoulder. 'In case you drink it, Emma.'

Oh dear, was this place really going to reduce me to drinking mouthwash?

I waited for her footsteps to disappear down the hallway and plonked myself down on the thin mattress, the bed squeaking loudly under my weight. Alone at last. I exhaled and looked around the little box room. Yellow walls. A red chair. A basin with a dripping tap. A window with an industrial-sized lock on it. So here I was then, home.

I lasted about half an hour in the room before I fled. I didn't even unpack. No one saw me slip out and the magnetic locked doors were easy enough to get past. Luckily, several of my friends lived in the area and I knew it well, so off I went, down to the local park where I rolled myself a joint. And here I was, first day of my last chance and getting stoned on my own. I felt guilty but equally I had had a massive overdose of reality, or something claiming to resemble it, and I needed a quick and easy escape. I say 'reality' but honestly it felt more like I had walked into an episode of *Eerie, Indiana*; all I needed was for those fat Tupperware twins to make an appearance and I'd be sure I was stuck in some sort of drug psychosis, one toke over the line. How had I ended up here? What was I doing? Could I really stay in that place, with those weird people, drinking my mouthwash like some kind of desperate lunatic? I lay back on the grass and closed my eyes.

The skunk-induced paranoia of traipsing back into the hospital wasn't fun. With more than slight difficulty I stumbled back into the 9/15 room. I saw them all from the driveway as I approached and in as sober a way as possible, mouthed 'sorry' as I came through the glass doors and took the seat closest to me. Unfortunately I'd sat right next to a girl called Stevie who was the main focus of the meeting. I kept my eyes on the floor for a while, hoping that the smell of draw clinging to my clothes wasn't wafting over to her or anyone else. After a few minutes I gathered the courage to glance up at her red eyes, crooked smirk, tapping foot and realised she was more fucked than I could ever hope to have been. It came to light that this was what the meeting was about – they were all accusing her of being on drugs – and she clearly was, but I didn't feel in a position to judge and just felt sorry for her as around thirty sets of eyes burned into her, asking over and over again, 'What have you taken?'

*

The meeting went on for what seemed like forever, everyone accusing Stevie, and Stevie denying it. She spent the whole time telling them all they were arseholes that didn't want her there and that this was just an excuse to get her kicked out. I spent the whole time hoping my dry mouth wouldn't result in my lips being welded shut for all eternity. Finally, at approaching 11pm, it was called off. Throughout the meeting I'd established that there were only two night staff there in the evenings and they weren't able to reach much of a resolve over the bickering and name-calling – only that Stevie must go to her room and stay there on 'seclusion'. The room dispersed and as the staff began their night rounds I scampered quickly back up to room twenty-six.

I sat there in the dark listening to the drip, drip, drip of the tap for what felt like a lifetime, trying not to breathe in the stench of disinfectant that wafted around me. I felt my phone vibrating in my pocket: it was Landon. I'd met him through friends a few years earlier and had always felt something towards him although I'd never acted on it.

'Hello?'

'Em, it's Lan. How's the madhouse?' Straight to the point then.

'They vote here! And I'm probably going to be drinking my mouthwash pretty soon.' He tried not to laugh but I heard a giggle. 'How are you, Lan?'

There was a second of silence. 'I miss you! Do you want to come round this week? If you're allowed out?'

I smiled and hoped he couldn't tell in my voice. 'Yeah, that would be really nice.'

'Okay, good. I've got to go, just a quick one to say hi. Keep your head up, Em. And text me, yeah?'

'Yeah.'

For the first time in what felt like forever I was tired; this had all been so much to take in, so despite the two-inch-thick mattress, the smell and the dripping tap, I felt myself slip into blissful unconsciousness.

2

PASS ME THE KOOL-AID

"Some are born mad, some achieve madness,
and some have madness thrust upon 'em."

— EMILIE AUTUMN, *The Asylum for Wayward Victorian Girls*

I woke up to the sunlight glaring through the paper-thin, might-as-well-have-not-been-there curtains, confused for a second as to where I was before the reality smashed back in me like a double-decker bus. Willing myself to get up, I found my way to the showers. Carefully stepping into the brown-stained enamel bathtub, I tentatively switched on the water. Nothing. I looked up at the dripping shower head and resorted to clasping my hands together to collect enough water to wash my face and not much else – the idea of a refreshing shower was clearly out of the question. I admitted defeat after a few minutes and got out. Wrapped in my dressing gown I opened the door and peered down the dark corridor to make sure no one was around and quickly rushed back to my room. I hadn't seen a single soul on that floor and was starting to wonder if I was the only one up there. I did my make-up as always: black eyeliner, mascara, foundation. Brushing my hair and pulling on my uniform black hoodie and jeans I reluctantly started to make my way downstairs for the morning meeting. The hospital felt cold and sinister; as I walked through the empty art room I felt like there were people watching me – you know that feeling? When you can't help but look behind you, certain someone's there, but when you turn around there's no one? That was what I felt constantly, in every room, like I was being watched. It smelt, too, old, like mothballs, like no one had opened a window in the place for fifty years. I had read about it before I had got here, of course; it was originally opened way back in the sixties to help World War II veterans with PTSD and then progressed to treating various other mental health problems. It was the first British hospital to 'use a patient-oriented approach to the treatment of psychopathic disorders'; in other words who else was better to understand the crazies than a bunch of crazies? They called it a 'therapeutic community' rather than a psychiatric hospital, and they didn't like psychotropic drugs here. Psychotropic means Sertraline, Xanax, Prozac, Citalopram, Lorazepam, or in other words anything that has the ability to alter one's mood; medication used for anxiety and depression will usually fall under this bracket. Psychotropic equals a yummy brain pick 'n' mix. This rule, more than any of the others, worried me massively, and was what I protested about most when my therapist said she was referring me. I had been on Prozac for four years (Citalopram before that), and I still felt like shit. Taking away my already wavering safety net seemed like a ridiculous idea... which is why I decided I'd just hide a stash of pills in my bag and continue to take them in secret.

Four flights of stairs later and I pushed open a heavy set of double doors that led to the kitchen. Susie, Augusta and a few others were sitting around the long wooden communal table drinking tea and eating toast; no one looked up or even seemed to notice me, it was like I was invisible. I walked through the room unseen, a ghost amongst ghosts.

I heaved open another set of doors and was back in the long beige corridor that led to the 9/15. On my right was a little room I hadn't noticed the day before with a sign on it that said 'Stores'. As I turned the handle and walked in I felt my senses simultaneously fill with joy and dread; it was stocked floor to ceiling with crisps, chocolate, sweets, fizzy drinks, biscuits… it was a binge-eater's paradise and an anorexic's worst nightmare; I quickly closed the door and headed for the next room.

The 9/15 was completely empty; I looked around deciding which chair was the safest bet and chose the one closest to the exit. Irfan was standing outside with a couple of patients, all smoking; he waved at me through the glass, a slight look of disappointment on his face when I didn't wave back. I had only been sitting down for a minute before I heard a cheery 'Morning!' Candace flopped heavily down next to me, still wearing her red poncho from the day before. She turned to me.

'So, how was your first night? Did you sleep?'

I wondered if she had a suitcase full of red ponchos; maybe there were other colours too that she would slowly introduce… maybe the colours were mood-based… like a mood ring for your whole body? I realised I hadn't answered her.

'Sorry, yeah I did actually. You?'

'Nah, not a wink. I listened to music and thought about how much effort it would take to break in to the meds room.' She chuckled to herself as if there were more to the joke that she hadn't said out loud.

By 9:05 the room was full with all the patients, most still in their pyjamas. I counted fifteen altogether, not including me. Ten women and five men. No one was really talking to each other, most just seemed to stare into space, distracted by their own thoughts. With the exception of Susie and her perfectly straight blonde bob and pristinely applied make-up, none of the other women looked like they'd even brushed their hair. I suddenly felt over-groomed... was there such a thing? Was I too turned out for being in a hospital? Should I have left out the eyeliner? Probably.

Pretty soon the seemingly endless number of therapists began to file in. Grant took up the main chair again and began by saying that Stevie (druggie Stevie from the night before) had walked out of the hospital and no one knew where she was, and that she hadn't called or told anyone where she was going. It was curious to me that no one seemed particularly concerned by this news; maybe it was something she did often. As if he'd read my mind, Lyle said, 'Well, that's nothing new.'

'Innit,' said the man sitting next to Lyle. He went on, 'Why is she being allowed to stay here, Grant?'

Grant clasped his hands together. 'Well, I think that's a discussion for everyone, Mike. How does everyone feel about Stevie's attitude to her treatment? Do we feel she's committed?'

The room fell silent for a moment until the girl with one hand spoke. 'I don't think she is,' she said looking demurely at the floor.

'Go on, Esther,' prompted Grant, 'what do you mean?'

'She doesn't want to get better. I think she treats this place like a hotel, and what's worse...' she lowered her voice as if she were afraid of Stevie hearing, 'she's always on drugs.'

Grant nodded along. 'Well, if this is how the majority feels, we will have to put Stevie on a vote and decide whether or not the Henshaw is the best place for her.'

The other therapists made little 'mhmm' noises in agreement. The best place for her? Can they kick her out then? Vote her out? God, this place felt like a really skewed version of *The X Factor*: if your performance wasn't up to par they'd just vote you out. And then what? Where would she go?

Once they'd finished talking about Stevie, the meeting quickly descended into a huge argument between a patient called Gareth and most of the other patients, or 'residents' as everyone seemed to refer to them. Gareth's issue was that Susie looked like his mother. His murdered mother. All at once the whole room broke out in a swell of name-calling and shouting, the main voices being those of Gareth and Mike. Mike was in his forties; at six foot two, he and his belly towered above me and most other people. He wasn't unattractive, with thick brown hair and dark eyes, but his face screamed that he had spent several decades drinking and doing drugs and it had aged him. His cockney voice boomed over everyone.

'Well, mate, I'm not being funny, but what do you expect her to do? She can't change her face, can she?'

Gareth, with his wispy blond moustache and blue eyes, was half the size of Mike; although around the same age, his voice sounded high-pitched in comparison. 'I'm not saying that, Mike, I'm just saying it's triggered me, okay? It's brought everything back...' He looked down as if he were trying to hold back tears.

Susie seemed mortified, and softly said, 'I'm really sorry, Gareth, I... I don't know what to do?'

Before Gareth could answer, Mike laughed, a strange noise somewhere between bewilderment and anger. 'You don't have to do anything! It's not your problem darlin', it's his!' he pointed aggressively at Gareth.

'Mike,' said one of the female therapists gently, 'I think we need to try and understand what Gareth needs from us and how best we can support him.'

'Support him?!' Mike snorted into his mug of black coffee. 'Oh do me a favour!'

'I don't think that's particularly helpful, Mike,' said Grant, chiming in again. It carried on like that for a while, this back and forth with no resolve – until, after about forty minutes, Susie burst into tears and ran out of the room followed by Augusta and Esther. Of course, Susie's departure didn't help matters; they all kept shouting and arguing with each other regardless.

*

'I hear you've all had a very difficult morning,' said a mousey-haired woman in a beige cardigan as she stood in front of us in the art room. There were a few grunts but no one responded. 'And we have some new faces joining us today. For those of you who don't know, my name is Blanche, I run the art therapy here.' She smiled at Susie and me.

The art group was run by two therapists, Blanche and Mona. The latter of the two took less of an active role in the sessions, sitting more in the background and from what I could gather silently judging us all with quiet disapproval. Every time I looked at Mona she did a strange smile back at me that seemed to say, 'I'm watching you'; it made me feel incredibly uneasy.

The residents were split into two groups for art, so after seemingly escaping the drama of the 9/15 I found myself yet again in a room with Susie, Gareth and the 'murdered mother' scenario.

I had always been uncomfortable with men crying – my father never really had a wide range of emotions, he was generally a laid-back man whom I had never once in my life seen cry. Iraqi-born, he had come to England when he was in his twenties and by that point the 'strong men don't cry' Middle Eastern imprint was firmly stamped into him. Gareth, sitting there opposite me in the art room with tears rolling down his face, should not have made me feel as on edge as he did, but if you've never seen a three-headed giraffe before you're going to stare at it; Gareth was my three-headed giraffe. Listening to him describing his emotions in epic depth as he snotted all over himself made me squirm uncomfortably in my chair.

Gareth told us that he had watched his father murder his mother in a violent and gruesome way. 'She pushed me and my brother through the window... we got out... she started climbing through but he grabbed her from behind and pulled her back in... he had the hammer in his hand... I wanted to go back but I couldn't... I couldn't...' He began to wail uncontrollably. I looked around the room, my eyes fixed on Blanche, who was now also weeping. Perhaps this gesture should have prompted me to warm to her, but instead it sent a wave of panic through me. Why was she crying? Why wasn't she saying something soothing and helpful? Gareth's sobs continued, interspersed with the odd gory detail of later seeing his mother with her crushed skull on the mortuary slab. I glanced at the other patients, a look of boredom painted across some of their faces; others looked mildly irritated – I wondered how many times they had listened to this macabre tale? A part of me felt it was just being told again for the benefit of Susie and me, like a rerun everyone was sick of watching. I kept silent and stony-faced throughout the session. It was as graphic as any horror film could get and there I was, not even twenty-four hours in, listening to the uncensored version of it; how the hell was this supposed to help me?

After art came 'sports and social'. Candace and Gareth didn't bother to get off the sofa or stop watching *Jeremy Kyle*, so I followed suit, snuggling into the warm armchair I had decided was mine from now on. There was no way in hell I was doing 'sports' and the social aspect didn't exactly fill me with joy either. I got the distinct impression that the patients here had their cliques and didn't trust newcomers. I found most of them unwelcoming and frosty, Gareth and Irfan being the only exception to this rule. I peeled myself off the chair at two o'clock to go and track down a nurse and get my medication while I still had the chance before they 'weaned' me off it for good, or at least tried to.

Hank was a nurse who I'd seen earlier in the 9/15. He stood behind the counter of the medication room and point-blank refused to give me my pills. He scrunched up his face. 'No. You're too late for your medication. Meds are before 10am.'

I tried to keep my tone level. 'But I didn't know, it's only my first day.'

He looked away sternly. 'Well then you'll learn by your second day hopefully.'

I had a banging headache; the 9/15 followed by art and now this was making my temples throb as if my brain were on fire. 'Can I get something for my head at least? I've got a headache.'

He paused, looking at me cautiously, and as if taking a big risk he sighed and said, 'You can have a paracetamol. But just one. And you have it here, in front of me.' He handed me the pathetic-looking little white pill and a cup of water, nodding for me to take it.

Was I some sort of reprobate that couldn't be trusted to take a tablet by myself? What did he think I was going to do, crush it up and sell it to the other patients? I swallowed the pill with a sip of water.

'Open,' he said, peering over the counter at me like I was a science experiment. I opened my mouth to show him. Satisfied, he turned away and carried on with whatever he was doing before I had appeared. With anger coursing through my body I went back to my room and rummaged through my bag until I found the supply of Prozac I had brought in should such an event take place. I popped two pills out of their little foil pockets and glugged them down with water from the tap. *Fuck you, Hank, and fuck your rules.*

*

Five o'clock eventually rolled around as I sat in my armchair watching all the therapists, doctors and nurses leave for the day through the glass doors and the two night staff come in.

Candace asked if I wanted to go and get a coffee with her. The idea of getting out of the hospital appealed greatly to me, so I happily agreed. We managed to persuade Susie into tagging along. I got the feeling she wasn't used to going out on her own much, even just for a coffee. As we walked down the road into the town centre the three of us giggled nervously.

'God, what have we got ourselves into?' said Susie as we crossed the main road towards the shops.

Candace shook her head. 'I don't know. They're all completely mad, aren't they? Like, actually mad! If I have to vote one more time I'm going to lose it, I mean seriously, who came up with this shit?' Susie and I laughed as Candace continued to rant about how ludicrous the rules at the Henshaw were.

The cafe was closed and so we found ourselves in the local pub. Candace and Susie got club sandwiches and washed them down with a couple of shots of a worrying-looking green liquid, which must have been undoubtedly, I thought, against the Henshaw's rules. I sat sipping my Diet Coke as they ate.

'Do you want half of my sandwich, Em?' Susie held the six-layer chicken and bacon monstrosity out towards me.

I shook my head. 'No, thanks, I'm not hungry.' I hoped they couldn't hear my stomach growling over the music. I learned that Candace was thirty-two, single and had lived in London all her life. She was a musician, a singer, and although she didn't have a nine-to-five job she would gig in bars with her band. She seemed such a happy little soul, I didn't really understand why she was in hospital. Susie was a different story altogether. She was married with two kids, a boy and girl. Her husband Carl was abusive, so much so that her ten-year-old son had severe PTSD and was in therapy himself, as was her fourteen-year-old daughter. They lived somewhere outside the city in a little town where no one asked questions about Susie's frequent black eyes and arm slings. Usually I would have judged someone in that situation, purely for staying in it with the children, but Susie was so visibly worn down and defeated. She shook constantly, her hands trembling, her eyes rarely leaving the ground… perhaps the Henshaw was what she needed to get some perspective, I could only hope.

We got back to the hospital after dark. The other patients had been fed, watered and were either watching television in the 9/15 or, I assumed, back up in their rooms.

*

On our tour I had noticed a small room, 'the blue room' as it was coined by the other residents due to the blue walls, blue sofa and large fish tank containing lots of neon tetras and various other tropical fish. It had a television in it, which was good enough for me, so I went and hid in there hoping to be left alone. However, the light under the door gave me away and after ten minutes of being in blissful silence I heard it creak open. It was Gareth.

'Hiya, mind if I join you?'

I wanted to say, *Yes I do mind. Yes please leave me alone so I can try to digest the fact I'm sitting in this nuthouse at twenty-one wondering what the fuck I'm doing here.*

'Sure.' I attempted a smile. He was so short his feet dangled above the floor of the sofa. It was quiet for a minute.

'So, how are you settling in?'

I was tired. Too tired to lie, too frustrated to twist the truth and censor it for him, especially as he had so willingly shared with me his mother's murder, whether it was part of some deliberate initiation or not.

17

'Shitty, to be honest. It's very insular here. Everyone keeps to themselves, they're kind of… unfriendly.' The truth eased out of me like a sigh.

'Well, be careful,' said Gareth warily eyeing the door as if someone were listening outside it. 'They won't like you hanging out with Susie and Candace; new patients are supposed to mingle, not stay together in a group. It's collusive.' The use of 'collusive' annoyed me; he said it like a child repeats a new word that they've just learned. I felt instantly irritated by him.

'How can I mingle when everyone ignores me, Gareth?' He didn't have an answer, just nodded sympathetically and swung his feet above the floor.

3

MIND WHERE YOU WALK

"I had no idea that the simple act of running a sharp blade across my wrist would change everything so completely. I wasn't after happiness anymore. I just wanted to survive."

— VICTORIA LEATHAM, *Bloodletting: A Memoir of Secrets, Self-Harm, and Survival*

'Come on, follow me.' Irfan was smiling.

'But, we'll get in trouble won't we?' I didn't want to follow him, but I didn't want to be standing outside in the freezing cold under the pretence of 'gardening and maintenance'. I hadn't eaten anything since the previous morning and I was starting to feel weak and dizzy.

'It's fine, just trust me.' I didn't trust him in the slightest but I followed him anyway. He led me to the pool room where a few other residents were also hiding from having to do 'leaf raking' on a storm-threatening day in late September.

I watched Augusta and Irfan play pool as a thin, pretty, bird-like girl came and sat next to me.

'I'm Chrissie, we met but you probably don't remember.'

I didn't remember. 'Hi, I'm Emma.'

'Yeah I know,' she said quickly, barely skipping a beat. 'How are you finding it here? I noticed you didn't get to sample dinner last night, were you out?' She eyed me curiously; something about it made me uncomfortable.

'Yeah, I went out with Susie and Candace, ate with them.'

'Well,' she said, relaxing into the chair, 'the food here is awful so I don't blame you. It's so greasy... not to mention fattening.' She scrunched up her face and made a disgusted sound, 'Ugh!' It felt like an invitation to me, like her comment had a multilayered meaning.

I wanted to test the waters and slowly said, 'Well, I've been on a diet and I don't want to wreck it by eating unhealthy foods. So I will probably just cook for myself.' I regretted my choice of words instantly but it was too late and her eyes flashed, meeting mine with a look of excitement.

'They'll put you on SIEs for that.'

'What's SIEs?' I asked, beginning to panic slightly.

She sat up in the chair, flicking her long chestnut hair back over her shoulder.

'Sleeping in extension. It basically means you get in trouble then put on a vote to see if you can stay the night.' She started to get up. 'You better not tell anyone else you're dieting.'

I stammered 'W... Well, it's not dieting, just healthy eating.'

She smirked, 'Sure. Healthy eating, dieting, starving, purging, binging, whatever.'

I tried desperately to compose myself and relax my furrowed brow but she floated out of the room without looking back.

*

Half an hour later I was still simmering with anxiety over my interaction with Chrissie but it was time for the 'discussion' part of gardening and maintenance, in which the therapists Cath and

Pierre were asking how people were feeling about going home for the weekend. We sat in a large semicircle, the tinge of the conservatory glass colouring the room a murky green as the sun began to set outside. Everyone remained silent until Augusta spoke.

'I was wondering how Chrissie was feeling about going home for the first time?'

All eyes turned to Chrissie.

'Okay! Nervous, I suppose.'

'Go on, Chrissie. What makes you nervous?' prompted Cath gently.

'Well, it's just that Derek is really strict about bedtimes.' There was a short silence.

'What do you mean, "strict"?' asked Irfan, his knee bouncing up and down hypnotically.

'Uh, well, just that he insists on tucking me in and reading me a bedtime story. And sometimes if I've had a bad day...' she paused, drawing in a deep breath, 'it's non-negotiable and I have to sleep in their room.' Derek was apparently the vicar she lived with along with his wife Barb. Chrissie's mother had been diagnosed with Munchausen's syndrome when Chrissie was a child and so she had been removed from her care and had been living with Derek and Barb since she was fourteen; she was now the same age as me. I tried as best I could to mask the horror that spread across my face the more she talked about Derek and his 'bedtime' routines, running her a bath, choosing her nightclothes.

'That's fucking disgusting,' muttered a man's voice from the other side of the room. It was Mike of course. Chrissie flinched, curling up in her plastic chair, and disappearing into her oversized jumper.

'That's helpful, Mike,' quipped Augusta.

'Well it is. We all know it is. We're just not saying it. And I for one...' he rose to his feet, 'am not staying to hear it.' The therapists pleaded with him to stay as he stormed out of the room slamming the door behind him; the glass shook as if it might shatter with the force.

Jess looked about my age, if not a bit younger. She was forthright and direct and it made me wary of her; whenever she spoke the whole room seemed to sit still. 'Does he touch you, Chrissie?' she asked, fiddling with her nose ring.

'Well,' Chrissie's already rosy cheeks began to grow redder, 'he tucks me in, if that's what you mean.'

Jess said it again with a slight irritability growing in her voice. 'But does he *touch* you?'

Chrissie suddenly erupted, 'No! No of course he doesn't. He wouldn't. Derek loves me, he cares about me and he looks after me. Why would you say that?'

Jess looked at the floor; she clearly wanted to say more but was choosing to hold her tongue. A minute or so passed. Cath looked at her watch and, breaking the now heavy sinking silence in the room, said, 'It's time, guys, session over.'

Saturday morning passed quickly. The 9/15 was less formal, with only a few staff present for it, and I once again avoided talking. I couldn't wait to get out of there; the last few days had felt like an eternity. I had a day planned in Camden with one of my closest friends, Cara: Cara, who no doubt would have a joint waiting for me and, most desirable of all, freedom.

I rushed upstairs to get my bag, calling Cara as I bolted down the drive to the bus stop. When she answered the flatness in her voice screamed down the line to me that my day was not going to go according to plan.

'I've been doing coke all night and I can't move, you can come and lie on my bed later if you want?'

I wanted to scream at her that I had been looking forward to this all week. That she knew I only had one day out of the hospital and how could she be so selfish? But I didn't. I clenched my teeth together and said I'd call her later, hanging up with no intention of speaking to her again that day. My fury had nowhere to go. So I took it back to my room and fell asleep with it, missing out on the rest of the day.

*

I woke up to a knock on my door. 'Emma, there's a meeting.' I recognised Lyle's voice.

'Okay, coming.' I put on my trainers and went down to the 9/15.

Stevie was back and again being accused of being inebriated. 'You've clearly taken something, love,' said Gareth as he sat perched across from her on one of the sofas, his little feet swinging above the floor.

'I haven't,' came her belligerent response.

'Get off it, Stevie, you're fucked.' Mike folded his arms over his belly as he half smirked at her, goading, waiting for a response.

'Stevie, I think it would be best if you just owned up to it.' Augusta attempted to force a smile; it felt as if this was as close to sympathetic as she could get.

'I haven't touched anything so why don't you all just get off my fucking back?'

Fiona, who I knew was to be my 'small' group therapist (although I hadn't attended one of these sessions yet), began to speak. 'Stevie, I think everyone here is very concerned for you right now, if you could try to be honest—' but Stevie cut her off.

'Why the fuck would I be honest with you lot? You don't give a shit about me.' She got up and walked out of the 9/15 slamming the door behind her.

The room fell quiet after that until Fiona spoke again. 'Chrissie, I heard that you have something you want to talk about?'

Chrissie was looking at the floor. 'Yes,' came her lilting, childlike voice. 'I'm sorry, but I thought you should all know I've been making myself sick again. I did it after breakfast this morning and after dinner last night.'

'What was happening for you to do that, Chrissie?' asked Louise, a severely anorexic patient whose age I wasn't sure of; the years of not eating had done extreme things to her figure – she looked like a tiny doll, the development of her body frozen in time, and she spoke too softly, like a little girl who was afraid of her own voice.

Chrissie shrugged her shoulders. 'I just felt so out of control, everything felt like too much to handle. I had felt really upset after gardening and maintenance.' Chrissie lifted her eyes off the floor for a second to shoot a look at Jess before going on. 'I couldn't stop myself. I binged. I binged on everything I could find. I ate until I felt like I was going to burst… and then before I knew it I was making myself sick.'

I wondered why anyone would confess to such a thing and listened as she got read her SIEs. Listening to Chrissie describe making herself sick triggered me horribly. I hadn't done it for a few months and it was not something I wished to return to or even hear about. I wanted to stick my fingers in my ears as she spoke but I had no choice but to listen, thinking about the fact that I had *not* thrown up this weekend, which in my mind seemed to explain why she was so thin and pretty and I was such an obese, ugly pig. I resolved not to eat for the day, it seemed like the only solution and a fitting punishment.

*

The revelations of Chrissie's bulimia had sparked off something in me and I wanted to cut. After the meeting I stood alone in the kitchen, motionless, blank, staring at one of the kitchen knives.

It had a green handle and a wide blade. I couldn't hear anyone outside; if I was quick I could use it. No one would know. Just as I took a step forward the door swung open; it was Mike.

'All right, mate?' I nodded and scurried past him out of the kitchen and up to my bedroom. I threw myself down on my bed in frustration and picked up my phone. There was a message from Landon.

'So, do you want to meet? xx'

I knew I probably shouldn't leave the hospital – there was art next and then another group after that – but I wanted to see him, and if I stayed here who knew what I might do? I did my make-up, grabbed my bag and snuck out.

I smelled the skunk and heard the dulcet tones of Oasis playing from a phone speaker before I saw Landon, sitting on a bench in the park where we'd arranged to meet.

'Em.' He stood up and kissed my cheek. 'Well, you look good, kid. Come, sit, smoke.'

He took the joint out of his mouth and passed it to me. I took a long drag, tilted my head back and exhaled. 'Thank God for you, Lan.' He laughed. 'It's so good to see you. I was starting to feel weird in there.'

'Weird how?' he asked.

'I don't know… just not myself… It's lonely and everyone is so fucked up!' I passed the joint back.

'Haven't any of the others been to see you yet, babe?' I shook my head, trying to keep my expression neutral. 'I suppose people get side-tracked without meaning to, we're all a bit too caught up in our own bullshit. But, I'm here.' He placed his hand on mine. There was something inside me growing for him; I knew it, I could feel it, but I didn't want it to get in the way so tried my best to ignore the feelings. I crossed my legs under me and turned to face him.

'How are you?'

He pulled his flat cap down over his face and laughed. 'Oh you know, stark raving mad.' He straightened his hat and took another toke. 'They're all freaking out, my mum, my brother. The shrinks are scheming, I can feel it… I think they're going to section me soon. They don't get it.'

'Well, yeah they don't. But you do need to talk to someone, you know that.' I sighed and looked at the joint hanging from his lips – I reached over and took it, took another drag and before I exhaled said, 'This shit isn't helping, and I shouldn't be encouraging it.' I let out a plume of smoke and threw the half-smoked joint on to the grass.

'Hey!'

'Hey nothing, it's not helping, you know that. You need to be careful, Lan.'

He slid over next to me and put his arm around my shoulder. 'I could say the same for you.' He tapped my arm gently. 'How is all that?'

I sighed. 'Can we not, I really don't want to talk about it.' I looked away from him.

'Okay, but I'm here if you do want to.'

I was already feeling stoned and suddenly felt nervous but managed a smile at him. 'Thanks.'

He reached over and picked up the joint that was starting to go out; he blew on the tip, the embers glowing orange again. 'You're special, Em. You're different,' he nudged me playfully with his elbow. 'Must be why we get along!'

We sat there, content in each other's company for a long while after that, listening to music and bitching about life, right up until it was time for me to go back.

I got to the hospital a little after dusk, the tall trees outside the building casting a dark shadow over the place that gave it an ominous, creepy feel. I knocked on the reception door and waited to be buzzed in. Through the glass I saw Stevie propped up in an armchair, a vacant look in her eyes; Blanche and another member of staff whose name I couldn't remember were sitting on either side of her. I stepped inside and quickly noticed small droplets of blood all over the pale green tiled flooring, I followed them with my eyes and they led me to Stevie's arms. She had a t-shirt on and what looked like new bandages on both her wrists. The bandages did little to soak up whatever she'd done to herself and in the few seconds it took me to walk through the room the blood was already soaking through the white material.

'Don't be alarmed Emma,' said Blanche. 'We're just waiting for an ambulance. Some stitches are required. Mind where you walk-' she pointed at the maroon puddle next to my boot. I stepped over it carefully, and began to make my way down the long corridor in the direction of my bedroom.

'That's what this place does to ya!' Stevie called out from behind me, her voice echoing alongside the thud of my footsteps, ricocheting off the walls like some sinister drumbeat.

I hurried through the deserted kitchen and up the endless flights of stairs to my room, collapsing on my bed in a heap. I closed my eyes, listening to the siren call of the ambulance as it arrived to take Stevie away.

*

The first time I cut myself I was twelve. I used a kitchen knife after an argument with my mother. I didn't know anything about self-harm: it was pretty non-existent in the media around that time, my only points of reference being a picture in Marilyn Manson's biography that my best friend Natalie had shown me and a small storyline on a particularly overdramatic teenage soap opera that I would secretly watch huddled around the television as if it were porn. The Internet was still in its early days: a twenty-minute dial tone and then five minutes of searching 'self-injury' and a final five minutes of deleting the browser history before my mother bellowed up the stairs that my half an hour of surfing the World Wide Web was over. I needed to relieve the pressure in my head and cutting myself seemed to work.

Standing in the kitchen that day at twelve, I hadn't realised I was opening a door that would lead to the longest and most profound addiction I would ever face. It would come to define me in ways, become my breathing aid, my living aid, and at times my everything. I went on cutting myself habitually every time I had an emotional reaction I didn't like. If I felt overwhelmed, I would cut. If I felt stupid, upset, irritated, humiliated, I'd cut. In the toilets at school. In the bathroom at home. In my bedroom. On buses. In parks. At friends' houses. It was never-ending and only got worse the older I got. The precursor to my ending up at the Henshaw had not been the years of secret therapy I'd been having since I was fifteen, but rather a suicide attempt followed by a cut that left me in A&E with my sanity being questioned and my arm being stitched closed. My parents knew nothing until I told them I was going into the Henshaw to be treated for 'depression' when I reached twenty-one. I kept them at arm's length, where I was safe from them, and they were safe from me.

My telling them, however, will always stay with me. My mother's response was a scene straight out of *Girl, Interrupted*: Joanna Kerns wailing into her hanky as Susanna asks Dr Melvin if borderline personality disorder is hereditary. As one of my therapists used to say to me, 'Let's park that for now.'

So, fast-forward six months from telling my parents I was going inpatient, leaving my dog, my friends and my strange semblance of a life, and here I was, surrounded by strangers who could potentially be axe-wielding maniacs for all I knew, with no lock on my door and not a clue in hell as to what I was doing there.

4

THE FABERGÉ EGG

"I been silent so long now
it's gonna roar out of me like floodwaters."

— KEN KESEY, *One Flew Over the Cuckoo's Nest*

It was another cold morning in the Henshaw. I looked out of my frosted window onto the damp green grounds below. I leaned out and spotted Mike and Jess smoking beneath me. It was Jess and another man called Brian's last day. I was mixed, glad I wouldn't have to face Jess's confrontational attitude, but equally I was pulled towards her and wished I had got the chance to know her. And with Brian's departure it would leave only four male patients in the hospital, compared to the nine women.

I sat in the 9/15 with everyone, listening to speeches from various therapists and patients about how far they felt the pair had come in their treatment over the last year. I had been told Jess had been severely anorexic when she was first admitted; she was still slim but looked healthy and I couldn't imagine her looking gaunt or ill.

An hour later we were told to gather outside on the patio as they said their goodbyes. As I watched Jess go from person to person hugging them, tears welling in their eyes, I dreaded my turn. What was I supposed to say to her? Thanks for saying I had cool hair? (She had said it when passing me one day in the art room.) It's been good knowing you for a week?

She managed to quash my preconception of her being intimidating as she approached me and carefully said, 'I don't know if you do hugs?'

I didn't particularly want to hug her with everyone watching – some of the therapists seemed to be scrutinising my every move, observing how I was dealing with the intimacy of this moment – but I smiled. 'Yeah, sure.'

We hugged, awkwardly, and as she pulled away she whispered, 'Stick it out, Emma, it'll be worth it.'

I breathed a sigh of relief as the goodbye scene seemed to come to an end, but then, as they both turned and began to walk up the drive towards Brian's Ford, all the patients followed, turning around and excitedly telling me to 'Come on.'

I wasn't sure what was happening and nothing could have prepared me for what was coming. They walked onto the pavement of the main road as Brian got in his car, Jess climbing into the passenger seat – it had been prearranged that he was dropping her off at her new flat only a stone's throw from the grounds. In perfect synchronisation with Brian turning the key in the engine, everyone standing next to me on the pavement began to whoop and cheer – so loudly that people walking near the flats opposite stopped and stared. A couple of kids riding their bikes came to a halt and, at first curious, quickly realised we were 'the hospital nutters' and began to laugh and point. Oh God, the embarrassment.

There was of course a part of me that wanted to join in, that wanted to jump up and down shrieking messages of good luck, but I couldn't. I was rooted to the spot of my humiliation. I could feel the eyes of ten or so psychotherapists on my back and I felt like a child at a tea party. I was supposed to be singing 'Happy Birthday' along with the rest of the children but I didn't want to, even though I could hear the silent criticism of my parents behind me. I clapped my hands together, but even that felt too much, so I just smiled and waved as I whispered to Susie who was standing next to me, 'When will this end?' As the car disappeared around the bend in the road I hurried back inside, relieved it was over, and confused at the niggling sense of loss that I felt.

As the other patients filtered back in we were asked to sit around and discuss our feelings. My irritation started to sizzle. Why couldn't an emotive reaction be simply that, why did it have to be immediately dissected? It reminded me of my annoyance in school, having to read and then tear apart Carol Anne Duffy's poetry line by line, the continual surmising of my seventy-year-old, miserable-as-sin hag of a Catholic school teacher who was sure it was all some 'homosexual' reference that she couldn't possibly debunk. Every lesson, I wanted to stand up and scream, 'We all know she's a fucking lesbian who writes depressing poetry, can't we just leave it at that!' Of course I never did... instead I flirted with Ruth, the beautiful Irish pixie who sat next to me. But not wanting to be insensitive to the other patients who were obviously upset, I sat and listened to those who were crying (Gareth) and the rest who had lost their good friends and were now panicked at the thought of carrying on at the hospital without them.

*

Brian's, and especially Jess's, departures affected the mood of the place terribly. It became even harder to be there, made all the more poignant as this was yet another thing I was excluded from. I should not be upset, I did not know them, this was not *my* loss. So my remedy to my feeling overlooked was to get out of there as often and as much as I could for the rest of the week. I was in most of my groups with Chrissie, and listening to her talk about her food-related issues was putting me in a constant bad mood. Every time she spoke about her slender body as being fat or disgusting I felt like it was a personal attack on me. Whenever she opened her mouth I imagined her looking at me saying those things about me, not herself – she became a mirror of my own making that was constantly being held up to me. If she thought her own size-eight body disgusting, what on earth must she feel about my plus-sized body? I cringed at the thought.

I was also in most of my groups with a girl named Megan, who was my age. She didn't wear a shred of make-up on her snow-white skin, her auburn hair was greasy, her clothes were boyish and unflattering, smothering her petite frame, but despite this, she was stunning and completely unaware of it. The image she saw when she looked in the mirror was so far removed from the reality of what everyone else saw and listening to her talk about how ugly and fat she was, was incredibly painful and frustrating. She carried around a selection of puppets and dolls in her bag – and when she didn't want to talk (which was often), she would talk through the puppets. Everyone at the hospital, therapists included, had completely acclimatised to this form of communication and would even address questions to the puppets at times: Fred, Beaker or Alice. She would use each puppet depending on her mood. Fred was a small frog with serious anger issues, Beaker was the shy assistant scientist from *The Muppet Show*, and Alice was a bossy mouse from the deep south who wore a wedding dress equipped with veil and was married to Fred (we were often subject to watching their marital disputes play out in the middle of art therapy or small group).

It was Wednesday and I had endured listening to Chrissie and Megan's self-hate campaigns, followed by Esther (the girl with one hand who had voted that very first time that she wasn't sure if I should be able to stay at the hospital because of my being late) talking of her rape by a Guides camp leader when she was thirteen, but how the whole experience, 'praise be', had brought her closer to God.

It wasn't even lunchtime yet and I had had enough of the day; I didn't want to hear another word from anyone. Before I could slip out of the back door I was ushered into 'psychodrama'. It was run by Kerry, a militant-looking woman with a crop, who walked with a distinctive swagger. I sat in the chair closest to the door, ready to make my exit if need be.

'Okay. I've been away as you all know so I haven't had a chance to meet the new people, but never mind, we'll be doing an exercise now. It's not optional, you will all take part.' I already hated her. She picked up a little blue velvet drawstring bag and pulled out a Fabergé egg. 'Pass the egg around and as you hold the egg you tell the group what you're feeling today. Okay. Go.'

I watched the egg slowly move from Lyle who simply said, 'I feel very angry', to Megan, or rather Fred: 'Megan is upset. She wants to go for a run but those stupid therapists have said she'll be put on a vote for over-exercising. They can all get fucked', to Chrissie who held it as she wailed about how disgusting and obese she was, and then suddenly, the egg was in my hand. I think the effort involved in trying to keep everyone at a safe distance had finally got to me and I snapped. I half shouted at them: 'I feel censored and suppressed. Censored by this environment and some of the people in it and suppressed by myself, my need to talk, but not being able to. By holding everything in for seventeen days and now not being able to articulate the feelings or know what they even mean any more.' My tears had entered into a race with each other and poured over my cheeks as if someone had opened a tap.

After over a fortnight of my barely talking, the other patients looked a little stunned – Megan tried to tell me that she was sorry I felt like that, but her own insecurities were crippling her and the words started and stopped like a faulty car engine until she finally gave up. A few moments passed. Kerry looked at me, confusion across her face, and tilting her head she said, 'What are the tears for, Emma?' I felt my stomach turn like a washing machine, anger filling up my insides. Had she not been listening? Why was she asking me such a stupid question? She knew full well why I was crying. I felt vulnerable and exposed; my annoyance slammed my lips together and I refused to answer her. I shoved the egg into Esther's hand and glared at the floor.

*

The next day I experienced my first 'Women's Group'. It was dull and I hated it. Was I supposed to talk about my period? Were we going to be subjected to a shoddy version of *The Vagina Monologues*? So far it was most of the men who had been nice to me, so I didn't feel like being in a group with just the women, a lot of whom hated the male sex as a whole and spent the entire session bashing them. It turned out that the Women's Group was no different from my small group, everyone talking, me listening.

*

For the second night in a row I found myself leaving the hospital with my friend Cara and her boyfriend Andy. I knew it would be frowned upon but I didn't care: I needed to see my friends. To be around normal, repressed people. As we sat in the pub, me sipping my Diet Coke, I was aware of Andy checking his watch. I tried to ignore it, pretending time had stopped and that I could stay out all night if I wanted. I regaled them with stories of the 'loony bin' so far, and laughed along with them as if it weren't my life I was joking about. The joke became less funny an hour later as Andy's Volkswagen pulled into the hospital's drive and I saw all the patients gathered in the 9/15 having yet another meeting. It looked heated. I could hear Mike shouting through the glass. I sighed, not undoing my seat belt or even attempting to get up.

Cara turned around, tears swollen in her eyes. 'I don't want you to go in there, Em.'

*

As I sat down inside the 9/15 I followed the snivelling sound through the room until my eyes landed on Esther. She had dried blood all over her forehead and a new bandage on her arm. It transpired that she'd banged her head repeatedly against her bedroom door and then burnt herself. As I listened to the shouting and crying that was going on I grew angry and resentful. My heart felt like it was breaking with loneliness and I didn't feel able to tell any one of them. The feelings were threatening to devour me: a swirling pool of upset that was growing deeper by the second. I wanted so desperately for someone to notice, for someone to ask if I was okay. But I was a face in the crowd, blurring into the background just like everyone else. I left the meeting a few minutes before it was due to end, slipping out of the door as Esther screeched into the night like a banshee.

There was no one about; they were all still in the 9/15 room. I walked into the kitchen, grabbed the biggest knife I could find, yanked up my sleeve and pushed it against my arm. Nothing. It was totally blunt. Of course it was. Why, after all, would they have let us have sharp knives? I clenched my teeth together trying not to scream. The feeling of powerlessness felt all-encompassing. I threw the knife down on the counter and ran up to my room, tears streaming down my face.

Something other than the stash of Prozac Augusta had failed to see when she glanced over my bag during her check was an orange-and-white disposable razor. I had brought it with the intention of using it to shave with, vowing not to use it for anything else. Suddenly vows meant nothing and I was crushing it under my boot, separating the blade from the rest of it. I twisted and ripped at the plastic until one end of the sharp gleaming metal was exposed. My hands were shaking with anticipation. Again I pulled up my left sleeve and before I knew it, there was blood everywhere. I wrapped my arm up in a T-shirt and got into bed.

*

It was small group time and once again we were listening to Esther talk about the rape – it had been one of the leaders that had done it, creeping into her tent when everyone else was asleep. She cried as she told the story and I felt guilty about the feelings of annoyance I had harboured for her the night before. I got a sense, though, looking around the room, that perhaps not everyone believed the tale she was telling. Megan was staring out of the window, a vacant expression on her face as she cuddled Beaker. Lyle's eyes were fixed on the floor, his chest rising and falling heavily, loudly, as if breathing in itself was an effort for him. Irfan seemed engaged enough, asking Esther lots of questions, telling the room proudly that if he ever met the Guides leader he'd 'be in serious fucking trouble'. Chrissie looked unimpressed though; she stared at Esther with disdain, playing with her long hair as she did so.

'It was just so awful,' Esther's lip was trembling. 'So awful,' she said again.

Chrissie's eyes narrowed. 'And no one woke up? No one heard a thing?'

Esther shook her head. 'No.'

'So strange...' Chrissie said, her voice perfectly even, 'that with all those people, all their tents side by side, and no one, not one single person heard even the tiniest noise.'

Esther's eyes met hers, and they exchanged a strange look I couldn't quite make out. Esther turned away to face Fiona, the group therapist. 'I can't talk about this any more, I'm too upset. Did I do well, Fiona?'

Fiona smiled warmly 'Very well, Esther.'

*

I decided to escape the hospital to nuzzle into the warm bosom of Starbucks for an hour, the only place I could get a fairly low-calorie drink and be able to sit and write for as long as I wanted. As I scribbled in my diary and knocked my coffee back, it suddenly dawned on me I hadn't seen the barista use the 'light base' for my drink. A lump rose in my throat. I was two thirds of the way through. A drink that I had thought was 150 calories was actually nearer 400. 150 calories had been carefully factored into my day. 150 calories took precedence over everything else I allowed myself to eat on a daily basis. 150 was barely acceptable, let alone anything else.

Within two minutes I was tying my hair up and locking the toilet door behind me. With the tap on, I stuck my fingers down my throat and retched until I was sure I had got the majority of it out of me. As I washed my hands I looked at myself in the mirror, feeling an enormous battle of relief and guilt going on as I watched my reflection. I was so glad I hadn't compromised my 700-calorie-a-day intake, but it had been a few months since I had last thrown up. I didn't want to start again. It had been hard enough to try and stop the first time around.

I walked back into the hospital grounds half an hour later. The ache of my ribs and back was already slowing me down and I quietly resolved not to make myself sick again. The hospital looked peaceful and still from the outside, but once inside the long white hallway, I heard a man's voice echoing. I strained to hear but didn't recognise it. It was coming from the visitors' room. As nosy as ever, I approached the door and standing on tiptoes tried to look through the glass window. Chrissie was sitting in there. An older man with white hair sat beside her with his hand resting on her thigh. He was reading aloud from a book – I pressed my ear against the door and heard what I thought were verses from the Bible. I ducked down before I was seen and continued down the hall. A few steps later it occurred to me that it must have been Derek. I thought of the way they were sitting, his pale hand just a fraction too high on her bare leg, fingers angled ever so slightly in the wrong direction and a wave of nausea ran over me as I recalled Jess's words: 'But *does* he touch you?' To my left the 9/15 door creaked open and Augusta wandered out, pausing to ask me if I was coming to gardening and maintenance. I nodded and followed her slick black ponytail down an adjacent corridor into the cold conservatory where the rest of the patients were sitting quietly.

5

DON'T MENTION THE HAND

"Everybody, everybody everywhere, has his own movie going,
his own scenario, and everybody is acting his movie out like
mad, only most people don't know that is what they're trapped
by, their little script."

— TOM WOLFE, *The Electric Kool-Aid Acid Test*

I had agreed to go on a gardening trip to buy some trees and bits
and bobs with Lyle and the two therapists that ran the gardening
group. I had been dreading it. But actually, when the time came
to escape for a few hours, the freedom was welcomed.

We got a taxi to the garden centre where Lyle and I were
allowed to help pick which trees we wanted to be planted in
the hospital grounds. I hoped no one would cotton on to the
fact that I didn't know my arse from my elbow where trees were
concerned and had merely volunteered to come on the trip to
get away from everyone else. I found Lyle a lot easier to get along
with outside the walls of the Henshaw, his dry sense of humour
finally having a chance to get out into the fresh air with us. As
Lyle and I stood behind Cath and Pierre, who were scrambling
around loading things onto the cashiers' conveyor belt, I picked

up a small geranium, the magpie in me attracted to the bright pink shiny pot. I timidly approached my flustered therapists and announced, 'Her name is Elsa. Please can I have her, Cath, pretty please?' I made puppy eyes at my somewhat bemused charge. Cath didn't know me well at all but had clearly picked up on the fact that when I set my sights on something, come hell or high water, it was going to be mine.

'Okay,' she said and squeaking a few thank yous I popped my new friend on the conveyor belt. I turned around to a bemused Lyle.

'Elsa?' he said, chuckling. I laughed with him knowing full well that he had seen through my little-girl manipulation routine. I clutched Elsa as we got back in the cab and began warning her about where our journey was taking us, Lyle smiling all the way as he listened.

*

I spent the rest of the day trying to be of help to Charis. She had been the third girl in my initial meeting with Susie, and had just been admitted to the hospital. She was jittery and her eyes darted from one corner of the room to another, constantly asking me questions, mainly consisting of: 'Is everyone usually this moody here?' I felt guilty as I said 'No.'

*

Afternoon turned into night and I sat in the TV room with a few people, watching the day staff all leave in their thick wool coats and bags. I hated watching them go, hated the fact that they could go, whilst I was stuck in the hospital.

I made a salad for my dinner. It lasted about fifteen minutes inside me before I snuck to the toilet and threw it up. The promises I kept making to myself seemed to fall to nothing in this place.

I spent the night in the 9/15 watching TV with Mike. He had managed to pull me out of my bad mood by telling me stories of his drug-addled past. He told me he was a former drug dealer who had done far too much of his clients' stashes and it had landed him in trouble various times. 'Shot me in the foot, those fuckers did!' he said shaking his head. 'I mean, bit of a fuckin' overreaction to a few g's going missing! I can't walk properly now. Every time it gets cold out my fuckin' foot seizes up!'

He had a similar sense of humour to me and it was a relief to be able to talk openly to someone without the worry of watching my every word. I warmed to Mike instantly and cried with laughter as he told me about his first month in the Henshaw, when he had gone out and got some EXTC from a 'hippy shop'. It was a legal high and Mike hadn't thought the pills he had popped into his mouth were going to do anything to a 'big-time drug user' like himself. He was wrong. And by the time he got back to the hospital his jaw and pupils were rolling around in his head and he could barely walk. He had been let into the building by anorexic Louise. He tried not to smile as he told me that he felt awful but had to feign a panic attack and told her not to worry as he staggered past her and up to his room, paranoia stopping him falling asleep for hours on end.

I discovered Mike had a severe dislike of Esther, whom he called 'Mother Teresa'. I wasn't keen on her either and told him she irritated me and, much like Chrissie had seemed to be, I was suspicious of the things she said… I couldn't tell if it was just that she was so very pious, or that she was in fact a liar – I was picking up on something, and whatever it was it made me uneasy.

He said he didn't touch hard drugs any more but asked if I could pick him up some skunk over the coming Christmas period, adding that he'd need it being stuck in the Henshaw with OCD Augusta and the equally OCD Lyle. I took £20 off him and agreed.

It was just after midnight and one of the night staff came in telling us we were having a 'referred' in ten minutes.

41

'What's a referred?' I asked him.

'A referred meeting, Em, like an emergency meeting, probably about absolutely fucking nothing.' He looked at his watch, rolled his eyes and went outside for a cigarette.

Ten minutes later and everyone had filtered into the room and were sitting bleary-eyed and agitated at being woken up. Esther sat in her pale yellow dressing gown chewing the sleeve of her missing hand, with her bottom lip trembling as puppy dog eyes almost dripped down her face – an expression I was growing familiar with and was already tired of. It wasn't that I didn't feel sorry for her, but it felt like everything she did in the hospital was so calculated, all an attempt to get as much attention as possible, and always to the detriment of someone else. As I looked at her other hand I realised for the first time that most of her fingers were missing from it. Mike caught me looking at Esther and smirked, again rolling his eyes and exhaling loudly.

'Top three' were a group of three 'voted in' patients (voted in by everyone else) who would chair the meetings. There was a new top three every couple of weeks with the aim that all the patients would have a go at taking responsibility and being 'in charge'. This evening's top three were Augusta, Irfan and Candace – they asked Esther what the issue was and she began a rambling diatribe about earlier in the day. Apparently Charis (the new girl) had said she had once known a woman with one arm. That was it. That was the reason we were in this meeting at gone midnight. Charis sat in shock trying to defend herself.

'Esther, I'm so sorry, I didn't mean anything by it.' Her apology did nothing to satisfy Esther's now bellowing guilt trip about how awful the comment had made her feel.

'Well whether you did or you didn't, you can't just go around saying what you want to people and triggering them. I was born like this! Do you know what you've done, how you've made me feel? The stress of it all was so bad that I had a fit. I actually had a fit!' She glared at Charis whose eyes had filled with tears. What did she mean a fit? A shit fit? Esther looked at the night nurse, Yvonne. 'I had a fit!' she repeated again like a demented yellow parrot.

'You mean your epilepsy was triggered, Esther? You should have come and got one of us,' said Yvonne. Oh, epilepsy.

Charis opened her mouth. 'I'm... so sorry... My friend was born with one arm, I just didn't think I was being offensive.'

Esther looked at her, outraged. 'Well, you were! Having only one hand and three fingers left on your other hand is not the same as having one arm; at least she has five fingers, I have three! Three!'

'Oh come on, Esther, she clearly didn't mean to upset you,' said Mike, an underlying tone of hatred in his voice. He paused for a second then said, 'Didn't you say you were in a car accident, and your hand got taken off?'

Esther's cheeks flushed red, 'No!'

'Yes, you did' mused Augusta from the other side of the room.

Esther scowled at them both and, ignoring the question, wailed 'I'm so uspet! I want to overdose now!' Her quest for attention was getting out of hand.

'Well, we need to make sure that doesn't happen and that you're safe,' said Yvonne. She smiled at Esther. 'How can we keep you safe? Do you need someone to stay with you tonight?'

Esther nodded.

'Okay. Who will volunteer to be Esther's support buddy for the night?' Yvonne looked hopefully around the room but was met with looks of annoyance. A couple of minutes passed, no one volunteering. 'We will have to stay here until someone offers. If Esther's epilepsy has been set off by the stress, it's important that she's not alone.'

'Fine, yeah, I'll do it.' Candace attempted some sort of smile at Esther.

'Thank you, Candace.'

When the meeting was over Candace called over to Esther, 'Just going to make a cup of tea then I'll come up, okay?' Esther nodded, wiping the tears and snot off her face with her sleeve.

'I have to go and get some meds anyway, so I don't fit again.' She followed the night staff out of the door.

Out in the hall I walked alongside Candace towards the kitchen. 'That was nice of you,' I said, gently nudging her arm.

'Nice of me nothing,' she replied, letting out a little laugh. 'I just want to go to bed, and the longer that little turd is allowed to keep me up, the more likely I'll strangle her.' She winked at me and walked over to the kettle. Susie and Charis were sitting around the dining table; Charis was crying into a wad of tissue. I sat down next to her.

'Please don't be upset, we all know you didn't mean it.'

Susie nodded. 'Em's right, no one thinks badly of you at all.'

But Charis was inconsolable, saying over and over again that she 'just didn't think'.

When the morning arrived, we found out she had packed her bags and left, saying she wouldn't be back.

*

'So, do you want to come?' It was halfway through the 9/15 and Gareth said he needed someone to go to 'Leavers' with him. Leavers was the outpatient group that residents who were about to be discharged from the hospital went to. It was made up of recently 'cured' patients and every week someone from the Henshaw had to go along with Gareth. He asked again if I wanted to go and I eagerly said yes, knowing it would get me out of afternoon cleaning and away from the solemn feel of the hospital after Charis's abrupt departure. They all had a vote, and agreed I could go.

*

After the 9/15 I walked into small group, groaning aloud at the thought of Esther using the time to talk about her 'traumatic evening', which she obviously did. I sat, bored, my knee bouncing up and down on my foot wondering why Fiona was indulging in Esther's melodrama by asking her questions about her 'feelings'. Towards the end of the session Lyle cleared his throat loudly and, slurring, he announced, 'I drank a bottle of vodka last night.' He paused for a second before continuing. 'And I've had about 90mg of diazepam this morning.' The resigned tone in his voice at knowing the amount of trouble he was going to be in, but being too out of his head to care, made me have to shove my hand over my mouth to stop myself laughing. The look of anger on Esther's face at having the limelight stolen from her was priceless. She glowered at Lyle, then at me as I took my hand away from my mouth a second too soon, revealing my smile. Lyle had officially become my hero, defeating Mother Teresa in one fell swoop. A referred meeting was called and he was taken to A&E in an ambulance.

*

I was glad to leave with Gareth by the time lunch rolled around. As we left the hospital he asked if I'd eaten. I nodded – what was another lie at this point? On the train he began to ask me what I thought of Irfan. I hadn't had much interaction with him since my initial induction but had noticed him paying a lot of attention to Chrissie – which didn't sit well with me as she seemed so vulnerable and childlike a lot of the time. Something about the way I had watched Irfan pursue her made me wary and, without thinking, I said, 'I'm not sure. He seems a bit predatory.'

Gareth was clearly bursting with some sort of gossip and said, 'Oh. Funny you say that because your name came up in men's group.'

I felt my face get hot as I said, 'What do you mean?'

'He was talking about you. He likes you. He thinks you're "womanly."'

I couldn't help the look of repulsion that spread across my face. There was something about the word 'womanly' that made me want to rip my skin off. 'That's vile.'

'Well, not according to him. He went on about you for a while. He's not right, Em, he's in here for some weird shit. You need to watch your back; me and Mike will too so don't worry.'

I looked out of the window wondering what 'weird shit' meant.

*

The leavers meeting was in Vauxhall, in a dank little room in an even more dank grey building that looked like it had been derelict for a decade. The standard two therapists sat with a group of ex-patients who all looked pretty worse for wear. We were only there for an hour and I wasn't encouraged or asked to speak at all, which I was glad of, but listening to them talk about how their drug problems, eating disorders and relationship issues were (collectively) 'worse than ever before' filled me with absolute dread… These were people who had left the Henshaw, presumably because they were better? A lot of them seemed worse off than the people who were still in there. After it ended they all wanted to go to the pub. One of the girls there, Lara, seemed very friendly with Gareth and they both tried to convince me to go, but I politely declined and made my way back to the hospital.

*

Evening rolled around, and as usual I watched the therapists leave, chatting to each other as they walked down the drive, unaware of my eyes boring holes in their backs.

Susie sat with me as we watched the darkness drift over the hospital. She began to tell me more about her life and her self-harm. She was a burner, usually with hair straighteners. 'I've had seven skin grafts now. And I've completely ruined this,' she paused to lift her left hand and wave it at me. 'I cut through the tendons a couple of years ago.' I tried to hide the sudden nausea that pulsed through me. 'I have no feeling in it any more,' she said looking down at her wrist and prodding her forearm. I caught sight of a thick white mark that looked like an acid burn and quickly looked away. 'I wish I'd been more careful with it all, but… now I've messed up my daughter too.'

'What do you mean, Susie, because she has PTSD?'

'Well, yeah that,' she yanked down her sleeve, 'but more that she's seen my scars, and she thinks it's how to handle feelings now. She's started cutting. Nothing serious, but, it never starts serious, does it?'

I really felt for her. 'You can't change what's happened, Susie, but you can change what *happens*… and that's why you're here. You can't keep beating yourself up for the past.'

She stifled a laugh. 'No! I have Carl to do that for me!'

Just at that moment Gareth walked in. 'Well if it isn't my two favourite people!' He fell back on the sofa next to me; the smell of alcohol was overwhelming.

'Oh dear,' I said, looking pitifully at him.

'Oh dear what?' he chirped, his eyes wide as saucers.

'Oh dear, you stink like a brewery!'

He dismissively waved his hand in the air. 'Oh bollocks, you should have come, it was fun. Lara liked you!' I raised my eyebrow at him as he continued. 'She said we should have a threesome, you, me and her.' He laughed as if it were the funniest thing ever said.

'I think me and Em better leave you to sober up before the staff find you and put you on seclusion!' said Susie standing up and reaching her hand out for me to take, which I did. We began to walk out of the room.

'Oh don't be boring,' he called after us as we left and headed up to our bedrooms.

6

THE VICAR AND THE DWINDLING MONEY POT

"I didn't want to wake up. I was having a much better time asleep. And that's really sad. It was almost like a reverse nightmare, like when you wake up from a nightmare you're so relieved. I woke up into a nightmare."

— NED VIZZINI, *It's Kind of a Funny Story*

'Pass me the knife… no not that one, the one with the yellow handle.'

I stood with Augusta cooking in the kitchen, finding her OCD a little amusing and equally worried about having to cook with her. I watched as she cut vegetables up into perfectly sized equal squares.

'They have to be the same size, or I can't use them,' she said absent-mindedly, no expression in her voice. I decided not to offer any help - my lack of coordination was a running joke among my friends and they would often fall about laughing as they listened to my tales of not being able to cut bread or cheese in straight lines, usually wielding a loaf at me asking me to slice it up, not even able to finish the request before collapsing into fits of giggles, arseholes. Mike came in, the kitchen door swinging back on itself loudly interrupting my thoughts.

'Oh, cooking with Augusta tonight, Em? Fun, fun, fun!' He poured some hot water out of the kettle into his cup and winked knowingly at her.

'Shut up Mike,' came the response. 'At least I can cook; what do you do, eat Mars Bars washed down with black coffee, a hundred cigarettes, fifty packets of crisps and call it quits? No wonder you look like you're eight months pregnant.'

I laughed at his feigned hurt expression. 'That's not very nice!'

'No, it's not,' she said, the knife almost cutting into the chopping board with each swipe.

'I have a body most men would die for!' he said, sipping the coffee he'd made.

She laughed. 'Yes quite, most *would* die.' They were funny together, these two, an unlikely comedy duo and an even more unlikely pairing. As cutting as Augusta was being, you could tell she actually really liked Mike and vice versa. Watching them both quip back and forth took me out of the hospital; it was like watching old friends try and 'one up' each other. Augusta finished the stew she was making single-handedly – all I did was shout to everyone that dinner was ready, set the table and pass her the things she asked for, but she was gracious and told everyone we had made it together. The staff took their seats with the patients around the dining table.

I began to leave the room as Yvonne called behind me, 'Not eating, Emma?' Her tone was questioning, accusatory. I paused, one hand on the door.

'To be honest I ate so much while we were cooking, I'm stuffed.'

Yvonne looked at Augusta. 'Is that true?'

Augusta looked at me, then back at Yvonne. 'Yes. She ate like a pig, I'm surprised she can even get up to her room.'

A couple of people laughed, Candace exclaiming, 'Fucking hell, don't hold back, Augusta!' I smiled at Yvonne and pushed open the door headed for upstairs – content that, somehow, although I wasn't sure why, it seemed I had yet another ally in this place.

*

Sitting on my bed preparing to summon the energy to take my make-up off, I looked at the yellow walls that surrounded me. There were so many small holes in them, some so deep they went right through the wall to the next bedroom. Paranoia suddenly began to fill my mind. The residents all knew which bedroom I'd be going into before I arrived. What if Irfan had made the holes? What if he was spying on me right now? The room next to mine was empty, he could be in there, watching, he could have used a drill to make the holes. No. I'm being ridiculous, aren't I? But, 'weird shit', what *did* that mean? I casually pulled my suitcase out from under my bed and removed the Blu Tack I had packed to stick pictures up with. I began to roll it into small balls and poke them into the minute holes all around me. As I lay down I quietly laughed about how paranoid I was being, but at the same time I felt a huge relief.

*

I woke up earlier than usual the next morning and got ready to go to Springfield hospital. I had been told by Augusta that the Henshaw was having some trouble finding funding. It cost around £15,000 – £20,000 a week for each patient to be in there and the NHS's money pot was dwindling when it came to the mental health end of things.

Most of the patients were going and although I didn't

particularly care about the future of the Henshaw, whatever that might mean for me, I decided to tag along. I climbed into a car with Chrissie. A nurse called Aidan got in behind us. I couldn't resist. I was in a mischievous mood and already bored of listening to crap FM.

'Do you remember me, Aidan?' I had recognised him the second I had seen him in the 9/15 in my first week of treatment. He didn't really contribute much in the meetings, but was always around. In college I had been friends with a guy called Kevin, whose brother used to deal weed to me, the brother being Aidan. It was a good eight years earlier and I hadn't expected him to remember me, especially with the amount of drugs he had taken. He looked puzzled, as did Chrissie, and said, 'No'. Playing with my prey was proving fun, so I carried on.

'I was friends with Kevin, we went to college together.' The colour began to drain from Aidan's face as he searched his memory for mine. I began to name mutual friends of Kevin's and mine, all of them notorious drug users.

After a few moments of silence he quickly glanced at me then back at the road in front of us as he said, 'Oh yes, I do remember you.' I felt a bit guilty and decided to put him out of his misery.

'Well, say hi to Kevin for me.'

When we got out of the cab at Springfield I found Mike and told him. He burst into laughter, patting me on the shoulder in approval. I swore him to secrecy, because even though tormenting Aidan had been fun I didn't want to get him into trouble. 'I won't say nothing,' Mike said as we followed Augusta into the meeting.

A small boardroom full to the brim of men in suits was waiting. I felt a surge of panic as I watched Augusta dart quickly away from us and to the back of the room to stand in the corner – I wanted to do the same but was being ushered by another nurse into a row of seats. I looked behind me but Mike had vanished somewhere in the crowd. Sitting in-between Gareth and Chrissie I listened to the debate unfold about my and all the other patients' futures.

At some point the panel broke away from what seemed to be their heavily orchestrated speeches to ask the staff and patients at the Henshaw what they thought. A few of the therapists stood up and began to reel off statistics, numbers of patients that had been helped by the Henshaw, the amount of people that had gone back into the world as productive members of the community. As I listened I couldn't help but think back to the leavers group I had been to... Those lot certainly hadn't been helped.

After a half an hour break to 'deliberate', a man called Eric Harper stood up in his grey suit with an equally grey expression. 'It is with a heavy heart that the choice has been taken to close the Henshaw hospital in the summer of next year. It is with great sadness that this decision has been made.'

And that was it. We filed out into the parking bay where the cabs were waiting for us. I looked at Lisa, one of the co-founders of the hospital. She was always there, in her office, but rarely came to meetings. Tears were in her eyes as her colleagues tried to comfort her. I spent the ride back to the hospital listening to Irfan chat to the Jamaican cabbie about reggae, the cabbie seemingly finding the whole conversation quite offensive, Irfan ploughing on regardless. As we pulled into the hospital grounds Irfan handed the cab driver his phone number. 'Call me, man, we should go for a drink, maybe hit up some strip bars, smoke some reefer.' I couldn't help but enjoy it slightly when later he got pulled up on inappropriate behaviour – which in turn put him in such a bad mood that he went out drinking by himself. He didn't get back to the hospital until the early hours of the morning and was put on seclusion in his room until he was sober. That suited me fine; after what Gareth had said, the less I saw of him the better.

*

Small group passed quickly the next day, with people discussing Irfan's drinking. Chrissie hadn't shown up, which was odd for her; they had a 'three strikes and you're in a referred' rule but I didn't think she was in any danger of getting into trouble. There was an air around Chrissie that prompted everyone who came into contact with her to suddenly become protective. She was twenty-two but she could have been four years old, and sometimes there was no distinction.

As I stepped out of small group into the hallway I heard Gareth shouting, 'Referred in ten.' I debated leaving but as he drew closer to me I saw a look of tangled excitement on his face – which must have meant drama was in the air. It made me curious enough to want to stay. I sat down with him in the 9/15 while the others got their last smokes outside.

'What's going on, Gareth?'

He turned to me, his eyes huge. 'It's big, Em.' Aggravated by not being told, I repeated myself, but before he could answer the door swung open and the therapists began to file in. He caught my eye and mimed the word 'Chrissie'. I instantly thought I was in for another discussion about her bulimia but when the meeting started, and Chrissie sat on the other side of the room from me curled into a ball, her face covered with the arm of her jumper – I realised this must be something else.

Top three were none the wiser than the rest of us as to why they had been asked to call a meeting; they slowly began to ask Chrissie questions about how she was and what was going on.

'Nothing. Everything is okay,' came the muffled, systematic response.

After some time of this, Gareth, looking as uncomfortable as I'd ever seen him, and yet somehow still being able to revel in the attention, said, 'Chrissie you have to tell them what we were talking about.' The other residents seemed more interested at this point and began sitting up in their chairs looking at one another. Chrissie didn't respond. Minutes passed like days before Gareth spoke again. My mind was whirring and I wished I could leave. 'What you were telling me about Derek?'

Oh God, the vicar. Not the vicar. Chrissie looked straight at him then, her eyes growing darker by the second as she hissed, 'That's private.'

Gareth stared back at her. 'People have to know, and if you don't tell them, I will.' She threw her face down onto the arm of the chair she was on and wrapped her hands protectively around herself. Was it too late to get out? My eyes darted from Gareth's mouth to the door. If I got up now, I could say I needed the toilet. But deep down, I knew I wasn't going anywhere. I knew I would have to sit through this with the rest of them. Gareth started again.

'Chrissie told us about Derek before, reading her bedtime stories and stuff. But it's more than that, isn't it Chrissie?' He looked at her for an answer but her hair was in a clump over her face. So he went on. 'It's sexual too.' I heard a few noises come from people in the room. I drew my knees up around me.

I want to get out.

I want to get out.

I want to get out.

The repetitive thud began in my temples. Chrissie wasn't speaking. She refused. And eventually, frustratingly, the meeting had to be called to an end.

'The staff will be having a meeting about this upstairs,' announced Grant as he left the room with the rest of them.

Susie had draped herself around Chrissie, and safe in the

knowledge someone was fulfilling this duty I crept out, up to my room, got my bag and left.

I came back to the hospital after the sun had set, made a salad and went and sat next to Mike in the 9/15. Whenever I was near him I felt safe; he was fairly emotionally shut down and I was happy not to have to talk about anything heavy. Unexpectedly, Chrissie walked in and perched next to me.

So here we were, Mike, Chrissie and me. I didn't want to bring up the meeting. I didn't want to hear about the vicar or the fucking, or the bedtime stories or any of it. Instead I wrote in my diary, totting up my calories for the day and casually spoke to her about the things I had bought when I was out. Chrissie was in a strange mood. More open than usual, but her eyes stayed fixed on the wall opposite her, unblinking, unfeeling. For some reason we began to talk about self-harm. I had never seen any marks on her pale skin so assumed she didn't cut herself.

'No, I don't...' she said. 'I use cannulas.' I felt my stomach turn. 'I lose a couple of pints every time... I've had to have a few transfusions.' I was suddenly grateful she wasn't looking at me as I silently retched. That was my idea of hell – though I was happy enough to whip out a razor blade at my every whim, the idea of needles, blood tests specifically, was enough to send me screaming into the next room.

'I've never been into cutting. It's messy. I prefer bloodletting.' I felt sick, and could quite easily have cried with joy when ten minutes later she got up and said she was going to bed. Mike had been off smoking and making his fifty-seventh cup of coffee for the day, and when he came back he must have noticed my face had drained of any colour.

'You okay, Em?' I puffed my cheeks out in a sick motion but before I could answer him my phone began to ring. It was my mother.

'Hello, Emma?'

'Hi, everything okay?' There was a pause and I felt my heart rate instantly pick up.

'No. I think Cassie might be on her way out.' Cassie was my dog. She was thirteen and she was the first dog I'd ever had. I'd saved up and paid £252 towards buying her. I was only nine, it was my life savings – every birthday, every Christmas, every chore, every car wash, every penny was saved meticulously for a time when I would be able to have a dog. She'd been my most loyal friend since I was a child and when I'd agreed to go into the Henshaw, it was her I didn't want to leave.

'Your father can come and pick you up if you want?'

I told Mike but no one else, once again slipping through the magnetic doors that were no obstacle for me. I wasn't in the mood for a referred; I didn't want to share this with anyone; I just wanted to go and be with my best friend when she needed me most.

I spent the night in my bedroom at my parents' house with Cassie. Her breathing wasn't good, slow and heavy. The enlarged heart she'd been diagnosed with some years earlier was finally getting the better of her. I sat with her all night playing music and holding her, supporting the weight of her chest so she wouldn't be uncomfortable. The next morning we took her to the vet's, and I left without her.

I felt like my heart had been ripped out. And it was a good thing I wasn't challenged by anyone about having left the hospital as it wouldn't have ended well.

'My dog died,' was as much as I said about it. I got a couple of 'I'm sorry's and the odd sympathetic smile and they were happy to leave it at that.

7

ANA, MIA AND ME

"Toilet water splashes in your face but you don't care, because all you can think of are calories, fat grams, *did I get it all out?*"

NICOLE JOHNS — Purge, Rehab Dairies

Media interest in the closure began to take off and it was only a matter of days until we were being asked to appear on various news stations to talk about the effect it was having on us 'mentals'. I declined all of these offers, but enjoyed standing with Mike watching a news crew interview Gareth and Candace in the driveway of the hospital.

In all honesty I didn't care about the closure. I cared about calories and losing weight. Everything that went into my mouth would make an appearance again within the hour and the weight loss was starting to show. I spent my days binging and purging, applying thick layers of concealer around my eyes to cover up the burst blood vessels. I carried on like that for week after week and it didn't stop when I was able to go home for weekend leave – in fact it got worse. I didn't have anyone to worry about watching me, so I spent what felt like the whole weekend locked in the bathroom. By the time my father drove me back to the Henshaw on Sunday night I was weak, ill and admitting defeat. I couldn't tell if I had a problem or not, but I knew I had spent the majority of the last twenty-four hours with my head down a toilet and I wanted someone to know. I needed someone to know. I was finally willing to admit that maybe there was an issue and perhaps I needed to start talking about it.

I spent the next few hours plucking up the courage to speak about the vomiting. I sat in the 10pm meeting feeling anxious and waiting for an opportunity to talk. Chrissie looked terrible; she had been as quiet as a mouse since what had happened in the referred meeting the week before. I didn't quite understand how it had been left like that, with this suggestion that the priest was fucking her, or abusing her, or God knows what, and that no one had brought it up since... I could only assume the staff were dealing with it behind closed doors.

'Chrissie, are you okay?' Susie asked, as if she had read my mind.

Chrissie didn't look up, her voice flat as she spoke. 'Fine.'

'You don't look fine,' said Augusta, who was on top three.

'What do you want me to say? Last time I said something people overreacted and I got in trouble.'

Gareth looked pissed off, his tone defensive. 'I don't think me telling people you're being abused was overreacting.'

She snapped her face upwards, her eyes meeting his and glared at him. 'I *am not* being abused.'

Gareth shook his head in frustration.

'I think people are just trying to establish if you're safe, Chrissie, and if you need some support you only have to ask,' said Fiona, who was on night duty.

Chrissie sighed, a sad, defeated little noise. 'I'm all right. I don't need support.'

It was left alone after that, no one daring to upset her further.

Augusta asked if there was anything else anyone wanted to talk about. I took a deep breath in.

'I've not been great. The food stuff is… bad. I have been throwing up a lot.' It was barely a sentence but saying it made me dig my nails into my hands, the exposure of speaking even just a few words always feeling like far too much. People were tired after their own equally upsetting experiences of going home and there wasn't much of a discussion, which didn't bother me, although I couldn't help feeling a little overlooked. It was a strange dichotomy for me of wanting people to know I was struggling, but not letting them tamper with what I was doing, a sort of 'hear me but don't help me' situation. I simply had to ask for my sleeping in extensions, which were granted.

*

In the morning my face looked a state. There is nothing glamorous about an eating disorder; anyone who's found themselves wrapped up in one will tell you that. My cheeks were puffy, my lips chapped, black circles sat under my eyes and I looked as though I had a bad case of chickenpox. I spent longer than usual applying my make-up, taking extra care to douse my eyes with foundation and glitter.

I took a seat next to Augusta in the 9/15 who reassured me that I was going to 'get got', as she called it, saying that 'of course' I would be on the agenda and would be grilled about the vomiting. I groaned and drew my legs up onto my chair with me, planting my head onto my knees.

'Don't worry, just be honest.' Her words didn't help to comfort me. Augusta smirked as she had to listen to a string of mumbled 'Oh fucks' as the room filled up, therapist after therapist taking their seats.

By the time my name was read out I was red-faced and

panicked. Top three asked me to explain myself again, which I did in about four words, covering my face with my hands the whole time – my explanation was delivered in one breath and consisted of mainly 'Sorry'. After my lungs had run out of air I pushed my head back into my knees and closed my eyes, pretending no one could see me. My eye caught Grant's, who I thought was gorgeous and had a big crush on – I hadn't realised he was in the meeting and felt mortified. I listened to the room talk about me for a few minutes, until Lisa broke away and asked me why I was 'hiding'.

My smart-arse fifteen-year-old self was in full defensive mode as, still not looking up, I said, 'I'm not hiding. I'm pretending to be a shire horse.'

I heard a few people laugh. There was a Christmas meal scheduled for that afternoon and people began to ask how Louise was going to cope. They then asked me. I couldn't have felt more stupid. Louise was probably six and a half stone at best, so why on earth was I being bracketed in with someone who had a real problem? I looked at Louise, the bones jutting out of her translucent skin, and then down at my own body, the rolls of fat that made up my huge stomach. I began to feel furious with myself for having told them. I didn't have a problem, I just needed to lose weight. Embarrassment began to smother me and I wanted the ground to swallow me up. Realising that the question of how I was going to manage the meal still hung in the air, I quickly said, 'Fine thanks. I'll ask for help if I need it.'

Gareth, who was on top three, said, 'There's that sarcastic little voice again, Em.'

I wanted to hit him, but instead said, 'Look, I was just being an attention-seeker. Just being irritating, I'm absolutely fine, really.'

Louise's voice squeaked across the room at me. 'I wonder how much of that is your voice, Emma, and how much of it is the eating disorder's voice?'

I didn't answer her. I heard someone meekly clear their throat and looked across the room to see Esther about to open her mouth. *This should be good.*

'Emma, I often sit with Chrissie during meals to help make sure she eats everything and that she doesn't go to the bathroom afterwards to throw up.' I couldn't help but glance at Chrissie, who looked like she wanted to punch Esther in the face. Esther carried on. 'It really helps Chrissie, and I'd be prepared to sit with you too, at the Christmas meal and at every meal.'

Oh do me a favour... you'd be 'prepared', you'd fucking love the drama, I thought, trying hard not to roll my eyes at her.

'Thanks but I don't need your help.'

But the therapists were loving it. 'What a great idea, Esther, and so helpful,' said Hank the nurse. Esther smiled triumphantly. I heard a 'psh' noise escape from Augusta next to me.

'Yeah, it is a nice idea but it's not needed. Cheers though.' I didn't care how sarcastic that one sounded. Esther turned to Hank, her eyes melting into black holes on her face.

'I think you need to say yes here, Emma, and ask for help. I think everyone in this room should agree that Emma sitting next to Esther is going to be the plan for the next few weeks.' Hank wasn't going to let it go, how was I going to get out of this?

'Emma,' said Grant carefully, 'you made a pretty big admission today, you asked for help and to be heard, and now you are being offered help, so I advise you take it.'

It struck me as weird that no one in this place had even realised up until this point that I never ever sat down for meals at the hospital. I hadn't eaten one dinner around the table since I'd been here, or had so much as a cup of tea in front of any of them. Just when it felt like I had nowhere to go, a shining light shone down on the room in the form of Mike.

'Em asks for help all the time. She has her meals in the 9/15 with me every night, she's been doing that for ages...' I could have kissed him. A complete and total lie, a beautiful fabrication that was going to be my saving grace.

Grant looked from Mike to me. 'Is that right?'

I nodded, 'Yeah, every night.'

'Well that's great; well done, Mike, for being such a support, and Emma for asking for help. Maybe in future just try and be a bit more open with the rest of the community so we know where you're at, okay?'

'Okay, Grant.'

Esther was furious, her little face bright red as if she might explode; she knew it was a lie but she wasn't going to take us on.

I asked for my SIEs again, not looking to see the people who declined granting them to me, and walked out of the meeting as soon as it was called to an end. I found Mike a few minutes later as he stood outside smoking.

'Thanks for that.'

He set his coffee down on the window ledge. 'Don't worry about it, anything to wipe the smirk off that little do-gooder's face.'

8

THE PHANTOM OF THE HENSHAW

"The possibility of physical and mental collapse is now very real. No sympathy for the Devil, keep that in mind. Buy the ticket, take the ride."

— HUNTER S. THOMPSON, *Fear and Loathing in Las Vegas*

At 3pm on the day of the Christmas meal I stood in the shower, behind the partially drawn curtain, fully dressed and silent. I heard someone's feet pad down the hallway past the bathroom and a knock on my door. My name was called a few times and then the footsteps were once more on the move. The bathroom door creaked as it opened and again I heard my name. I couldn't place the voice and stayed completely still. Whoever it was left and I felt content that it would be reported back that I had gone out and was therefore going to miss the meal. Yes I'd get in trouble, but it was better than having to sit in the packed 9/15 with fifty people all shovelling roast potatoes and turkey into their mouths like animals at a trough.

I couldn't actually get out of the hospital now without the

risk of being seen so instead decided to nosy my way around the floor I was on, poking my head into all the empty bedrooms. I rummaged through drawers and wardrobes and found old residents' leftover belongings. I took a table lamp out of one of the rooms deciding it might make my own bedroom feel a bit more cosy. With my lamp in hand I walked through a door marked 'Floors'. All I knew about this room was that it was where the other group had their therapy and that this was where people who needed support would sleep at night – along with whichever resident had offered to stay with them. The door squeaked a little as I opened it and stepped inside. The large space had about ten chairs in it, all in a semi circle; I sat down and looked at the artwork on the walls, most were swirling vortexes of colour, red and black hurricanes with words like 'trapped,' 'pain,' and 'hurt' scrawled all over them. Haunting drawings of tormented faces with black hollows for eyes, their mouths open and twisting. Why would you ever put those on the walls? They didn't evoke calm, healing feelings – where's a fucking unicorn or a rainbow when you need one? A small TV under an adjacent chair caught my eye. I plugged it into the wall and smiled as the set lit up and it switched on. I had missed having my own television so much; I picked it up and took it back into my room.

I cleared a space on my dresser and placed the lamp down along with the TV set, sitting back on my bed as I did and finally feeling less like I hated the room. I determined that if anyone said anything I'd just say I didn't know I wasn't allowed to have it. But there was no way I was letting them take it away; I'd found my salvation. No longer would I have to rely on Stuart, the big spider that lived in the corner of my ceiling, for company. Stuart and I had the world at our fingertips now! Filled with a new sense of motivation I got all the photographs and pictures out of my suitcase and began to stick them up onto the walls. Perhaps I could make this room bearable after all.

For some reason I wasn't pulled up on missing the meal. Perhaps no one had noticed I hadn't been there; perhaps it was too close to the Christmas break for the therapists to care. The next morning a lot of people left to go to home. I wanted to stay at the hospital for an extra few days, but decided to leave on Christmas Eve.

*

My eyes opened and fixed on the ceiling of my bedroom in my parents' house on Christmas Day, my insides quickly filling with dread. The morning moved slowly and as lunchtime rolled around and people took their places around the kitchen table I asked my mother if I could serve myself. The amount of food she was piling on everyone else's plates was making me dizzy with anxiety. Through her gritted teeth but still maintaining her smile at the rest of the family she quietly hissed, 'Stop being ridiculous, Emma, for God's sake.' She filled up the plate and passed it to me. As soon as she turned her back to top up my grandmother's champagne glass I tipped half of it back onto the baking tray. I managed about four Brussel sprouts, half a parsnip and a mouthful of a roast potato before excusing myself and rushing to the bathroom to throw up. Christmas for the eating disordered is as good an idea as white water rafting for a haemophiliac – sure, you can give it a go but don't except to come out of it without some internal bleeding.

*

On New Year's Eve, my friends and I went to Landon's house for a party. Just like most nights out with my friends, I had a few lines of coke and hid in Landon's bedroom by myself trying to work out what was wrong with me and why I found it so difficult to socialise with people. I tried to find Landon a few times, as the lure of getting some empathy and attention from him was fairly enticing – but after not being able to find him I asked one of his flatmates, who reported that he was in the spare bedroom 'with some girl'. I put my coat on and left through the back door without anyone seeing me go.

Back at my parents' house I didn't sleep. I lay awake for hours on end feeling like I was going mad and remembering why I hated drugs so much. The only chance I had at falling into a slumber of any kind would mean cheating on one narcotic with another. Abandoning my aggressive white drugs and replacing them with something green and lazy might work; failing that I'd have to crack out the blues – the 10mg Valium's that sat in my bedside table begging for a chance on centre stage. I rolled myself a joint, then not hesitating, swallowed two of the blue pills – why wait?

Soon the sun was shining through my window and my head was pounding. I reluctantly got out of bed and went downstairs, deciding to call Natalie and see if she wanted to meet me. Collapsing on the sofa, I dialled her number. Her mum answered. 'Hi Emma.' I sensed something was terribly wrong instantly.

She told me that her dad (Natalie's granddad) had died in the early hours of the morning. Oh no. I had been dreading this day for years now. It had been chasing me, ever present, waiting to pounce. Nat's grandfather was her everything, and now with my coke hangover and depression sitting on my chest like an all-too-comfortable overweight black cat, I was going to have to be of help. I was part of the cavalry. No matter how I felt in my self-inflicted drug-induced stupor, I was the one who Natalie needed. I told her mum I would be round within the hour and, hanging up, moped into the kitchen to make a quick cup of tea. My mother stood stirring something in a pot on the cooker. I told her the news. She huffed and asked if I was going to the funeral, the tone in her voice already suggesting that any answer

I gave would be the wrong one. I answered yes and she launched into a speech about how I had 'not bothered' to go to my own step-grandfather's funeral – a man whom I had not been at all close to, and who had died four years previously. And so began a blazing row, a back and forth of fuckery and shouting with no end in sight. My mother was 'cold and unfeeling'; I was 'spoilt and rude'. And so it went, on and on.

As I got ready to leave I began to regret the interaction, and wanted to try and fix things before I left to see Natalie. I cautiously approached my mother as she sat at her dressing table fiddling with her hair. I cleared my throat.

'I'm sorry for shouting. I was upset about Natalie's grandad dying.'

Without turning her head away from her reflection in the mirror, she said, 'You have it very cushy here, Emma. Everything comes easy for you. You need some hardship in your life, you've had an easy ride so far.' She paused and pulled a clip from her hair and turning to face me she continued, 'I think you've been coming home too much. I will phone the hospital tomorrow and tell them it ought to be looked at. You shouldn't be coming home so often, if at all.'

I chose not to say anything and walked out. The swell of anger and lack of control I was feeling was stirring in me like a tidal wave. My ears filled with the noise of klaxons. But it wasn't about me. I had to be there for Nat. I pushed the feelings down as far as I could, knowing if I did that they would eventually consent and silently lie in wait until the evening, an unwritten contract between me and the voices in my head.

*

By the time I got to Natalie she was in the pub with several of our friends and her boyfriend Chris. I wrapped my arms around her and sat with her as she cried, saying the sort of things you are expected to say in that situation, not sure if I believed any of them, but hoping I was being believed.

I got home a little after midnight. The house was quiet and still so I crept up to my bedroom where the unwritten contract had come to an abrupt end and the voices were competing for attention. Regardless of the sixty-watt light bulb that hung over my head, the room was dark. I was once again alone with the guilt of my actions from the morning, and the night that stretched seemingly endlessly out in front of me. I reached into the top drawer of my bedside table and pulled out a razor blade. Peace would be mine tonight, one way or another.

*

The train back to Henshaw was empty as I stepped on. I winced as I sat down, the pain of so many cuts shooting up my leg. I had sliced my shin to ribbons; not only was it hard to walk, but going back and forth from my bedroom to the bathroom in my robe was going to prove an impossible task, both at the hospital and at home – that said, once my mother had phoned the Henshaw it might be a while before I got to actually go home again.

Walking back into the hospital was filled with as much joy as I had predicted: a miserable atmosphere and miserable faces, most of whom couldn't even raise their heads to say hello. I decided not to tell anyone about Natalie's grandad, or the cutting and quietly hurried up to my room where I sat in the dark watching TV all night.

*

The next morning I sat in art therapy after having put a poem down on the floor for the group to read, regretting my action almost instantaneously as Esther began to pull her turkey-faced expression and mumble that it had triggered her. I swooped down and picked it up off the floor –: an act that was heavily frowned upon – I was supposed to leave it there and 'fight the vulnerability'. Mona stared disapprovingly at me.

'You need to put that back, Emma.'

I eyeballed her with disdain and held the paper close to my chest.

'Emma?' she said again, the annoyance showing on her face.

Mirroring her expression right back at her I said, 'I don't *need* to do anything, Mona.'

She turned to face the rest of the room. 'What does everyone else think of Emma's behaviour right now and its impact on the group?'

Esther opened her mouth to start to say something but I wasn't going to have any of it.

'Oh just fuck off,' I muttered under my breath as I got up and walked out.

*

It was a couple of hours later and 'group cleaning' was interrupted by the call of top three announcing a meeting. We were told that Lyle had left the building, not before handing a note to Gareth, which he proceeded to read to us. It said: 'Don't worry about Lyle, he is safe with me and Christine now, we will look after him.' Gareth looked up for a moment, then back to the note, confusion scrawled on his face. 'It's signed "Eric".'

There was a long conversation about who Eric was; no one knew. A couple of people volunteered to walk to the bus stop to see if they could find Lyle before he got to wherever it was he was going, and confront this 'Eric' fellow who he was presumably with.

Two hours later, a very vacant Lyle was found wandering around the town centre and brought back by Irfan and a few others. In a matter of minutes we were all once again sitting in the 9/15 asking him what had happened. I'd been placed on top three for this meeting and so sat on the sofa in-between Mike and Gareth. The two men were finding Lyle's disassociated state of mind difficult to communicate with, so I did the majority of the talking.

'Who's Eric, Lyle?'

It was a good three minutes of breathing in that heavy, laboured way before he answered, 'He's me.'

Gareth turned toward me, confusion splattered across his face and whispered, 'What the fuck?'

I ignored Gareth and kept looking at Lyle. 'You invented him?' I asked.

Again there was a long pause. 'Yes, sort of. He is here to protect me.' I was about to ask another question when Lyle's huge stomach rose, inhaling deeply and with great effort he opened his mouth. 'Eric is evil though. He tells me I should be alone... that I can't trust anyone. That I can't trust any of *you*.'

Megan, who was usually very quiet in meetings, cleared her throat. 'Why can't you trust any of us, Lyle?'

He didn't look at her, but in an almost melancholy tone said, 'He told me you're all trying to kill me, and that *she*,' he pointed at Chrissie, 'is poisoning the food.'

Chrissie opened her mouth to speak but no sound came out.

'Why would Chrissie be poisoning the food? Chrissie barely cooks, I do most of the cooking and I'm certainly not poisoning the food.' Augusta was trying to help but seemed upset and defensive.

Lyle took in another deep breath. 'Eric came to me earlier today and spoke to me. He said we needed to talk, he and I. He said that I should get *you all*, before *you* get me. So that's why I left. Because I didn't know what he'd make me do.' Talk of Eric was massively freaking the other patients out, their eyes wide as they looked for reassurance in the night staff's blank faces.

I heard Mike's voice from somewhere beside me. 'And who's Christine?'

Lyle's eyes stayed fixed on the wooden floor as he said, 'Eric made her. For me.'

I felt my own mouth open slightly as I fought the strong urge to start nervously laughing – I didn't find it in the least bit funny but for some reason laughing was all I could think of to do. I glanced around the room: Candace sat opposite me pulling a face that suggested she was finding this both amusing and horrifying. Susie had her hand over her mouth. Even Esther was uncharacteristically silent. I glanced over at Chrissie who just looked terrified.

Lyle went on, 'He said Christine is mine. So I won't be lonely any more, she's my… girlfriend.' The nervous laughter instantly left my body then as a deep sorrow settled in around me – that's how alone he is, I thought, that's how much he needs someone to care about him. I knew from things he had said in our small group that his father was an abusive and uncaring alcoholic and his mother was much the same… He was an outcast at home, and it made me sad that he felt like an outcast here as well – in the one place where he should feel like he had people who understood.

We were an hour into the meeting and Lyle was coming round ever so slightly but was not in any place to discuss in detail what had happened to him mentally over the last few hours. From what I could gather he'd basically had some sort of psychotic break, or maybe Eric and Christine were Alters? Separate parts of himself? True enough I didn't know what was 'wrong' with Lyle; schizophrenia, dissociative identity disorder, or maybe he was just lonely, it could be anything. We were patients not doctors; all we could do was ask if he needed support. But every time it was asked he would say no. I looked at the night staff hoping they would suggest he went somewhere more secure for the night – perhaps an acute unit – but they didn't utter a peep.

*

Lyle was supposed to be cooking that evening, and as the meeting ended the other residents scurried away for fear of being made to cook with him. I had also been wary, especially after hearing about Eric, but when Lyle had told us about Christine I felt so desperately sorry for him that the paranoia around my safety melted away and I volunteered. Hearing this had made Augusta a little braver and she offered to sit in the kitchen with us, as long as I 'understood' she would not be helping – I chuckled at that but was glad of her company. She had been hanging around me more and more lately and I felt like she was fond of me, though I wasn't sure why.

I realised quickly that Lyle was in absolutely no state to cook. I wasn't overjoyed about him using one of the large kitchen knives to chop up vegetables, as blunt as it may have been, so just asked him to stir the various things I threw into the cooking pots (under instruction from Augusta, of course, who by the way didn't count micromanaging me as 'helping'). I talked to Lyle, though, almost constantly, insistent that he be part of the conversation. I thought that the more I spoke, no matter how benign the subject, the more it might make him feel grounded and 'back in his body' kind of thing, as he'd clearly been out of it for most of the afternoon.

An hour later than usual, the chicken and vegetable curries were served. Augusta meandered around the hospital shouting

'Dinner' and, episode aside, the other patients appeared one by one to take a seat at the table. Lyle, more lucid by this point, sat down with them and even managed a smile as the night staff complimented him on the curry.

As I watched them eat from the kitchen my phone vibrated in my pocket – Cara and Andy were outside in the car for a surprise visit. Opening the kitchen door with all the stealth I could muster, I crept out and met them in the driveway. The amount of curry I had consumed whilst doing my various 'taste tests' during cooking had caught up with me, or rather the guilt had. So when Andy and Cara stood at whatever pub we were in ordering drinks, I went to the toilet and threw up.

9

CONFESSION TIME

"Tough old world, baby. If you're not bolted together tightly,
you're gonna shake, rattle, and roll before you turn thirty."

— STEPHEN KING, *The Shining*

The three-month review was something all patients had to
endure. It was basically to check in and check up on my progress,
see the ways in which I was improving, and the areas which
needed more 'work'. From what Augusta had told me it usually
consisted of two therapists and three or four other residents.

I saw it as my chance to be honest, my attempt at redemption,
my confessional. I had cut myself around six times now since
being in the hospital… at first I had thought about fessing up
about all of these incidents but as I also added to that the vomiting
the night before… that was seven sets of SIEs. I decided to pull it
back to three counts of self-harm, and only one of making myself
sick. That seemed about right. I knew that whatever I said I would
be stopped from going out at the weekend, so I may as well be as
honest as I felt I could be without serious repercussions.

The dread in me was bubbling from the knowledge that
my least favourite staff member was working that day. Bernard

was in his late forties, thin with angular features. He had a grey complexion that swirled around his deep Scottish accent and a prominent lisp that unfortunately made him sound like he was hissing every word at us. He was a bully, and he liked nothing more than verbally ripping apart his victims. Bernard and I had forged a mutual dislike of each other very quickly – not that I was special in this regard; most people avoided him at all costs. I had seen him go for various residents over and over again in the 9/15; his random attacks seemed like they only came about as a result of his own bad mood.

I walked into my small group room – the place my review was scheduled for. Inside sat Chrissie, Megan and Lyle, along with two therapists, Fiona and Matt. Before I knew it, I was crying and telling them all that I was suicidal and that I'd made myself sick. I said that I wasn't coping without my medication (I had completely run out of my stash by this point, and the staff had 'weaned' me off my restricted supply) and that I'd cut myself on three separate occasions.

My three fellow patients were surprisingly supportive, trying to point out the good and saying I could get past the bad – that it was an important step that I had told the truth. I cringed a bit as they said this thinking, *If you knew the amount of cutting, drugs and vomiting I've actually been doing you'd kick me out*, but instead I tried to smile back across the room at them.

As I walked out of my review, Megan, who was on top three for the week, pulled me aside and whispering said, 'They'll want a referred now, because of what you've admitted to… so don't go out, or go out this second, just don't get caught, and don't tell anyone I said this.' I thanked her and decided to stay and face the music I had created.

Sure enough the referred was called within ten minutes. I found my way into the corner of the 9/15 and tried to make myself as small as possible.

Unluckily for me, Esther was chairing the meeting and was on a mission to get me. She had been seeking a reason ever since Mike and I had duped her in the 9/15 over the food issue. Her pious platitudes were in full flow as she announced her revelations to everyone as if she were a politician at a press conference.

'Emma,' she said, pausing for dramatic effect, 'has been keeping her self-harm a secret for weeks, and lying to us all.' *Oh I fucking loathe you, you scheming little shit.* She continued, 'And not only has she been self-harming, but has made herself sick.' Megan sat looking guilty next to her, smiling at me from time to time – a big feat for someone who barely lifted their gaze from the floor. I braced myself, expecting to get the grilling of a lifetime, but for some reason it didn't happen. The meeting seemed more of a formality than anything – Esther was enraged that I wasn't getting in any trouble.

'Well done for speaking up, Em,' said Susie, smiling sweetly.

'Yeah, well done, that took a lot of courage,' added Louise.

Esther looked aghast at them both. 'But she self-harmed, several times! And didn't tell anyone! She lied!' She threw the line again and again, but no one bit. As much trouble as I knew I could potentially be in, I couldn't help smirking at her when Candace shouted for her to move on and ask me for my SIEs. 'But, we need to discuss this!' she stammered.

Augusta groaned. 'We've discussed it enough, come on I need to cook!' As if an invisible gun were being held to her head, Esther, through gritted teeth said, 'Those in favour of granting Emma her SIE'S?' Everyone's hands went up. 'Against?' No one raised their hand. Esther looked almost overtaken by fury, her pale cheeks flashing burgundy. 'And undecided?' she half spat, throwing her arm up so fast in the air that it was a wonder she didn't give herself whiplash, joined as I had suspected she would be, by Bernard. There was a short pause before Megan happily chirped 'Okay, SIE's granted. Meeting over!' Esther stormed out of the room slamming the door behind her. I'd got away with it, for now. I knew the morning meeting would be an altogether different kettle of fish but I had all night to run around assuring Mike, Augusta, Susie and anyone else I could find who would stick up for me if I lost my voice.

*

I was up early and on time the next morning, dressed, hair washed, make-up on and first in to the 9/15. I sat cross-legged in the chair closest to the door and felt my palms grow more and more wet as the room filled up. I tried not to count the number of people that were steadily filling up every chair and in my mind kept going over answers to any potential questions that might be asked.

The meeting began. Megan was chairing and as she read out the agenda I realised she had not mentioned my name – a flash of relief shot through me but just as she began to talk about the first thing on her list Esther's voice interrupted.

'Um, what about Emma?'

I tried to stop myself from mumbling the word 'bitch'. Poor Megan then got in trouble for not having put me on the agenda. She huffed and scribbled my name down on the list before carrying on.

'Before we talk about Emma, you should all know Stevie left this morning; she said she'd had enough of being here, that she didn't feel supported.' I breathed a long sigh of relief as everyone began to talk about Stevie's departure and that most of them felt she had not taken her treatment seriously and was on drugs for most of it.

As much as I had hoped we would run out of time, we didn't, and before I knew it I could hear my name in the thick of a discussion I hadn't even realised had started. The residents tried their best to skim over the details and prompted me to ask for my SIEs but the staff – aided by Esther – were having none of it.

Grant sat opposite me in his usual pose – feet square on the floor, hands clasped together over his groin. I had secretly coined him 'Lestat' (the antihero and antagonist in *Interview with the Vampire*) due to the air of authority that lingered around him – none of the other therapists dared to disagree or interrupt when he spoke. His shoulder-length dark brown hair combined with his dark eyes and high cheekbones all made him look like he had just stepped out of an Anne Rice novel. He looked at me for a moment and then began, 'I think you need to go to the nurse's room and have your self-harm checked out, Emma.' Though it was delivered casually this suggestion prompted a surge of fear in me. Show someone my cuts? My scars? My body? No way. Not in a million years. I snapped back that I had been self-harming long enough to know the difference between a superficial wound and one that needed medical attention. But Lestat had me by the throat, and was just toying with me before biting down.

'You need to be checked out by a nurse, this isn't a request, Emma.'

I wasn't going to submit. 'No, I'm sure it's not, but I'm all good. Thanks for the concern though.'

He didn't want to give up. 'So you're just savaging your body? With no one knowing the extent of the damage you're doing to yourself?'

'Savaging? Jesus, Grant, come on! That's a bit extreme.' I chuckled aloud as I said this, bemused. The rest of the room melted away in those moments and it seemed to be just me and him; our eyes were locked on each other – predator and prey.

'That's another thing. Where does humour come into your self-harming?'

I looked at him, puzzled. 'Well, it's not as though I tell jokes as I'm cutting myself.' This image made me laugh again, spurred on by the smile that fought its way across his lips. He glanced down to compose and refocus himself and then looked back up at me.

'Can you stay with being serious, Emma?'

I sighed. 'But being serious is so boring.'

He chuckled this time. 'That may be the case, but we cannot have you up in your room, destroying your body and not letting the community in.' His eyes were still fixed on mine, neither of us prepared to back down.

This battle of wills was eventually stopped by Megan squeaking from somewhere far away, 'So, can Emma ask for her SIEs now?'

Grant, perhaps internally reconciling that the war was more important then this battle he had inadvertently found himself in, looked at her and with an air of all-encompassing authority, nodded once.

'All those in favour of granting Emma's SIEs, hands up.'

The majority raised their hands in the air, smiling at me as they did so. I saw Grant's go up along with my friends.

'All those opposed?'

I kept my eyes down at this point; I didn't want to know who didn't want me there.

'And undecided?'

I saw Esther's arm shoot up, accompanied by a few other staff, Bernard and Yvonne to name a couple. The meeting came to an end and as I walked out of the room I got my various congratulations from Mike, Susie and a few others – they patted me on the back and smiled at me as they walked past, small simple gestures but ones that said they were happy I wasn't going anywhere. I'd survived, my throat intact.

Augusta followed me into the kitchen talking incessantly about the various interactions that had taken place in the meeting. As I squirrelled out my bag of porridge to prepare she was so incomprehensibly fast that I had to ask her to repeat herself.

'Sorry! Sorry! I can't believe you're making food by the way! You do know where you are, don't you? Or have you really gone mad? Can I sit with you while you eat? I know you don't like it but I won't look at you and—'

I interrupted, fearing her head was about to roll off. 'It's fine, Augusta.'

We sat down at the long table in the kitchen next to a few others. Augusta was still talking at a speed that suggested she was about to implode, her ponytail whipping and jerking with every movement of her head. I felt as if she was gearing up to something and eventually it came.

'So, um, would you like to come?'

I looked up from my bowl, suddenly realising I had been doing calorie maths in my head and not listening.

'Come where…?'

'To Jess's flat… with me tonight? She said she wanted me to invite you.' I knew Augusta and Jess still kept in close contact and the offer of going to her place seemed more interesting than a night in at the Henshaw.

'Uh… yeah sure, thanks.'

*

We were called into a meeting in the afternoon and what followed was what we had been expecting for a couple of weeks now. The staff very matter-of-factly announced that they had contacted social services and reported Derek for what they were coining 'inappropriate sexual behaviour' towards Chrissie. I felt it was slightly cruel that they were delivering this information to her in such a public forum and hadn't pulled her into a private meeting to tell her… but this seemed to be the Henshaw all over: if it wasn't discussed publicly, it wasn't discussed. If it couldn't be put to a vote and deliberated on, then what was the point?

'You can't!' she screamed.

'It's already been done, Chrissie.' Blanche attempted to sound empathetic but it was useless even trying, her voice was lost amid the flames of Chrissie's internal raging forest fires.

'I'll deny it. He never did anything to me anyway! I'll say you're lying, all of you, I'll tell them you are trying to get me in trouble, trying to make me stay here in this awful place.' She was clenching her fists, her face turning more and more red.

People interjected, or tried to, calmly saying to her that what he was doing to her was wrong, that he was taking advantage of her, regardless of whether it was consensual or not. Susie's honeyed tones swept through the room.

'Sweetheart, it's not right. It's not okay what's happening. I know you're frightened but…'

'What's not right? A kind, caring man taking me in? Looking after me all these years? Making sure I had a roof over my head when my own mother couldn't even be trusted to not try and overdose me, or poison me, or push me into the road? She was the one abusing me, not Derek!'

'You don't know what's real and what's not,' said Candace looking at Chrissie as compassionately as she could. 'You can't even tell at this point what's okay and what's not okay. And I'm telling you, what he's doing to you is not okay. Everyone just wants you safe. We all care about you.' But something had been awoken in Chrissie and it was very obvious to me at least that she was not going to let anything happen to take her away from Derek.

'It's not safe for you to be living there. You haven't been open with us, Chrissie, we don't know how long this has been going on for, or to what extent,' said Meg, one of the outreach therapists.

'I'll leave here. I'll leave here if you do this,' came the shrieking response.

Blanche looked at her, resigned. 'It's been done. Whether you leave or not, he'll be investigated.'

Poor Chrissie had completely lost the plot now, realising there was no control to be gleaned. 'He never did anything I didn't want to do! I wanted to! I wanted it!' She was beside herself and it was horrible to watch.

'He is abusing you, Chrissie, because ultimately he is abusing his power; you are a young, vulnerable woman in psychiatric treatment, under his care. We can't and won't just ignore it,' said Grant firmly from his chair – daddy at the head of the table.

'He is *not!*'

They kept trying to make her understand, but to no avail.

'You can't do this! You can't do this!' She was standing up in the centre of the room, tears streaming down her face.

'You need to try and calm down, Chrissie,' said Augusta coyly, as if she were bracing herself for an onslaught.

'Augusta is right,' continued Meg again. 'You need to calm down immediately or we may have to call an ambulance for you to go to a secure unit.'

'Call it then! I don't care! I don't care what happens!'

As usual it was left to Grant to have the last word. Calmly and without apology he spoke. 'Chrissie, the decision was made and has been actioned. It's out of our hands, and yours. We will not and cannot turn a blind eye to abuse, of any sort, and if you cannot calm down we will have to do something to help you.'

'I hate you! I hate you all!' She ran out of the room, Augusta and Esther rushing after her.

To my surprise it was Mike and Gareth who were most involved in the following conversation – both shouting and hollering that they were going to rip Derek's 'fucking head off' if he came anywhere near Chrissie or the Henshaw. And the usually passive Susie was also shouting, shaking as she did, a look of anger I had never seen before on her face as she stood up and cried, 'You're just pushing her into a corner, she'll leave now, she'll go back to him, you are supposed to protect her!'

The staff had obviously prepared for this reaction and were solemn in their resolve that they would not let Chrissie be abused without telling anyone. They would not be enablers. I silently agreed, but also felt the same as many others that all we were doing with this ultimatum was pushing her further into Derek's arms, into some dark corner of hell none of us were privy to. The room was split, a mess of raised voices, questions and accusations. Eventually Augusta pushed open the door. I could tell by her face more bad news was coming.

'She's gone.'

At that point we saw Chrissie fly out of the front door, a duffel bag over her shoulder, car keys in her hand; Esther was hanging onto the door handle, shouting after her as she turned the corner, her chestnut hair disappearing down the drive as she ran.

There was a silence. After a minute Mike bellowed at Grant, 'Well that's fucking fantastic isn't it, well done.' He stormed out of the room, followed closely by Susie, who was still shaking.

*

I didn't see much of anyone for the rest of the day, although uncharacteristically for me, I stayed within the grounds. By 3 pm I was bored out of my mind and slightly manic, bouncing around the hospital looking for someone to talk to. I knocked on Mike's door and got no reply; he never went out so I assumed he must be asleep. The art room was empty and silent but I was too hyperactive to sit down and do something creative. So, singing to myself, I bounded down the four flights of stairs, through the kitchen and burst into the 9/15. Tara was sitting in the corner of the room rolling a cigarette. Tara had only been in the hospital a week, she was quiet and I had barely said more than hello to her since she arrived.

'Hiya!' I called as I walked in and plonked myself down a few chairs away from her.

'Hi?' came the slightly wary response.

'Tara,' I said, my voice having turned into that of a two-year-old child that wants something.

'Yes, Emma?' she said smirking back at me.

'Candace told me you cook, make cakes and stuff?'

She eased into the conversation at that point. 'Oh, yeah I do. I love baking.'

I carried on. 'Well, I'm terrible at making cakes, and I was wondering if you could teach me? I'm really fucking bored and I need something to distract me from everything that went on today.'

She looked down at her watch, for what reason I'm not sure as neither of us had anything to do. She put a cigarette into the corner of her mouth and pulling out a lighter from the massive pockets of her long thick jumper said, 'Okay. Let me have this and then we can have a go.' I squeaked a few thank yous and waited in the warmth of the hospital as I watched her smoke under the grey clouds outside.

*

The kitchen was always fully stocked with anything and everything you could desire – it was a scandalous paradise of naughty but nice treats and it was no trouble finding all the ingredients we needed for the cake-making lesson. I stood next to Tara with a notepad and pen watching as she meticulously laid out bowls, eggs, butter, milk, sugar, flour and began to take me through what it was she would be doing. I watched her, mesmerised for a time as without using measurements or spoons she sifted, stirred and poured. Candace poked her head around the corner of the serving window.

'Oh yeah, what's this then?'

'Tara is teaching me how to bake,' I beamed back at her.

Candace nodded in approval then once again disappeared around the corner. When I turned back Tara was taking off her jumper. She was about a foot taller than me, with dyed hair that was the colour of amber. She pushed her glasses back on her nose with her slender fingers. But it was only when she turned around to face me in her fitted black T-shirt that I had to dart my eyes quickly away from her arms.

Her skin was so pale, the most perfect canvas for the hundreds of bright red raised scars that seemed to cover every centimetre of her exposed flesh. She was too busy greasing baking trays to notice what was now me gawping at her body. I could hear random words coming from her mouth: 'icing'... 'mix'... I nodded but my brain struggled to focus on anything but the scars, and the occasional fresh cut.

Half an hour had passed. Tara opened the oven and pulled out two symmetrical sponge cakes. 'So we just wait for them to cool then put on the icing sugar.' She pulled her jumper back on. 'I'm just gonna go for a smoke.' I smiled robotically, forcing an 'Okay', and flopped my head down on the counter next to the perfectly golden cakes as the kitchen door swung shut behind her. The image of her arms was sure to become the screen saver for my mind over the next few days.

*

I didn't expect Augusta to be impressed by my baking skills as she herself was an extraordinary cake maker, so I was a little surprised when she praised my wonky vanilla sponge, the too-runny icing dripping off the sides of the plate and onto my hands. Mike was first to have a piece and I couldn't help but smile when he said it was good. Next Yvonne took a slice exclaiming in her French accent, 'Wonderful, Emma. You and Tara have done very well today.' I even took the praise from Esther, though had the fleeting urge to shove the whole cake in her face. Needless to say I didn't have any. I wanted to try it, just a little bit… but every time I picked up a slice I felt overwhelmed by how many calories were in it and put it down; thankfully everyone was so grateful of the mood lift after the morning's mess, that my not eating went, as usual, unnoticed.

We sat in the 9/15; almost all the patients came down and it was strangely comforting to see everyone just chatting, relaxed, laughing, eating cake and drinking tea. I gazed around the room and, with the exception of a couple of them, I realised I was starting to look at these people as though they were friends.

Having run it by the night staff, Augusta announced we could leave to go to see Jess at around six, saying to them we would have dinner at her house. It was becoming apparent that for some reason Augusta was more than happy to lie for me when it came to food, which felt strange as she was so adamant about sticking to the rules with everyone else.

It was a short bus ride to the estate and after a ten-minute walk Augusta was pressing the buzzer for 'Flat 4'. I was a bit anxious about going to Jess's although I had felt a little pull towards her at the Henshaw, especially after her heartfelt goodbye to me.

Happily, though, the evening was a lot of fun. She was welcoming and friendly from the second she opened the door to the tiny, one-bedroom flat. I discovered Jess and I had the same sense of humour and spent the evening roaring with laughter as we watched various TV shows and gossiped about the Henshaw. Oddly enough, as quickly and effortlessly as I eased in to Jess's company, Augusta seemed to stiffen, getting more and more stressed out. All her OCD traits were bubbling to the surface – she refused to sit on the sofa with us and crouched uncomfortably on the floor, quietly counting under her breath. I would hear her get to a hundred, watch as she patted her knee several times, then restart the counting once more – much, it seemed, to Jess's annoyance – she then began, completely unprovoked, proclaiming to us both every so often that she was 'fine'.

It was nice to be away from the hospital, and from everything that had gone on with Chrissie. I tried to stall going back as long as I could, but Augusta had almost seemed to want to go within half an hour of getting there. I had, rather selfishly, ignored her attempts at suggesting we leave, until eventually her anxiety had turned her voice into an inaudible squeak. 'I really think we need to go back, we told them we'd be back by now.' I decided I had better oblige and so we said goodnight to Jess and headed home to the hospital.

10

MR JONES AND ME

"Soon madness has worn you down. It's easier to do what it says than argue. In this way, it takes over your mind. You no longer know where it ends and you begin. You believe anything it says. You do what it tells you, no matter how extreme or absurd. If it says you're worthless, you agree. You plead for it to stop. You promise to behave. You are on your knees before it, and it laughs."

— MARYA HORNBACHER, *Madness: A Bipolar Life*

I had known about the date for Natalie's grandad's funeral for a few days but had not asked for time away from the hospital. I knew if I brought it into one of the morning meetings I would be made to dissect how I felt about it all, or rather everyone else would try to – firing hundreds of questions at me about my 'feelings', whether or not I would be safe, if I should take someone from the hospital along with me, if perhaps I shouldn't go. Subconsciously I'm sure a large part of me didn't want to answer any of their questions because I knew the answers, that actually, yes, I was struggling with this massively and that death of any sort affected me horribly. I sat in the 10pm meeting deliberating whether I should tell them, or just go… I left it to the last possible moment then put in what they referred to as an 'emergency extension'. The night staff weren't keen to grant it as they argued I was being manipulative waiting until the last second to tell them (which I was). One of those night staff was Bernard, who used this brief show of me actually needing something to utilise his power and dangle the extension in front of me like a carrot. The reason I think Bernard couldn't stand me was that he knew no matter what was said I would go and do what I wanted, and that whenever I brought anything into meetings it was merely to cover my back. It was all a formality, a game, a vote wasn't going to stop me going and he knew that.

'I just don't see…', he drew out the word 'see', his lisp lingering in the air like a hiss, 'why you waited to bring this in. It seems very manipulative, and extremely calculated. You know full well, with the staff-to-patient ratio in the evenings, we are outnumbered and whatever we say, the majority of the patients will vote in your favour.'

Yes, I thought, *they will, that's exactly why I did it.* I pursed my lips as though I was contemplating what he was saying as if it was a new concept. 'I suppose, with everything that went on with Chrissie yesterday, I just didn't feel right bringing it in; I felt as if everyone had enough to worry about.'

He uncrossed his legs, then crossed them again. 'That sounds like a very convenient answer.'

'That's not really fair, Bernard,' interjected Susie, 'we all know Em struggles with speaking up in meetings, and asking for things.'

He uncrossed his legs again. 'I'm not commenting on that, I'm saying this all feels very orchestrated.'

Esther's well-tempered voice squeaked out from behind the sleeve of her bath robe. 'I don't know about any of that…' I should have timed how long it would take her with her bullshit to weigh in – any excuse. She went on. 'But I don't think it's safe for Emma to go. I think someone needs to go with her, and it definitely needs to be discussed in the morning meeting.'

'The funeral starts at nine, so I'll be needing to leave long before the 9/15,' I said, smiling at her with a quiet 'go fuck yourself' in my eyes.

'Yeah, see, this is what I mean, calculated.' Bernard was enjoying the idea of me wriggling on a hook. I needed help. I looked pleadingly across the room at Mike and Augusta; my SOS was quickly received.

'That's a bit harsh, mate.' Mike's booming voice was like music to my ears. 'You can't say that, it's not on. If she has to go, she has to go. It's her best mate, end of.'

Before Bernard could say anything Augusta chimed in, 'Emma, will you ring us if you feel like you are struggling while you're there?'

I nodded at her. 'Yeah I will.'

She looked at Bernard. 'There, she'll reach out and ask for help. I vote for her to be able to go.'

'Same,' said Tara from next to me.

'Yeah me too,' added Candace. I watched Bernard squirm uncomfortably in his chair as I fought the desire to laugh in his face.

Fiona was the other therapist on night duty. Bernard turned to her. 'I'm sure Fiona agrees with me?'

Fiona cleared her throat. 'Well, Emma is working hard in small group to be more open and ask for help, and actually I think asking to go to the funeral, even though I agree it has been left late, is proof that Emma is trying to let people in.' She looked at me. 'I know it would have been easy for you to just go without saying, but you are letting us know and I think that shows a lot of growth.'

Bernard flushed red with a look of fury that I'd never seen his expression escalate to before. *Oh dear, Fiona, I think you're off the Christmas card list.*

'All those in favour of Emma being able to go?' said Megan, stifling a laugh. Everyone apart from Bernard and Esther raised their hands. 'Cool, call us if you need us, Emma. Meeting over.' My little saviours, I could have kissed them, each and every one.

*

St Mary Magdalen was a decadent red inside, rich, bold colours swirling around a gold altar. Apparently this place had been Natalie's grandad's church and he used to attend Mass here twice a week. My friends and the family went and sat up at the front but I continued to loiter where I was at the back.

As with a lot of things that I found it hard to be mentally present for, my mind and body began to disconnect from each other. I floated off from the service thinking about weight and diets, calories and purging, Tara's arms, my own scars... just about anything I could to keep my mind off the touching speech the priest was giving. Every so often I'd tune in for a moment, feel my throat constrict and go back to thinking about how I could orchestrate having less than 300 calories for the day.

I stayed lost in my own world for the remainder of the morning; the only thing to occasionally bring me back into the room were the sounds of Natalie and her mother's quiet sobbing, but even then I couldn't stay with it, it was too painful, too real.

At the British Legion's club afterwards I listened to speech after speech from their friends and family – all the while holding Natalie's hand and trying to perfect my reassuring smile. I checked my phone for the sixth time as we all stepped out of a black cab by a nearby pub; I was worrying about getting back to the hospital. Natalie's mum grabbed my arm, and through the smell of alcohol and tears said, 'You'll stay a while won't you? For Nat? You will, won't you, Em?'

'Of course,' came my response. While we all filed in and stood at the bar I tried to work out how long I had to get back to the hospital before the night meeting started, and how much shit I would be in if I didn't make it. It was 7pm and I'd been out all day at this point. I was already pushing it.

After the eighth and ninth rounds of cans cracking open, I knew I had to go – the alcohol would now serve to help my friends in their time of need, as well as to help me to slip out unnoticed. I rushed to the train station but I wasn't alone; something had crept into me. I wasn't sure when, or at what point, but some awful heaviness had begun to pollute my mind and as I got on the train I felt like I was floating above myself, watching my own reflection as if it were a stranger. I stared vacantly out of the window miming along to 'Mr Jones', the song I was currently holding hostage on my Discman, the repeat button being pressed every few minutes. The further along in my journey I got, the further from myself I seemed to travel.

*

It was a couple of minutes to ten. The lights of the 9/15 came into view, everyone having already taken their seats as I walked up the driveway dragging my feet behind me as though they had weights tethered to them.

The feelings of vacancy and disassociation that had wrapped around me like a blanket over the last few miles had somehow begun to twist and turn themselves into a lurid, searing anger the closer to the hospital I got. A furious stabbing pain in my stomach started up and felt as if it was gnawing at my guts; what was happening? I didn't have the energy to figure it out.

I walked into the 9/15, sitting in the furthest corner from everyone, my CD still hot as I twirled it on my index finger. I tuned in and out as if the meeting wesre a radio station I had no inclination to hear, the noise coming into focus every now and then, just enough to hear them discuss Megan's over-exercising, Esther's latest headbanging episode, and Irfan's 'feelings of abandonment'. At one point somebody, although I can't remember who, asked if I was 'okay' – it felt like an afterthought, as if I'd been totally overlooked and had to make way for everyone else's feelings. They all knew where I'd been, why had it taken half an hour to ask if I was all right? Without meaning to, I snapped back, 'Fine.' The room was going black and the only thing I could hear was the voice in my head telling me to go to the seldom used squash courts. *It's quiet in there. No one will find you. You can be angry in there and no one will have to know. You can play 'Mr Jones' over and over and over again and they won't be able to hear it.*

As top three closed the meeting book I was up and out of the room; systematically and without the need for thought, my feet directed me. Turn right, then left, through the double doors, down the hall, no light whatsoever, through the next set of double doors, this room is cold, walk straight ahead, get the CD player on your right, turn left, take the first door to the right, find the handle, go in. I quietly shut it behind me and stood for a moment with my back to it. The white walls of the squash courts created a light amid the total black. My chest heaved up and down though I had only walked for a few seconds. I fumbled around the walls with my hands, reaching, trying to find a light switch. Finally I landed on something and with a flick of my finger, the room lit up, neon white. I looked to my left at the narrow wooden staircase that led up to the mezzanine level of the court. Within a minute, or an hour (time had lost all meaning by this point) I was loading Counting Crows back into the CD player, hitting play and sighing with relief as track three began to boom out, blocking out the voices in my head that were narrating my every breath. I sat quietly with my eyes closed and mouthed the words. The mouthing turned into singing. And the singing to shouting. My hands were shaking and whatever had started happening to my head was happening again, the thudding now competing with the music. Flashes of the day were slipping through my mind, turning me into a washing machine of vision after vision, Natalie, the coffin, the crying, the flowers, my mother, me, inadequate, out of control. And just then, the true cause of my grief crashed against me like a tidal wave, the image of my dog in her last moments a few weeks before, the feelings of uncontrollable grief and loss, the back-breaking heavy guilt of letting a man whose surname I did not know inject her with a poison that stopped her heart beating. The look of trust in her black eyes as she stared at my face, the convulsing of my body as he shaved her leg and told me to say goodbye, the seconds that passed at a speed that had no meaning.

He flicks the needle.

Mr Jones and me...

The needle's going in.

Look into the future...

Time moves and I am now in the vet's room, and I am watching her chest rise, and fall, and rise, and I wait, and I hold my breath with her.

We stare at the beautiful women...

And the vet is telling me it's over.

She's looking at you...

But I will not move.

She's looking at me...

'She's gone.'

Standing in the spotlight...

No she's not, she'll breathe again.

I bought myself a grey guitar...

I hear myself shrieking 'Is she definitely dead?' over and over and over again, and he answers me with the same awful three letter word, 'Yes, yes, yes.'

When everybody loves me...

'But her eyes are open!' I scream at him, his fingers move quickly over her face onto her chest lingering there for a heartbeat that never comes and her body suddenly looks heavier and more still.

I will never be lonely...

I am back in the squash court and I am watching myself smash a racket against the wall, it's splintering and the wall makes a loud noise with every strike.

I will never be lonely...

I throw it over the mezzanine and the echo of the bracket hitting the floor does nothing to obscure the sounds of myself.

Said I'm never gonna be...

My hands are in my black bag and they are pulling out a razor blade that has been sitting for months in my wallet.

lonely...

I roll up my sleeve.

lonely...

And I am plunging the blade into my skin repeatedly as I shout through the tears that are all over my face, dripping into my mouth and being spat out with the force of my shouting the words I can hear. And before anything can make much sense, the images in my head have stopped and there is blood all over the perfect white of the room, all over my clothes, all over my bag and I can hear screaming, awful, terrifying screaming, and I am flying back through the darkness alongside the screaming, following it, trying to find where it is going, where it is coming from, someone is in a lot of pain, someone is very hurt and they are making one of the worst noises I have ever heard. All of a sudden I am back in the main hall and Irfan is staring at me as if he has just seen a ghost, his mouth is moving but I cannot hear a word over the screams, I want to ask him why he looks so worried but for some reason I can't, and then somehow I am not steering myself any more, someone is pushing me from behind and all too quickly I realise that the screaming is coming from me. And I can't stop. I bend over like I am going to retch, but every time I do the screams come out. There is some sort of door around me and there is someone I know watching me, Augusta perhaps, or Esther; I see my hand move in front me as the door slams violently shut in whoever's face it is. And then there is nothing. I look up and I am silent. It happens all at once and everything has come to a complete stop, though the floor is still shaking along with the whole room. Pierre, the gardening and maintenance therapist, is standing in front of me shouting. I try and concentrate on what sounds he is making and I try not to smile as finally I hear him, his voice a high-pitched shriek.

'Does it need stitches? Does it? I don't know! Does it? It does need stitches!' I look at my arm then back at him and suddenly find this situation hilarious. The more panic that spreads across his face the funnier I find it. He is pulling gauze and bandages and antiseptic wipes out of every cupboard so manically that he is dropping most of them. They hit the floor gently and when he tries to pick them up he drops them again, still shouting. He repeats his question about stitches and rather aggressively now. I laugh.

A sort of expression washes over my face that I imagine looks like that of Regan in *The Exorcist* when she is telling the priest his mother sucks cocks in hell and I half scream back at him, 'No it doesn't need fucking stitches, just give me a bandage and I'll do it myself you fucking incompetent idiot', but then I am crying again, and the sadness is all around me and I wish I hadn't shouted at poor Pierre who is now trembling as much as I am. Brianne, a tall redheaded swanlike therapist, is behind me asking what has happened. I ask her for a hug, she refuses and I begin to shout again. I shout that she is a '*cold, heartless bitch*'. I scream it again and again from the top of my lungs, '*cold, heartless bitch; cold, heartless bitch; cold, heartless bitch*,' until she leaves. And then I am still and quiet. I let Pierre bandage my arm as I sit on the bed. I begin to talk to him about gardening and trees and say I really enjoyed our trip out with Lyle and Cath. He doesn't respond. There is sweat dripping down his temples and sliding onto his neck. His hand is weaving over itself again and again and my arm is covered with white gauze. I am back in the hallway and someone is taking me to my bedroom. The room is dark, and so quiet. Crawling into bed I am asleep as my head hits the pillow.

*

The next morning I woke up with dread holding me in place. I groaned aloud as the thought of the 9/15 meeting swirled in my head. I knew that getting in there first would be to my advantage but I couldn't make myself move quickly. I raised my arm up and looked at it, and as embarrassed as I was about the night before I had a gnawing feeling of annoyance at how badly by arm had been bandaged. I began to unwrap it, eventually finding my skin buried beneath what seemed like twelve metres of gauze. Several cuts lined my arms, some deep; they probably could have warranted a couple of stitches, but I wasn't about to hold that against Pierre. I threw the bandages in the bin, re-dressed my arm properly and began the arduous task of getting ready. I looked like shit, pale and ill no matter how much eyeliner and mascara I applied.

Once again the meeting went much more smoothly than I had imagined it would. I was asked what had happened and I responded, as honestly and as in lacking in detail as I could. Unfortunately for me Brianne was in the meeting – perhaps she hadn't gone home purely for this purpose – and just as everyone else seemed happy to have me asking for SIEs she kicked her long leg out and crossed it over the other. 'The thing that strikes me, Emma, is that you asked me for a hug. And when I didn't give it to you, you became very, very angry.'

I wanted to punch her. I wanted to get up right there and then and throw her through the glass doors behind her. Her mouth was in such a pout I imagined she had half a lemon inside it. In as much of a controlled way as I could I said, 'I was having a panic attack, Brianne. A bit of human contact would have been helpful.'

She went on, purely it seemed (in my eyes at least) to expose and try to embarrass me. 'But you almost seemed *desperate* for me to hug you – what was that about? It struck me as almost odd, Emma. And then the screaming and raving when I wouldn't, they could hear it from the garden.'

You bitch, you stupid, cruel bitch. Gathering myself up, slowly, carefully, I said, 'I think my reaction was normal, I think it was yours that was not.' I refused to engage with her any further although she kept trying, inviting others to talk about their 'experience of me'. Some of the other therapists, Grant namely, seemed to feel sorry for me and, as Brianne went on and on, I looked at him with begging eyes that he had probably never seen before.

He cut her off. 'Okay, I feel like this is enough of a discussion about it today. Emma had a very bad night; my recommendation is she talks about it in her small group. Can I ask what's next on the agenda please?' They talked about Esther banging her head against the wall next; I had never been so relieved to hear her drone on. It was obvious now that I was not going to be allowed out at the weekend; perhaps they all thought that was punishment enough.

*

The next day I felt more myself again and was able to talk in the morning meeting about the funeral and what a strain it had been to see the people I loved in such distress and feeling useless against it. I didn't talk about my dog as it felt too private and, more to the point, as if they wouldn't understand, or worse, would judge me for behaving so 'dramatically' over an animal. Some things truly are better left unsaid – or at least held in until the right audience is available.

11

IRFAN

"All creatures must learn that there exist predators. Without this knowing, a woman will be unable to negotiate safely within her own forest without being devoured."

— CLARISSA PINKOLA ESTÉS, *Women Who Run With the Wolves: Myths and Stories of the Wild Woman Archetype*

'Welfare' was a group we had to endure three times a week, which was run by Magda. To say I didn't like welfare would have been an understatement. While other people would spend the two-hour session ringing the housing association and securing flats for when they left the Henshaw, I sat there thinking about returning to my life at home. The welfare room was bright yellow and far too small for my liking. I felt like I was sitting on top of everyone and the claustrophobia was overwhelming at best, unbearable at worst. It had been two days since my eruption, and this particular morning everyone had shown up, meaning the group was more full than usual. I quite liked Magda; she was strict, but seemed to be able to see into my head without me saying anything and would constantly challenge me, asking things like: 'How do you feel about your fellow patients refusing to give you any sort of attention when you need help? That they just let you get away with everything?' She would do this in front of them to provoke a response; they would bite, but I never would. This was one of those mornings. After we had done our hour of phoning up welfare advisors and planning for the 'future', we would fill out forms the Henshaw gave us about how we felt we were progressing in treatment and how we would cope once back out in the big, bad world (I spent this time writing down obstinate and ridiculous answers to these questions 'I think I shall become a homeless artist. I will commandeer a small army of rats and utilise their skills to steal cheese from the rich' and so on). Then, once the forms were completed, we collected back in the welfare room to discuss how we all were. Magda used this time to ask provocative questions and generally, it seemed, to try and rile everyone up. On this morning in particular Irfan was sitting next to her just out of her line of view, but directly in mine. He spent the whole of the session staring at me, smiling, and laughing hysterically whenever I told a joke (my constant role in any and every social situation).

'I'm guessing no one's followed up with Emma? I heard about the other night. Just ignoring it all, are we? Letting her get away with everything as usual?' She was so obnoxious it was almost funny to me.

'Oh fuck off,' I heard Gareth mumble under his breath.

'What was that Gareth? Do share.' She smiled at him as if she hadn't heard exactly what he'd said.

'Nothing,' he grumbled.

She kept going but they all ignored her attempts and when, a few minutes later, she finally called time on the session, I was relieved to get away from Irfan's beady eyes peeping out from behind his glasses.

*

After welfare came cleaning, and then the dreaded psychodrama – which I had grown to loathe horrendously and would refuse point-blank to get involved in, often saying I needed the toilet at least six or seven times during the session. These trips would last about ten minutes each and if Kerry challenged me on it I would act as if I was terribly hurt and say something like, 'Kerry, why do you want me to get kidney stones? Why do you want my bladder to rupture?' She, like most other authority figures in my life, would give up after the third or fourth round of this and seemingly ignored my fellow patients' giggles as I skipped out of the room grinning like a Cheshire cat.

*

That night, I sat in the 9/15 with several other people. They were chatting, watching TV; I felt my phone vibrate. I looked down to see a new message from a number I didn't know. I picked it up and pressed open. The message read: 'You got me really hard in welfare today.' I shoved the phone onto my lap then picked it up again. 'You got me really hard in welfare today.' A shiver of disgust ran up my spine. My phone beeped again with another message: 'I want to fuck you.' I stared at the TV blankly, praying it wouldn't vibrate again, but it did... perhaps I shouldn't look? I pressed open. 'We're going to have sex. Come to my room tonight. Irfan x'. I instantly thought back on my actions and how they could have been misconstrued. Had I been flirting with him and not even realised it? I somehow must have evoked this reaction with my behaviour although I wasn't sure how. Should I tell someone? Should I tell Mike? No, best not. I must have made too much eye contact with him? Smiled too much? It didn't once occur to me that perhaps I hadn't done anything, and that maybe Irfan was just a predator. I wanted to tell someone but felt I couldn't. It was embarrassing, and I was certain I had somehow done something to have made him send the messages to me in the first place. I switched my phone off and pushed it into my pocket.

An hour later, as I sat opposite Mike still in the 9/15, Irfan walked in. He smiled at me, a smarmy look spread all over his face. I tried not to look at him, my eyes darting away to the TV, but he kept asking Mike and me questions. 'Are you having a good night, Emma? You look tired, better get yourself to bed soon?' I carried on staring at the TV and didn't answer him. I was more than relieved when he got up to go and 'listen to his music in his room'.

A few minutes after that, Mike, his eyes fixed on the TV, said, 'I don't trust him as far as I could throw him.'

I tried not to seem overly interested in his statement and said as casually as I could, 'Why's that?'

Still not looking at me, Mike shook his head as if trying to shake an image from his mind. 'There's something wrong with him. He used to stalk his ex, one of the reasons he's in here. I wouldn't be surprised if...' his voice tapered off and I started to lose my cool demeanour.

'If what?'

He pulled a face as if he had a bad taste in his mouth.

'If what, Mike?' I repeated.

'I don't know. I don't know if he'd understand the word "no" if a girl said it to him. And I don't like the way he is with you and how he was with Chrissie. He fucked Jess when she was vulnerable, and he fucked another girl before that, same thing, vulnerable, she didn't know any better. The staff knew about Jess, but not the first girl; if they had maybe he would have been chucked out, you know, if they realised it was a pattern. Just be careful. And tell me if he tries anything.' He picked up the remote and began channel surfing.

I should tell him, this was my chance. But what would happen if I did? Would he go and confront Irfan, would they fight? Then a referred would be called; I'd have to tell them all about the texts, I'd probably have to read them aloud... then what if they said he had to leave, where would he go? Or worse yet, what if they said he could stay and he was angry, came to find me, to punish me? Or what if Mike got in trouble for fighting him, and was told he had to leave? No. No, I couldn't, there were too many variables, too many ways it could go wrong. I gave it some time then said goodnight. I chose to go the longer route to my bedroom, which meant not having to pass Irfan's. It was late and most of the lights were off. I walked through the dark building as silently as I could, barely making a sound on the stairs, or through the art room. As I opened my bedroom door I flicked on the light before I went in, peered inside and bent down to look under the bed, I breathed a little sigh of relief: nothing there. Without making a sound I closed the door behind me, sat down on my bed and for the first time in the Henshaw felt as if I wanted a lock on my door. I lay on top of the bed sheets fully clothed and unable to sleep, straining to listen for any sound outside in the hallway. After a while I got up and propped my chair up against the door; at least this way if he tried to get in I'd have fair warning.

12

BORDERLINERS

'Borderline what? Borderline between what and what?'

Girl, Interrupted

BPD. The three letters kept being repeated. I pulled out my phone and checked to see if I had any messages to distract me from the current conversation that was going completely over my head. No new messages. Back to the speech then. June was a woman who had come into the Henshaw for the day to give us all a talk on borderline personality disorder, or 'BPD' as she kept referring to it. I stared at her as she wrote down things on the whiteboard in the 9/15.

'Frantic efforts to avoid real or imagined abandonment.'

'Pattern of unstable and intense interpersonal relationships characterised by alternating between extremes of idealisation and devaluation.'

'Identity disturbance; markedly and persistently unstable self-image or sense of self.'

I looked over to Candace who was sitting next to me doodling in a notebook. I nudged her with my foot.

'Why are we listening to this?' I whispered.

She didn't look up. 'So we can be educated on it, the symptoms and all that.'

I glanced back at the whiteboard.

'Recurrent suicidal behaviour, gestures, or threats, or self-mutilating behaviour.'

Charming. I gently kicked her foot again. 'But why do *we* have to learn about it?'

She looked away from her drawing and, bemused, loudly whispered back, 'Because we have it, Emma! That's why we're here, obviously! Now ssh, I want to draw.' She turned back to her notebook.

Sorry what? We 'have it'? I don't fucking 'have it'! I kicked her again; she huffed loudly and slammed her book down on her lap as she turned to look at me with wide, questioning eyes.

'Candace, I don't have this—'

She interrupted, 'Emma! This hospital is for people *with BPD*. Everyone in this room, bar June over there, has been diagnosed with borderline. Maybe they just didn't tell you, but you've been diagnosed somewhere along the line, which is why you're sitting here. Ask your doctor or something, it'll be in your notes. Now please shut the fuck up, I want to draw!'

I turned back to the meeting and felt my brow furrow as I actually tuned in and listened to June. 'So that's it really, guys, that's what the DSM categorises the symptoms of borderline personality disorder as.' She flicked over the page of the large book she had in her hands and began to read from it. 'A pervasive pattern of instability of interpersonal relationships, self-image, and affects, and marked impulsivity beginning by early adulthood and present in a variety of contexts as indicated by five or more of the symptoms we've discussed.' She gestured towards the whiteboard. 'Chronic feelings of emptiness. Affective instability due to a marked reactivity of mood, for example intense episodic dysphoria, irritability, or anxiety usually lasting only a few hours and only rarely more than a few days.'

Who didn't have irritability? Or a 'reactive mood' or occasionally feel 'empty'? Okay, yes, I did feel empty a lot of the time but didn't everyone? And yes my moods did swing from hour to hour but whose didn't?

Tara raised her arm. 'June, sometimes I feel myself making very snap decisions, sometimes they get me into trouble, is that part of BPD?'

June walked over to the whiteboard. 'Yes, you can see that here in the fourth point.' She tapped her red nail on bullet point four. I squinted as I read her wonky handwriting.

'Impulsivity in at least two areas that are potentially self-damaging.'

I kept reading over the nine symptoms on the board. 'Inappropriate, intense anger or difficulty controlling anger.' My anger wasn't inappropriate. Yes, I was often angry about something or other but it was always valid, wasn't it?

I felt a huge surge of relief as I read the final point on the list. 'Transient, stress-related paranoid ideation or severe dissociative symptoms.' Ha! I don't dissociate. I sat there for a minute safe in my resolve that despite being able to tick every other criteria I didn't have that one. Of course, my mind chose that moment to project me back to the squash court incident that I remembered so little of. I still wasn't sure how I got from place to place, how long the whole thing went on for and I certainly didn't remember getting up or down the stairs or back to my room. But, that wasn't dissociating, was it? My feeling of relief was short-lived as I realised that probably was dissociation in one form or another.

As soon as the meeting ended I went up to my room and dialled my GP's surgery. I bypassed the receptionist by saying Dr Khan, my GP of the last six years, had personally asked me to call him – I doubted she believed me but she put me through.

'Hello Emma, how can I help?'

'Dr Khan, have I been diagnosed with borderline personality disorder?'

There was a short pause before he spoke. 'Why do you ask that?'

'Because I'm in a hospital for people with it.'

'Emma,' he cleared his throat, 'I really didn't think the diagnosis would be helpful for you at the time, so you weren't told.'

I was stunned. My own doctor had kept this from me.

'When was I diagnosed?'

He inhaled loudly. 'A few years ago.'

I hung up and sat on my bed staring at the window for what felt like a lifetime. So I did have 'it'. I had had 'it' for years. And he hadn't thought to tell me. Hadn't thought that it might be helpful to know that my behaviour all this time could actually be attributable to something else? Maybe if someone had told me this when they diagnosed me I could have got real help for it instead of resorting to trying to kill myself in a miserable house in east London the year before, the suicide attempt that was the appetiser to my ending up in here. Do you want to hear about it? The suicide attempt? I suppose you probably do, that's where the fun lies isn't it? In the gore. Well sorry to disappoint you, but there was none of that, no wrist slitting, no railway tracks, no ceiling beams, not even a head in the oven type of scenario. I was staying in a bedroom with no light fixtures in it, on a single mattress in the basement of a shared house in east London. The walls of the room were infected with rising damp and had black mould creeping up them. I was surviving on plain boiled pasta because that was all I could afford, and smoking more skunk then my already struggling brain could process. I'd taken myself off my mood stabilisers and as my depression reached it's glorious peak I decided to fully, wholeheartedly, commit myself to suicide. With the house empty for the weekend, I wandered the local shops accruing enough paracetamol, codeine and ibuprofen to take down a small horse. I went back to my room, wrote a goodbye letter to Natalie, put Sarah McLachlan's *Mirrorball* on the CD player and began the arduous task of swallowing pill, after pill, after pill. I lost lost count after number 67. And then off I went into blissful unconsciousness. It was ethereal my suicide, painless, serene, a thing of beauty; waking up covered in my own vomit, however, was not so beautiful. It was dark outside and raining, Sarah McLachlan had long since abandoned me and I felt sick, sicker then you could even begin to imagine, I'm talking about the type of nausea that makes you wish someone would take a sledgehammer to your head just to get it to stop. The room spun like a cheap fair ground ride that you know is going to break apart at any second and all I could do was crawl, on my hands and knees to the bathroom. The vomiting was endless. I somehow managed to lift myself in to the bath tub where I stayed, retching, for the better part of 48 hours, watching what looked like an explosion of discoloured Smarties flow out of my body like a Charlie and the Chocolate Factory acid trip, until finally, eventually, yellow, stringy bile began to appear. The pain was excruciating: my back, my insides, my mind. Never, ever, ever again. And then of course came the shame, the voice louder than ever before screeching into my ears as it laughed maniacally, 'Well fuck me, you couldn't even kill yourself properly.'

Several days after the 'attempt' I sat facing a young blonde woman, in an airless room in my GP's surgery. Dr Khan wasn't available, so Dr Sarah Deacon it was. I didn't want to open up to her, I had never met her before, and I was exhausted. 'So Emma how can I help?' she asked flatly.

'I feel terrible. I feel like I'm going to kill myself. I *want* to kill myself.'

She rolled her chair towards her computer and began to type on the keyboard, her long fingers barely hitting the keys. 'And what brings this on?'

'I took an overdose a few days ago; it didn't work. I feel like I might try something else, something quicker this time.'

She turned back to face me, 'And did you go to hospital, for this "overdose"?'

I shook my head, 'No.'

She made a little 'mhmm' noise, ever so slightly rolling her eyes as she began to type again.

After a moment Dr Deacon pushed her chair away from her desk. 'Well I see you're already on 60mg of Prozac daily, which is obviously the highest dose, so increasing it isn't an option. Have you got a friend you could chat to about how you feel? Or how about some self-care? Having long baths, things like that?' She paused, perhaps waiting for a response which she wasn't going to get. The sunlight shone through a small window above her, making her pearl necklace shimmer brightly; it hurt my eyes to look at it. She carried on, 'Exercise often helps with low mood too... Do you do any sport?'

'Look,' I felt my hands squeeze in to fists as I stared her in the face, 'I need to be somewhere safe, like, right now. I don't need a bath, I don't need to go jogging, what I need is for you to refer me. I'm going to kill myself if I leave your office with no help!'

Dr Deacon sighed loudly, 'Emma, it's 3pm on a Friday before the bank holiday.' She held her palms out, 'I can't refer you anywhere today, it's completely out of the question!' She paused for a second, 'But, we can meet again next week and see how you're doing?'

Why wasn't she listening to me? What bit about 'I'm going to kill myself' was hard to understand? Did she think I was being melodramatic? Throwing out buzz words for fun?

'I really need you to refer me to somewhere. I can't be alone.'

She began looking at a pop-up diary on her screen. 'How about...' she made a clicking noise with her tongue as she skimmed the dates with her mouse, 'next Wednesday morning? 10am?'

'Why aren't you listening to me?' I felt my cheeks begin to flush.

She pulled out an appointment card and started scribbling something down. 'I am listening to you Emma, but it's not going to be possible to arrange a referral now. So I suggest you go home and find someone to talk to, practise some self-care and we'll meet next week.' She handed me the card, 'Okay?'

I ran home. My brain like fog, my mind whirring. I'd just told her I was going to kill myself if she let me leave and she couldn't care less, that's how little I matter! No one was in as I turned my key in the lock and sprinted up the stairs to my bedroom. Who could I call? Anyone? I paced up and down my room feeling like my chest was going to explode, my breathing getting quickly out of control. 'No one cares!' I screamed aloud to myself. 'No one fucking cares!' I pulled open my bedside table and reached for one of my new Gillette razor blades. The room was spinning, shaking, I rolled up my sleeve, and with more anger then I had ever felt dug the blade against my skin, once more shrieking 'NO ONE FUCKING CARES!' as I dragged the razor with a desperate force down my forearm. My skin parted instantly, it was so deep that it didn't even bleed at first. I looked down at the white fat, the horrible gaping of my flesh, the inch and a half wide, six inch long horror show, and watched in alarm as the blood began to gush. Oh my God. I grabbed a t-shirt and wrapped it quickly around the wound trying to ignore the intense nausea and dizziness that was quickly coming over me. What the fuck have I done? I took my phone out of my pocket and, like one of those terrible nightmares, my hands were shaking so badly I couldn't unlock the screen; every time I tried my fingers clumsily hit the wrong buttons. Panic hurtled through me until eventually, thank God, I tapped in the right number and the screen unlocked. I called Natalie and within minutes she was outside my house in a cab, waiting to take me to hospital. A few days later I was referred to the Henshaw, not by Dr Deacon, but by my therapist.

*

It had been a week since Chrissie had walked, or rather, run out, and no one had been told anything or heard from her. There was a vague mention of it in one of the 9/15 meetings saying that if they didn't hear from her soon they would discharge her, which as you can imagine went down like a ton of bricks with most people. But what could the staff do? Because of Chrissie's age, technically whatever was going on was consensual. Sure, it likely started years ago, but in the eyes of the law she was now an adult – legally they didn't have much of a leg to stand on as far as I could see. We all knew it was a problem, but if Chrissie couldn't see that then no one was going to convince her otherwise... I tried my best not to imagine where she was, who with, or if she was okay.

13

TOP 3

"Here's an easy way to figure out if you're in a cult: If you're wondering whether you're in a cult, the answer is yes."

— STEPHEN COLBERT, *I Am America*

Elections were held in the hospital every three weeks. I had so far managed to escape being elected for top three, the dread in me stirring every time it was mentioned… I would sink low in my chair hoping no one would think to suggest me, and so far it had worked, bar having to stand in on that one occasion when Lyle temporarily lost his mind. But having escaped four elections unscathed, the fifth got me, and though I tried every excuse under the sun to get out of doing it, they of course voted and to my horror I was elected.

Every single meeting that we had was recorded verbatim by the 'scribe' who was also elected (in this case it was Tara), and everything was scribbled down in the 'Referred Book'. I had tried being the scribe on one occasion and my hand had nearly fallen off, but Tara, curled up in her big cardigan, seemed to enjoy it.

There weren't any benefits to being on top three, other than having a say about what went on the agenda. Every night at eight o'clock top three, the scribe and the night staff would have to go into a room called 'summit' and have a discussion about what should be put on the agenda in the 9/15 meeting, who was struggling, what had happened in the day and what needed to be addressed. It mainly felt as if we were just mini dictators, having our secret meetings and deciding whose heads would be going on the chopping block.

Other than interfering with my regimented mealtimes, and meaning that I had to stay in the hospital all night, the meetings weren't too bad. I used summit as an excuse to bitch and moan and make people laugh. The morning meetings were the nerve-wreckers. Sitting in front of thirty or so people having to read out an agenda, start and stop discussions, and grant people their SIEs. It wasn't hard to see why people got slightly drunk on power whilst doing top three – I had been so nervous at first, sitting on the edge of the sofa quiet as a mouse, but was soon the one who chaired the meetings. I'd often refuse to start if anyone was talking and more often than not when the staff were chatting amongst themselves I would say something like, 'When you've quite finished, Grant and Lisa, we can begin.' They would automatically look up like naughty children and I would loudly clear my throat and begin with a 'Now that everyone is paying attention, we can commence. Good morning.' This would often produce a lot of laughter, from patients as well as staff, and the meeting would be off to a relaxed start, which in turn made the whole thing seem to flow with more ease than usual.

Of course I was told off by some of the staff (and Esther) for not taking it seriously, and in a lot of ways I didn't. I thought it was all far too rigid; the rules annoyed me and the voting was just bizarre. I'm sure it had worked once upon a time, but now it just felt strange, and oftentimes rather ominous – like your fate could at any moment be changed by other people. It gave me *Lord of the Flies* vibes watching some of the votes take place and a part of me felt it had all turned into a convoluted mini dystopia where it wasn't quite clear who was in charge, and where more often than not a lot of the decisions seemed to be driven by ego. In the wrong hands I could see this type of group dynamic, this strange institution (especially back in the seventies where a generation of twenty-something's were slowly coming down off the psychedelic roller coaster of the sixties) being used to breed Jim Jones types, like one big narcissistic fuckfest. If I closed my eyes I could easily imagine Marshall Applewhite and Bonnie Nettles sitting around the smoking area discussing their religious beliefs with David Koresh. Is that what this was? A cult? It didn't feel too far off sometimes. Perhaps Grant was trying to indoctrinate us all, grooming us with the voting system, seeing who could be easily swayed to turn against their peers... You needn't bother, Grant, with those cheekbones I'll just join: 'Henshaw family' here I come.

*

On my third night of top three I sat in the garden smoking a joint with Mike; we were red-eyed and bleary as we stumbled back in through the 9/15 doors. Mike collapsed on the sofa and half ordered me to 'get junk food' from the stores room. I walked down the hallway and, as I stood there looking at the hundreds of boxes of crisps not knowing what to choose, suddenly there was a crashing sound from somewhere down the hall. I picked up a twelve-pack of Penguin bars, pushed open the 9/15 door and threw them at Mike.

'Did you hear that?' I asked him.

He didn't look at me, too busy wrestling with the Penguin packaging. 'Do they actually want me to be able to eat one of these fucking things? How the hell... do ... you ...'

I rolled my eyes and started off towards where the noise had come from. By the time I opened the door to the kitchen Susie and

Augusta were bent down over Esther, who was convulsing violently on the floor. What amazed me was how calm they both were. Susie looked up and softly said to me, 'Esther's having a fit, Emma. She's going to be okay, but could you get the staff?' I nodded and bolted for the staffroom. This was the first time I'd actually seen her fitting, although I knew it had happened a few times since I'd been there.

*

Five hours later I was sitting in A&E next to Lyle, as Esther lay on a hospital bed. The doctors had told us it wasn't uncommon to suffer from short-term memory loss after having an epileptic fit. Esther began to ask where she was and who we were. The doctors wanted to do further checks on her because she had apparently suffered multiple fits. As there were only two night staff, neither could be spared to come with us so we'd gone alone. It was 3am and Lyle couldn't keep his eyes open any more. I offered him a stick of gum.

'Why don't you go back? I'm fine on my own.'

He took one and put it in his mouth. 'No. No, it's not fair. I'll stay.' He yawned for the twentieth time in a row.

'Lyle, go. Honestly I'm all good.'

With a little more persuasion he got in a cab and went back to the Henshaw. I was exhausted, I felt ill and for once I actually wished I was back at the hospital.

'Why do I have a cross around my neck?' said Esther, her eyes melting down her face as she fiddled with her crucifix.

'Because you're religious. You're all about God and the church most of the time.' The flat, uninterested tone in my voice resonated around the room.

'Oh. Yes, God. I think I remember him.'

'Good stuff,' I said as I took my gaze off her and began rummaging in my bag. I had been concerned for her at first –

she obviously had fitted, I had seen it happen in front of me – but I was convinced that, three hours after regaining full consciousness, she was now putting this on.

'Do you think God will forgive me for what I've done?' She looked down at the cat-like scratches on her arm that she must have done pre-fit.

'Probably.'

'Why am I in a mental hospital? Where is my mother?'

'At home I would think, having a large glass of wine. And you're in a mental hospital because you're mental.' I finally felt the little lump of skunk in my bag I'd been rummaging for. 'Okay, I'm going to go have a cigarette and then we'll see about getting you out of here.'

I rose to my feet and as I began to push the door open she said, 'But you don't smoke?'

I smirked as I turned around to look at her. 'How do you know? You've lost your memory, right?'

She began to stammer over her words as she attempted a response, her face growing redder by the second. 'Well, um... I have... you just don't look like a smoker and, I, um...'

I smiled sweetly at her. 'Don't worry, you're probably just dehydrated, I'll get you some water.'

*

The next day I was shattered after having only an hour's sleep. I was late for the 9/15, which I was supposed to be chairing, and subsequently got in trouble for this, despite having been up supporting Esther at the hospital. Esther, who of course said nothing in my defence. I was too tired to argue with any of the staff and let them hammer on about my lateness being a commentary on my attitude to therapy. It seemed they linked everything back to our attitudes to therapy. If I wore my hair up in a ponytail it was a commentary on my attitude to therapy; if Mike farted it was a commentary on his attitude to therapy. They were obsessed.

It was both Gareth and Louise's last day, so thankfully that took up a lot of the meeting, the staff and residents chattering about the pair's individual journeys through the Henshaw, the highs and lows. I wasn't particularly close to either of them so their leaving wasn't going to affect me massively, but if anything it was sad to lose two familiar faces. I opted to miss out on the goodbyes, hiding in my room and watching from the window as Louise was collected by a plump, older looking woman who I assumed must have been her mother. Everyone did the whooping and cheering as she drove off, Louise happily waving from the passenger side of the car, blowing kisses with her hands and smiling. Gareth followed suit not twenty minutes after. As he climbed into a taxi the staff and patients once again cheered for him. He cried (of course he did!) and like Louise, smiled and waved the whole way down the drive.

*

That evening Lyle was due to cook but said he was far too tired after being at the hospital with Esther the previous night and called a referred to try to get a vote on us being able to order Chinese food. Of course the two night staff had no chance and were outvoted. The Chinese was soon laid out in front of me with everyone tucking in. I sat with my eyes fixed on the television screen and refused to even look at the food. I hated the smell of it. I hated everyone eating it. I hated myself for wanting it. Magda kept asking me why I wasn't eating, as did some other patients. I fought off their questions but, eventually, my will failed me and I began to spoon noodles into my mouth, followed by sweet and sour rice, crackers, and just about everything I could see. I hadn't even finished chewing my last mouthful before I was racing up the stairs with a bottle of water in my hand. The disgust I felt for myself was unimaginable; I wanted to claw my skin off. I could literally feel the grease of the food on my face seeping in to my pores, the fat around me expanding. I had discovered a toilet in the art room that no one seemed to know about, set back through the pottery workshop. It was the perfect place to make myself sick. With a quick check to ensure no one was around I ducked inside and silently locked the door.

After fifteen or so minutes I was back downstairs shovelling more Chinese food into my mouth, and once again before the last mouthful was gone I was back in the art room toilet. This binge/purge session went on for hours. Mike was the only witness to it but, in-between flicking through TV channels and going outside to smoke, he did not suspect what I was up to. The ninth time I was bent over the toilet that night, blood began to flood the toilet bowl. Every time I threw up, another lot of it appeared. This should have stopped me. This should have been all the shock value I needed to go and seek help, to go downstairs, to tell someone. But I didn't. Instead I hunted through the freezer until I found Chrissie's stash of Ben and Jerry's ice cream and, deciding that she probably wouldn't be returning any time soon, I ate that too. I spent the rest of the night running up and down the four flights of stairs from the kitchen to my room: I'd time myself and try and beat my record each go. My legs were shaking by the thirtieth attempt at this. Doubled over and gasping for air at the top of the stairs, I debated stopping. But all that food… what if I hadn't got it out? What if when I weighed myself at the weekend I had gained? I couldn't bear it; I had to make sure those calories weren't staying inside me, and if that meant spending six hours running up and down the stairs, so be it.

*

My head throbbed as I pulled back my curtains and finally let the sunlight into the room. I stood looking out onto the grass of the front lawn and smeared the morning's condensation off the inside of my window with my hand. I turned my head and looked at myself in the mirror. Oh no… I took a step closer and stared at my reflection. There were hundreds of burst blood vessels all over my face, mostly around my eyes, even on my throat. Black bags hung like crescent moons on my skin and my lips were chapped and flaking. I rushed through a shower then poured what felt like a whole bottle of foundation over my face and layered concealer under my eyes. It still didn't cover up the red spots on my eyelids, so delving deeper into my make-up bag I found my eyeshadow palate and applied 'Pink Pizazz' over the dots, surely that would hide them?

We were told that morning that Chrissie had 'left' the Henshaw. The staff said that, after multiple attempts to get her back, she was adamant that she wouldn't return so they granted her what she wanted and officially discharged her, saying that as far as they knew she was back living with Derek and Barb. As was expected, the shouting began – staff vs patients. How could you let her leave? How could you endanger her? You aren't helping people, you're harming them, and so on and so forth. I sat quietly with my eyes fixed on the floor thinking, *I knew she wouldn't need the ice cream.*

*

I barely consumed anything that day. And even after my routine coffee I threw up. My back and ribs ached, I felt sick and I was walking like a eighty-year-old woman with severe arthritis. Sitting in my room with the hospital walls spinning around me, I rang Dr Khan and asked to go in and see him the following day; he made me an appointment for eleven. My annoyance at him not telling me about my borderline diagnosis was lulled considerably and most of the time I felt like he was the only true confidant I had.

The rest of my evening was spent meticulously preparing a salad, measuring and weighing every ingredient to make sure I was not going over 150 calories – this process always took forever because I had to stop every time someone came in the kitchen so as to not be spotted weighing my food. Huddled on my bed and watching *Supersize vs Superskinny*, I shovelled it into my mouth. Halfway through (no doubt prompted by the 'superskinny' anorexic woman I was watching cry over having to eat a '*whole*' slice of toast), I decided I did not deserve my salad and ran to the art room toilet. I sat in the evening meeting not contributing to what should go on the agenda, hardly talking, staring at the floor and fighting the feeling of being hungry with the feelings of being fat and undeserving. I left the meeting halfway through to throw up, suddenly fearing that I had not got all of the iceberg lettuce out of me the first time.

14

WHEN DANGER COMES KNOCKING

"The wolf said, 'You know, my dear, it isn't safe for a little girl to walk through these woods alone.'"

— *LITTLE RED RIDING HOOD, The Fairy Tales of The Brothers Grimm*

I lied to the staff saying my doctor had asked to see me as he wanted to know how I was getting on at the Henshaw. They didn't appreciate this and insisted on having a vote before I could leave. Luckily for me, my friends shot their hands up without being prompted and I was allowed to go.

I watched Dr Khan's fingers move briskly over his keyboard as he typed what I was saying. He seemed distant and mainly focused on scaremongering, obviously hoping that telling me my body would not have time to shrink and that saying I'd be left with 'a lot of loose hanging skin' would be enough to encourage me to stop making myself sick. I asked him why blood was coming up, and he explained that I was most likely tearing my oesophagus when I retched or perhaps had cut my throat with my nails. I left feeling as though he wasn't overly concerned.

If you were thin enough, he would be worried, he'd tell you to stop. It's because you're still obese that he doesn't care. See? You're fine. The blood isn't a worry – just cut those fingernails. Keep doing what you're doing. Three more pounds until you're skinny. Three more pounds until you win.

That voice. That voice that had come out of nowhere but was now always with me. Always there. Feeding off my energy. In my moments of weakness, when I had eaten too much, when I had eaten *at all*, it would start its whispering. And it lied! How it lied! It would always say the same thing. Three more pounds until I was skinny. But it never was three pounds. I'd lose three pounds and it still wouldn't be happy. It would say three more. I hated it. But did I hate it because I was weak and greedy? Wasn't it, at the end of the day, just trying to help me attain my goals of being thin? When it came down to it, it didn't particularly matter if I believed it or not, it wasn't going anywhere and I knew it.

I professed to being tired earlier than usual and went up to my room where, illuminated by the light of the television, I cut repeatedly. I'd sought help from Dr Khan, or tried to; I'd opened my stupid mouth for nothing and I needed to be punished. I needed a reminder to never do it again. As I lay down with my arm wrapped in a T-shirt I decided not to tell anyone; they would only keep me from going out at the weekend anyway. Had I stayed downstairs with everyone I would have known Irfan came back from 'seeing his friend' completely wasted and was banished to his room. Unfortunately, he refused to stay there. He began hammering on my door a little after midnight. I crept out of bed and picked up the chair, again wedging it under the door handle.

'Hey, let me in. I just want to talk.'

I sat on the floor in the dark, barely breathing, the razor blade I'd used to cut with in my hand – it was all I had to defend myself if he did get in.

'Emma, I know you're in there, I've looked everywhere. C'mon, don't be like this... don't be a bitch.'

The handle of my door turned slowly. I shoved my feet against the chair and as I'd hoped it would, the handle jammed on it and didn't open.

'Emma, open the door, you're being really over the top right now.'

Was I? Was I being over the top? Maybe I was? Maybe he did just want to talk... As my will started to waver his voice turned to anger.

'Open the fucking door!' I jumped as he hit what sounded like his fist against it. My phone was on the floor next to me... Should I call someone?

As I sat frozen, not knowing what to do, I heard the art room doors swing open and Magda's voice loudly say, 'What are you doing wandering around, Irfan? You're not allowed to be out of your room.'

'I, uh, oh, I thought this was my door... I went to the toilet... I got confused.'

You fucking liar.

'You're drunk, that isn't your room. Follow me, right now!'

I listened as the sound of their footsteps disappeared down the hall. I barely slept, curled up around the chair on the floor, but got some relief when in the morning meeting he was reprimanded badly by the staff. Although no one knew he had tried to get into my room, I sat there with the secret sitting in the palm of my hand like a grenade that I could pull the pin out of and throw into the middle of the room at any second. But I still felt unable to tell anyone, and I didn't know why. They decided he would be put on a vote at the end of the week to determine if he could stay or not. They didn't think he was 'taking his treatment seriously.' Many patients agreed. Grant looked across the room at Irfan.

'So can you tell me what progress you feel you've made since you've been here?'

Irfan cleared his throat. 'Well, I think I've built some really good relationships with people and been able to look at my issues around attachment,' he paused, 'plus I've been able to support others here when they needed help.'

'You are joking?' Mike's expression was somewhere between bemusement and disbelief.

Irfan looked up at him. 'What?'

'Good relationships? Support? You've shagged two girls since you've been here! You fucked them when they were at their most vulnerable! You *pretended* to support them and then persuaded them into having sex with you!'

Irfan was starting to noticeably sweat; small beads of perspiration were forming on his forehead. He pushed his glasses back on his nose and tried his best to respond to Mike whilst still playing the role of victim for the staff.

'I had mutual sex with *one* person. And I had strong feelings for her.'

Augusta scoffed and I heard her quiet voice from behind me. 'Yeah, right.'

'You are completely full of bullshit.' Mike was pointing at him now as he stared at Grant. 'Two, he fucked two girls, not one, two, and you probably would have tried to fuck Chrissie given half the chance, and others...' His voice trailed off and I silently prayed he wouldn't look at me.

'I think we need to bring this down a level,' said Grant calmly, but Mike was fuming, bright red with saliva spitting out of his mouth every time he spoke.

'*He* is a sexual predator. He's dangerous, Grant. He shouldn't be in here.'

Grant gave Mike a reassuring look that seemed to say he agreed.

'I am not,' came Irfan's response, 'and I'm not sitting here being accused of this.' He stood up and began to quickly walk out of the room.

'Irfan, can you stay?' asked Meg but he kept walking towards the door.

Mike shouted after him, 'Go on, run away. You can't face the truth, you fucking pervert.'

Mike had also got up now and was heading to the garden. As Irfan slammed the door to the 9/15, Mike turned around with his unlit cigarette in his hand and looked again directly at Grant. 'You need to get rid of him, mate, he's trouble. You need to trust me on this one.' He pushed open the glass door and walked out. I twiddled my hair in between my fingers and didn't look up.

*

The end of the week came around quickly, and after Irfan had once again gone out drinking, it was fairly obvious how the vote was going to go. But, in true martyr style, at the beginning of the meeting he interrupted everyone and said he had decided to leave. He gave a big speech about 'not wanting to make people vote' and that 'the Henshaw wasn't helping him anyway'. It was hard not to join a few of the others in sneering at him as he did this, Mike literally beaming with a sadistic joy as some of the staff suggested Irfan should still be put on vote and was merely 'escaping a possibly negative experience'. But despite this, it was not voted on, something for which I was grateful as I hated playing God in these situations, regardless of how little I liked the defendant. My only hope was that he didn't expect a hug from me when he left.

Susie had walked out of the meeting before the end. Augusta and I offered to go and check on her when, after ten minutes, she had still not returned. As we walked down the hall to her room we heard a loud smash. I tapped on her door, Augusta loitering nervously behind me.

'Susie?'

'Yes?' came her steady response.

'It's Emma and Augusta. Can we come in please?'

There were more sounds of commotion and eventually her door creaked open a couple of inches. She stood in the doorway not letting us in, but even with her blocking most of the view I could see she had smashed and broken just about everything she owned. We managed to talk our way into the room and helped her to pick up some of her non-repairable belongings. She was rambling, and absent-mindedly blurted out that she had been self-harming but that she didn't want to tell anyone.

'Are you both okay, carrying this? I just don't want anyone to know yet.'

'Has something happened? To bring this on?' I asked sitting on the edge of her bed. Her eyes filled up.

'Carl...'

The husband, I should have known.

She carried on, tears starting to run down her face. 'He's blaming me for everything... he wants me out and he wants custody of the children. He's got the courts involved and told them that I should have to live somewhere else and have supervised visits with the kids... because...' she began to wail, 'because I'm not stable enough!'

Augusta handed her a tissue. 'He's a pig, Susie.'

Susie nodded as she blew her nose. 'I know, but what can I do?'

'So if we tell anyone about the self-harm... it could affect you seeing the children?' I asked.

She nodded again. 'Yeah, Em.'

I looked at Augusta and took a deep breath. 'Susie, you have to promise to come to one of us if you feel bad, okay? Before you do anything? Promise?' She nodded again. We reluctantly agreed not to say anything. Leaving her room we headed back to the meeting to tell everyone she was fine but just felt light-headed, agreeing between each other that we would work as a close team to keep an eye on her.

A few hours after the meeting I sat in the 9/15 on the big red velvet sofa sandwiched between Mike and Augusta. Megan lay on the floor reading a fitness magazine and Susie was curled up on an armchair staring into space. The door creaked open. It was Irfan.

'I'm all packed and my cab's on the way. I just wanted to say bye.' He stepped inside the room.

'Oh,' said Susie somewhat vacantly, turning to look at him. 'Bye Irfan, good luck.' She got up and gave him a hug, followed by Megan. I pushed myself as far back into the sofa as I could, hoping that sitting next to Mike would deter Irfan from coming any closer.

'Bye, take care,' said Augusta coldly from next to me. Irfan looked at me and held out his arms. Oh God.

'Bye, Em.'

I reluctantly got up and hugged him, keeping my body as far away as I physically could.

'Be safe,' I said as I hurriedly sat back down next to Mike. Mike picked up the remote and started channel surfing. Irfan stared at him for a moment, debating, I'm sure, whether to get one final comment in; he must have thought better of it and walked back to the door.

'Well, good luck to you all. And you all have my number so keep in touch.' With that he walked out. A few minutes later we watched him getting into a cab outside. 'Good fucking riddance,' said Mike as the car drove out of sight.

*

I sat in Jess's flat later that night, relieved to be with my new friend and away from everyone at the hospital. Having lost Chrissie and now with Stevie and Irfan walking out, as well as Gareth and Louise leaving, the patient numbers were dwindling fast, which we had been told would speed up the closure. Added to that Megan had also said she wanted to leave – she had told us she didn't feel like the hospital was helping her get better.

'They just try and stop me exercising… but there's so much more that's wrong…' she trailed off. I gently put my hand on her arm hoping she could tolerate my touching her.

'Is there anything I can help with, anything I can do?'

Megan shook her head. 'No. I just… I can't be here any more.'

I didn't want her to go, but I was feeling the same way about the hospital, so asking her to stay would purely be for my own selfishness and not for her well-being; I just hoped that maybe she'd change her mind.

*

Jess and I had taken to chatting on the phone or MSN Messenger most nights and I had completely moved away from the first impressions I had made of her. I couldn't have been more wrong, in fact. She was incredibly caring, funny and spending time with her was like being back in the real world, despite the fact that the majority of things we spoke about were the other patients. She was glad Irfan had left, even more so when I sat next to her on the sofa and showed her the text on my phone that he'd sent me about being 'hard'.

'Mike's right, Em, he's dangerous.' She asked about various people and when I brought up Augusta, she began to squirm around in her chair. I looked at her, confused.

'What's wrong?'

Jess suddenly began speaking at the rate of someone who had snorted a gram of speed as she said, 'She told me not to tell you, but I think you should know, and frankly, Emma I can't hear about it any more, I really can't. It's every day, all the time!'

'About what? What are you talking about?'

She exhaled loudly. 'Augusta. She fancies you. Really badly. She thinks she's in love with you. You're all she talks to me about, she's obsessed.'

I suddenly felt stupid and nervously began to laugh. 'Are you joking?'

'No, I wish I was fucking joking. You need to tell her you don't like her or something because she's driving me mad.'

Of course I couldn't keep what I had just learned to myself for long and was soon standing in the garden with Mike watching him smoke a joint and whispering about what I had been told. I regretted telling him as he spent the rest of the night taking the piss out of me. Every time we were alone in the 9/15 he'd make some stupid quip.

'Fuck, it's already midnight… Em, does your girlfriend not want you up to bed?' He'd laugh hysterically like he was the funniest man in the world.

I decided to basically forget what Jess had told me and pushed it as far back in my mind as I could, hanging out with Augusta as usual and not letting on that I knew. I didn't want to embarrass her and I certainly didn't want to acknowledge that someone found me attractive.

*

It had been a week since Megan had mentioned that she wanted to leave. She came down the stairs as I sat in the 9/15 with Mike and Augusta.

'Guys, I'm going.'

I looked up at her. 'Going where?'

'Going. Leaving. I can't stay here any more.'

'But why?' Augusta looked as if her world was collapsing.

Megan sat down next to her. 'I feel as though I'm getting worse. I'm sorry but this place isn't helping me.'

'But... but...' Augusta was in shock.

'But nothing, Augusta,' said Megan, her voice calm. 'I've been here for six months. I've wasted six months basically getting more ill. This place is going to shit, we all know it. It's collapsing. I need therapy, real therapy. I'm sorry.' Within an hour of telling us, she was disappearing down the drive with her huge backpack and Beaker under her arm. She hadn't wanted to wait until Monday when the staff were all there and they could have a meeting about it (which I didn't blame her for) but seeing her go was just another stark reminder of how the hospital seemed to be falling apart around us.

*

By the time word had spread on Monday of Megan's departure and further news came that Susie wanted to leave, the 9/15 turned into crisis talks with the staff about the closure. Some of the therapists said they thought the Henshaw was becoming a damaging environment, others disagreed. But this notion in itself of the staff disagreeing and publicly contradicting each other spoke volumes of its own. People argued back and forth, suggesting things like making the inpatient programme a three-day week, or just using the hospital as an outpatient facility. As I listened I didn't really understand why they were having these conversations in front of us all. I obviously knew they wanted us to feel somewhat involved in the decision-making, but this was just a shit show of watching them all bicker and come up with solutions that were so far-reaching they'd make you throw your back out. All that became apparent was that no one knew what was going to happen or how to solve it and the only thing this meeting was doing was stirring up major anxiety in all the residents. I wondered if Grant would soon be suggesting we all 'drank the Kool-Aid'… it didn't seem that far off.

As I watched the nurses and therapists contradict and talk over each other I knew it was time to start making some decisions – I wasn't going to be able to stay here; this boat was sinking and I needed to get off.

15

THE UNRAVELLING

"If I died tomorrow, I would be a happy girl."

—AMY WINEHOUSE

My self-harming was becoming a running nightly theme. I had stopped telling anyone altogether, there was no point. I was cutting more deeply every time but I didn't care, I felt I was slipping away again and if no one noticed, all the better. The only thing getting me through each day was not eating and purging. The control I felt from consuming only a few hundred calories and watching my ribs begin to protrude without the need for me sucking in a mouthful of air was all the propelling forward I needed. I would obsess over images of anorexically thin girls. My only motivation to go out began resting on printing off random Google images of (sick) women I did not know in the nearby Internet café, only to spend the evening up in my room gluing them into a notebook and coveting what I deemed perfection. I truly thought if I lost enough weight, things in my life would suddenly get better. I believed my relationships would improve, that I would find a boyfriend who would save me from my need to self-harm, that I'd get a job and make money and move out and everything would just finally fall into place. A modern-day Cinderella. The problem was that every time I managed to achieve the weight goal I was setting myself, nothing had changed, apart from the goal itself. The glass slipper still didn't fit; would it ever?

My CPA (care plan assessment) had been scheduled for the next week. Every resident had one of these. It was a meeting between staff at the Henshaw and, in my case, staff in another local borough who were financially in control of my care. Its purpose was to go over a treatment plan for me – to find out whether, when the closure finally came, I could be happily released back into the general population or if I needed further treatment somewhere else. I already knew what my options were: leave the Henshaw and go home, or possibly transfer to the Caddick, a nearby hospital which I'd heard basically did the same thing as the Henshaw. I failed to see how it would help me; this place had been slowly destroying me for months. I'd come in with the intention of getting better and currently I was more ill than I had been in a long time. I was dreading the CPA and hoped it would be put off or cancelled.

*

During welfare group I used the time to phone home and speak to my mother about the state of the hospital. She didn't know anything about the closure, so I filled her in, telling her it was falling apart and that I wanted to come home. She point-blank refused, saying I was not allowed to go home – that I was mentally ill which is why the doctors had 'put' me in there in the first place. 'I really don't have time to discuss this now anyway, Emma.' She told me she had to go and hung up. I sat there for some time, shell-shocked. If I wasn't allowed to go home, where would I go? I knew staying at the Henshaw until the closure, which was now only four months off due to how few residents were left, was not an option. Every time someone left, the PCT (primary care trust, the NHS bigwigs who were responsible for deciding which services got funding and which didn't) used it as an excuse to bring the closure forward. I was literally watching it unravel before me every day and it was stifling. A transfer to the Caddick seemed like the best option, but if it was built on the same model as this place, would I just get even more ill? Was that even possible? Plus I had waited so long for funding to the Henshaw, and that waiting period had been so hellish… It could be a year before I could get into the Caddick; what would I do in that time if I couldn't go home?

I hadn't realised I had left the hospital grounds as I found myself standing at the nearby train station watching train after train arrive and depart. As I stood there, I did my best to figure out what the perfect moment to throw myself under would be. What would ensure I would not survive? I moved my feet closer and closer to the edge of the platform, leaning over and looking at the different railway lines. A few commuters gave me slightly nervous glances but instead of saying anything chose to look in the other direction or walk further down the platform away from me. Not that I blamed them: not many people would approach a spaced out, ill-looking girl on the brink of tears, teetering on the edge of a train platform. The reality of what I could so easily do dawned on me and I started to cry. Images from a documentary I had watched some years earlier began to flood my mind; it was about people trying to kill themselves and failing, one of whom was a guy who had jumped out in front of a train and instead of dying he was dragged under it for miles, his poor body being battered and broken so badly that he was now a paraplegic. The thought of being that out of control of my life scared me more than the thought of living, so mopping up my tears with my sleeve, I left.

My depression turned into a searing rage as later that day I sat in psychodrama listening to Esther make Susie and Lyle act out her life. The dwindling number of patients meant that, without Irfan, Chrissie and Megan, our group now only consisted of Lyle, Esther, Susie and myself. It was harder to hide in these tiny groups; but contrary to what you might think it wasn't as if you could really focus in on the therapy. The closure was the hot topic, and whatever was brought up would be related back to it.

I watched from my chair as Esther made Lyle and Susie play out some long-lost memory from childhood, driving in the car with her parents. They sat on the floor, Susie and Lyle in the 'front seats' and Esther loitering behind them. In these scenarios, you weren't supposed to play yourself, you were supposed to direct someone else to be you. So Lyle played the role of both parents, Susie played Esther and Esther was the sort Stanley Kubrick of it all, standing around ordering everyone about and feeding them their lines, who said this, who did that.

'Esther, you have another seat in the car, perhaps Lyle can just play one parent and someone else can play the other,' said Kerry, not looking at, but obviously meaning, me. Esther glanced at me, then picked up a cushion.

'Okay, Lyle can be my father and this cushion can be my mother...' Was a cushion really taking preference over me? I felt my body start to stiffen, the anger pulsating through my blood as if it were now a part of me that could only be got rid of by being drained out. The worst part was, I couldn't tell if Esther was just too terrified of my general demeanour in these groups to ask me to be part of her performance – worried in case I told her fuck off – or if this was (yet another) dig from her, just a subtle, underhand gesture that was designed to rile me up... Both options seemed plausible. I went back and forth in my mind, for a moment frustrated that I didn't trust myself enough to figure out which it was, so I got up and walked out of the session before I erupted all over them and their imaginary car.

*

It hadn't escaped me that it was the 14th February, Valentine's Day. I had been sitting in the 9/15 with Candace, Tara and Mike watching TV and chatting. We had seen Lyle walk down the drive some time earlier and now he was walking back, a Clinton's bag in hand and a worried expression on his face. He poked his head around the door.

'All right?' asked Mike throwing down his newspaper as if he were happy of the distraction.

Lyle cleared his throat. 'Yes...' he pursed his lips together quizzically, 'Yes, I'm fine... I was just looking for Esther.'

Mike shrugged his shoulders. 'Dunno where she is, mate.'

'She's in her room sleeping,' said Tara. 'She was tired after your drama group.' Lyle smiled, the anxiety melting away from his face leaving in its place a strange glimmer of relief.

'Oh! Okay.' He vanished behind the door, his heavy footsteps padding quickly down the hall.

'Tsk tsk.' I looked at Candace who had a knowing expression on her face as she played on her phone.

'Why "tsk tsk"?' I asked.

'He likes her,' she said, without looking up at me.

'What, Esther?'

Candace nodded. 'Yeah, of course. Haven't you noticed?'

I thought for a second; I suppose he was *always* with her, always following her about. 'I guess...' I said scrunching up my face without meaning to. 'But, Esther?'

Candace laughed 'Yes Emma, Esther.'

I didn't understand; all she ever did was play the martyr and try and get everyone else in trouble. I wondered if maybe

Candace was just reading in to something that wasn't there, but as it turned out, she was right.

A few hours later a referred was called; everyone wearily lumbered into the 9/15 where I was still sitting with Mike. The night staff, Meg and Hank, took their places like dutiful dogs next to top three, Susie, Augusta and Tara. I looked around the room trying to see who, if anyone, looked upset, when as usual my eyes landed on Esther – eyes red and teary, chewing on her sleeve.

Augusta began, 'So top three have called a referred because Esther approached the night staff a little while ago very upset. Esther, do you want to say what's happened?' Esther slowly took her sleeve out of her mouth.

'I was in my room asleep, I was tired after psychodrama and everything it had brought up.' I heard a groan come from Mike and tried not to laugh – I'd filled him in on the cushion situation while we were watching TV.

Esther went on, 'there was a noise outside my door, and then this was pushed under it.' She held up what looked like a Valentine's Day card. 'Lyle had pushed it under my door.' Esther opened the card and began to read aloud from it: 'Dear Esther, you are amazing. Thank you so much for being there for me, happy valentines day, all my love, Lyle.'

Lyle sat a few seats away from me looking beyond mortified. What was happening right now? Why was I being forced to endure this this ritual humiliation of another person? Purely for Esther's own self-interest, her own incessant hunger for attention. It made me despise her even more than I already did and before I knew it I felt my mouth opening.

'Aw, that's really nice. What a kind gesture, Lyle.'

Esther looked at me as if I had just tried to conjure the devil. Mike snuffled into his coffee, shaking his head as he tried not to laugh.

'It's not *nice*,' Esther spat at me red-faced, the tears magically drying up.

'How did it make you feel, Esther?' asked Meg, a look of compassion on her face that in turn made me scowl at her. I was fuming, raging actually, and didn't let her answer. Instead I bellowed, 'Maybe, Meg, we should ask Lyle how this is making *him* feel right now?'

'And we will, Emma, in a moment. Esther?'

Fuck off, Meg.

'I just feel so triggered… so violated. I don't think I can stay on my own tonight, I need someone to stay with me.'

I looked at Mike, who nodded in Lyle's direction and mouthed to me, 'Lyle?' We both burst out laughing, I couldn't help it and I had totally stopped caring what Esther thought, or the staff for that matter.

'Mike and Emma, can you stop?' said Hank fidgeting in his chair.

'We could,' I said, 'but then who else would bother to call out the bullshit?'

Hank didn't know what to say to me; a look on his face suggested he knew he was standing at the mouth of a cave that had a hungry wolf inside it, and just looked away.

'Who's going to stay with Esther tonight?' he asked.

Susie raised her hand.

'I would just like to say, I am truly, truly sorry, Esther. The last thing I wanted to do was make you feel uncomfortable or upset. You have been a real friend to me,' said Lyle, looking at the floor like he might cry. It broke my heart for him, and not for the first time. The meeting was closed and everyone started to leave.

Candace playfully kicked me as she walked out. 'Troublemaker!'

After a few moments it was just me, Lyle and Mike left in the

9/15. I threw a cushion at Lyle; he looked up at me, the tears now brimming on the edges of his eyes.

'How about a cup of tea and a Jammy Dodger?'

He smiled, 'Got anything stronger?'

'I could probably stretch to a Hobnob,' I said making my way to the door before adding, 'but God help us if anyone finds out!'

He laughed, wiping his eyes.

'Do I get a cuppa?' called Mike as I opened the door.

'You get a "fuck you"!' I shouted back throwing my fingers up in the air at him. The door closed behind me to the sound of their laughter.

16

THE BIGGER THEY ARE

"What strange phenomena we find in a great city, all we need do is stroll about with our eyes open. Life swarms with innocent monsters."

— CHARLES BAUDELAIRE, *Les Fleurs du mal*

It was the weekend. I hadn't been home as my mother still wasn't wanting me back, so I'd spent Saturday night at a house party shoving cocaine up my nose and Valium down my throat, telling all my friends how much I loved them despite the fact that only four of them had been to visit me since I'd been in the Henshaw.

I'd also spent a large portion of the night with the razor blade I'd used to carve up lines of coke locked in whoever's bathroom it was, slicing into my arms. After what felt like a year of staring at the white tiled walls, there was a knock on the door.

'Em, it's Landon, are you okay, babe?'

'Yeah, all good,' I called back.

'Can I come in please?' I pulled down my sleeves and opened the door. He stepped in, closing it behind him. I followed his eyes to the sink, which was covered in blood; usually I would have made some attempt to conceal it but I was too fucked and too upset to care.

'Em, what the hell?... No, no more of that. Where is it?'

I stared at him blankly without answering.

'The blade, or knife, or whatever it is you've been using.'

I held out my clenched fist, opening it to reveal the small razor blade. He flinched a little, but took it out of my trembling hand. Landon put the toilet lid down and sat on it, pulling me onto his lap. I began, despite my best efforts, to start crying and once the taps opened I couldn't stop.

'Emma, I don't think this hospital is working. Look at you... you're not okay... and you've lost so much weight, hon. Can I see your arms?' I was crying so hard I couldn't answer but shook my head. 'Fine but we're leaving. I'm taking you back to mine, you shouldn't be here.' He made a quick call to order a cab and before I had time to protest he was holding my hand as he led me out of the house and to the car. We sat there in silence as the cabbie drove, the empty 2am roads a still, peaceful stretch in front of us. As we pulled up outside his flat I'd managed to stop crying but felt horribly numb. He paid the driver and, getting out, opened my door. 'Come on.'

I sat on his bed and watched him make us both a cup of tea. He walked over and sat next to me, passing me one of the mugs. I took a sip and cleared my throat.

'I can't go home, and I don't want to go back to the hospital... Is it okay if I stay here tonight?'

He put his cup down. 'You are staying here, you shouldn't be alone tonight. But, do you need to go to A&E or something, get stitches?'

'No, I'm fine, it's not that bad.' Sure enough the cuts weren't stitch-worthy but I'd made a horrible fucking mess of myself, the coke-induced haze blurring my sense of when to stop.

'Okay, well I'm going to get you some bandages and one of my T-shirts.'

I shook my head. 'You don't need to do that…'

'Hon, you're covered in blood.'

I looked down; I hadn't noticed but he was right. A little while later with my arms clean and bandaged I lay facing him in his single bed.

'I'm sorry, Lan.'

'You have nothing to be sorry about. I don't want you hurting yourself any more… in any sort of way. You know I care about you, don't you? You do know that?'

I didn't say anything, just leaned over and cuddled into him. He wrapped his arms around me and I fell asleep feeling safe and protected.

*

'Well, you look like shit,' said Mike as he slurped his coffee.

'You are so charming, tell me again why you're single?'

He stuck two fingers up at me. 'You been on it all weekend then? Looks like it! Bring me any party favours back?'

I sat down on the sofa alongside him. 'No sorry, they all went up my nose.' I pulled one of the sofa throws around my shoulders. 'So, any weekend gossip?'

He began to laugh. 'Just a fucking bit, Em! You sure you want to know?'

'Don't I always?'

He smirked and began. 'On Saturday night someone started banging on my door at midnight. I ignored it for a while but they wouldn't fuck off, BANG, BANG, BANG, so I got up and Esther is standing there crying saying Lyle went into her room, she said she ran out but she didn't know if he was still in there. So I told her to wait in my room and went and got Magda out of the staffroom – we walked around and found him in the kitchen with a fucking carving knife! He starts cutting himself with it, then all of a sudden he collapsed.'

I sat gawking at Mike as he continued. 'You've waited all night to tell me this?'

He laughed and went on, 'Eventually he came round; I tried to make him just sit there and calm down but he got past me, and how the fuck was I supposed to stop him? I mean, what is he, forty stone? I had no chance! Magda told me to phone the coppers, so I did, then we went to his bedroom.' He took another glug of his coffee. 'I was shitting myself to be honest, but I opened the door and he was there in the corner, sitting in the dark on the floor, with this fucking Barbie doll, hugging it. Then he started hissing and spitting at us like a cat. He looked evil, Em, his eyes were all black.'

'Did you go in?'

'Did I fuck! No! I closed the door and the "popo" came ten minutes later and carted him off. He's down the road in a secure unit.'

'Poor Lyle,' I said, hugging the blanket around me.

'Poor Lyle? Poor me! I thought he was going to kill me, and Magda, and probably fucking Esther too!'

'Well, this is on her, Mike, the whole Valentine's thing, she tipped him over the edge.'

He stood up, pulling out a cigarette. 'Yeah I know, but still, he looked demonic.' Mike walked outside to smoke and I thought about what he'd just told me. A sober Lyle would not hurt anyone, but drunk or drugged, at his size, he would be a force to be reckoned with. It's not that I advocated him going in her room, and yes I can imagine it did scare the shit out of her and it definitely wasn't 'okay', but I had such a hard time sourcing any sympathy for Esther, she had tried to fuck me over on so many occasions that I was pretty much devoid of all empathy when it came to her. I knew that Lyle would be on a vote once he got back, I'd be opting for him to stay, but I didn't know that the others would be so forgiving.

17

CPA

"The nail that sticks out farthest gets hammered the hardest."

— *PATRICK JONES, Nailed*

The day of my CPA drew closer and I was adamant I did not want any other patient in my meeting with me, which was unheard of and, of course, frowned upon. But I didn't want someone else in there who would then tell everyone what had gone on.

This CPA was going to be my opportunity to break down, come clean and to say it wasn't helping. I didn't feel as if I could do any of those things with someone else in there. Naturally, this was dragged into every meeting, over and over again, with everyone, staff and patients alike, telling me that I should have a fellow resident in there with me, and the more I refused, the more they persisted, to the point where I eventually refused to speak about it. As far as I was concerned, it wasn't technically in the 'rules' – they couldn't stop me or put me on a vote, they were powerless against my obstinacy and I knew it. This was one fight I was determined not to lose.

The morning of my CPA came and as I sat in the 9/15 I was still being urged to take a patient in with me. It had been eight days of this now, over and over again, and I was sick of it. I did not need an audience for my falling apart and begging for help. Very luckily for me, the two staff members I had in the CPA were Andrew and Blanche. Andrew worked in outreach and, in the long waiting process for my funding to come through for me to be admitted to the Henshaw, he had been the person I would meet with twice a week so he could check in with me and see how I was doing. He had basically been my therapist for six months before I'd got here and I had really grown to like and trust him; unlike a lot of the other staff at the Henshaw he knew me, the real me, no bullshit, no pretence. He would occasionally come to the hospital to be present in these CPAs as he was instrumental in patients' funding and the comings and goings of money. And although I wasn't that friendly with Blanche, she seemed good at her job; in the art groups she was always pretty stoic and structured and I felt like she liked me.

So it would be those two – Andrew and Blanche – and then Dr Carter the consultant psychiatrist (aka the head honcho), from the larger borough that was responsible for my funding and his co-worker who I'd never met called Nicole. Dr Carter and I had a long history marred with difficult interactions and I was dreading seeing him; we'd met several times over the years and he had always seemed patently uninterested in my issues and there was also a 'pull your socks up and get on with it' type of attitude emanating from him.

*

At 11am I sat with Andrew and Blanche around a table with six chairs in a room in the Henshaw I had never been in before. Time passed slowly and when it got to twenty past with still no sign of Dr Carter or Nicole I began to cry. The reality of not being helped at all dawned on me, tangled with the feeling of being overlooked again. Blanche and Andrew did their best to maintain boundaries but tried to comfort me at the same time, saying they were bound to turn up. 'But they're twenty minutes late!' I wailed. 'They don't care! No one does – I'm on my fucking own to sort it out, as usual.'

It probably sounds horrifically overdramatic. After all, people are late all the time, and really twenty minutes wasn't even that bad. But you have to understand what the Henshaw was creating in me: a desperate clawing creature that was making a last-ditch attempt to save itself while its head was on the chopping block. The hospital was making me worse and, even if it hadn't been, it was closing very soon. The staff felt I was unreachable or difficult (which I was), the 'therapy' wasn't helping and I couldn't go home. So what the fuck was I going to do? Suicide was an option, of course it was, but I wasn't 100% sure I wanted to die. What if there was a chance for redemption? What if my 'happy ever after' really did exist? What if my life wasn't in fact doomed to be hospital wards, toilet bowls and bandages? And that there, *that's* why I was crying, that's why I was sitting in that stupid little room loosing my shit. Because in true borderline style I was seeing black and white. This CPA was either going to save me, or condemn me.

Ten minutes later, through my snot and tears, I saw a Jaguar pull into the drive and out stepped Carter with a tall, dark-haired woman I assumed was Nicole. Soon enough they were in the room apologising for their lateness while giving me empathetic looks as I tried to compose myself and stop snivelling. But my composure had long since left and I spent the rest of the meeting virtually comatose, tears pouring from my eyes with such ferocity that eventually I stopped wiping them away. I felt like all the strength, all the pretence, and all the effort I used keeping everyone at arm's length had left me in those moments and I was a baby again, arms outstretched, screaming, waiting for someone to pick me up.

It was hard, almost impossible, to tell them why I was so upset. I was terrified of anything I said getting back to the rest of the staff at the Henshaw. But somehow I managed it, saying it wasn't working for me, that I needed medication and that I was suicidal. Andrew, kind as ever, spoke for me when I couldn't manage it. However, Blanche, to my surprise and detriment, said I was 'not signed up' to treatment and therefore may be asked to 'leave anyway'. I looked up at her, my mouth hanging open wondering why she would choose this moment to say such things. In one breath I was saying I was suicidal and in the next she was saying the Henshaw might not want me after all.

I caught a glimpse of Nicole's face, who seemed particularly irritated by Blanche's statement and began to console me. 'I will be there to support you and you most definitely won't be alone should that happen, Emma.'

I felt acutely betrayed by Blanche. The gloves were off, if she wanted to fuck me over, I could do the same. I began to talk about the closure and how detrimental it was to the patients.

'This place is a sinking ship. People are bailing left, right and centre. They're getting worse, there's a huge underworld of drugs, eating disorders and self-harm here which is just growing by the day because the staff are too taken up with the closure to notice. I know I'm not good at talking in groups, I know that. But even when I do, it's linked back to the closure; every problem I have, the staff attribute to the funding.' I glanced at Blanche whose eyes were now forming needlelike dark slits. I didn't care; she'd proved she wasn't on my side.

After a long silence Dr Carter said, 'I think the Caddick would be better for you,' something that they all seemed to agree with him on. 'However,' he continued, 'we would have to apply for funding again, which may take a while. The problem is, where do you go in the meantime? Going home would be counter-therapeutic. I think we need to get you into shared housing, or a flat, whilst we request funding.'

I left the CPA feeling as if, by some miracle, I had been taken seriously and that, after all, help was once again on its way.

*

Life at the Henshaw in the days that followed was even less pleasant than usual. Blanche and Andrew had fed back what had happened in the CPA and the rest of the staff were pissed, to say the least. It felt as if they were out to get me for 'not talking about my issues within the community.' They just did not seem to be able to understand that I couldn't speak in groups, that I was not comfortable expressing my vulnerability, or any sort of flaws (of which I knew I had many) in front of an audience. The smaller groups were slightly easier to talk in, but even then I found it excruciatingly difficult, often feeling the need to leave the hospital instantly after telling anyone even one small detail about myself. I felt as though the wolves were baying at the door. All I was hearing was that I had had 'a lot' to say in my CPA and why wasn't I sharing it with my fellow patients? They kept throwing that line again and again in front of everyone else – and of course it made the other patients paranoid, wondering what I had said. It seemed almost as if the staff were trying to turn the residents against me. They knew I wouldn't open up, but the continual questioning made it seem like I had something to hide. I wanted so desperately to escape, but I had nowhere to go.

18

WHEN THE WOLVES GET RESTLESS

"For hunters, the kill is in the climax –
the most important moment. They are not driving into the
woods (or sometimes actually walking) for the sake of beauty,
but in the hope of a kill."

LISA KEMMERER, 'Speaking Up for Animals: An Anthology of
Women's voices'

Lyle had been under section for a few days, but the secure unit
had soon deemed him stable and had sent him home. So he
went back to his small flat on the outskirts of London and we
were now called into a referred meeting to discuss him coming
back to the hospital. I was on top three again and I wished
desperately that I wasn't; I didn't want any part of deciding
Lyle's fate. It was fairly unanimous that no one felt safe with
the idea of him being in the Henshaw, mainly, as I suspected
would be the issue, due to his size and strength and the risk he
potentially posed to everyone when he was drunk or drugged.

Esther, of course, made the whole thing about herself,

whimpering that she was not safe and that he was 'after' her. She droned on and on, 'It's me he wants, I won't be safe, I'll be in danger.' Eventually, the vote came. And before I knew it I was up with top three listening in to Mike telling Lyle over the phone that he couldn't come back.

'Sorry, mate,' said Mike, genuine remorse in his voice. The guilt I felt was unbearable as I listened to Lyle on the other end of the line.

'Oh. Okay. That's fair enough.' It was awful, that defeated, broken tone. As Mike hung up I prayed Lyle would not kill himself.

*

Out with the old, in with the new, it seemed. The Henshaw *had* to keep its patient numbers up in order to keep the closure at bay; the men in suits were less likely to bring the hammer down on a hospital full of patients, so the staff tried to keep the numbers up and the wolves from the door.

And so on one cold day in February appeared Lana and Katie. Both late twenties and both as loud as each other. Lana was an ex-heroin addict with a history of attempted suicide and an abusive, militant Catholic mother. During her introduction she held up her wrist to reveal a thick white scar.

'I slit my wrists when I was thirteen,' she said in her heavy Scottish accent. 'But my mother didn't want anyone to know because it was such a sin, such an embarrassment so she got out her sewing box and sewed them up herself, she did an all right job, I suppose.' I moved my eyes quickly to the floor fearing if I looked at the scar for even another second I would projectile-vomit. Katie's explanation of why she was there seemed slightly tamer after that, telling us about her history of eating disorders and a fiancé who had killed himself.

I fought the urge to dislike Lana; she was so abrasive and came across as a know-it-all, whereas in contrast Katie was warmer and I appreciated her more gentle approach to getting to know us.

The two women were put into my small group, which now consisted only of Esther and myself. For the first five minutes, as they both talked, I was relieved not to have to be listening to Esther's voice. But five minutes was all it lasted for. Katie's booming Irish accent tangled with Lana's Scottish one and the noise they produced as they both fought with each other for the limelight was almost unbearable. Neither of them had social awareness enough to not talk over each other, us, or the therapists and would just bulldoze over everyone verbally as they competed for the floor.

I had felt under so much pressure from some of the staff since the CPA that I was making more of an effort to talk. I was worried that they may delay my funding to the Caddick, or worse yet say if I didn't work at the Henshaw that I wouldn't work at the Caddick and ruin my chances for me. I took a deep breath and opened my mouth. Lana let me get about four words in before interjecting and steering it back to herself. It was exhausting and I bolted out of the small group fifteen minutes before it was due to end, my ears ringing all the way to my room, frustrated and angry that I had bothered to open my mouth at all.

*

The top three rotation meant that I only had to endure being on the red velvet sofa of all-encompassing control for a fortnight and being back off it was a huge relief, and I certainly relished in my freedom. Not having to attend the summit meetings every night and discuss everyone else's problems when I could barely find the will to get up in the morning was a huge weight

STORM IN A TEA CUP

off my shoulders, although not having to chair the 9/15s any more meant my time-management skills reverted to type, and in my first week of being off top three I was late for the morning meeting three times. This was an automatic 'assessment' – three strikes and you're on a vote. I had debated in my lateness not to go down at all but this would mean the 'new' top three coming to find me and even more attention being thrown my way. So, shaking at the thought of walking (yet again) into a packed room, I creaked open the door and found the closest seat to me.

I should have been on time. This was the perfect opportunity for the staff to ask me question after question about 'what was going on' with me. What had happened in the CPA and why was I not 'sharing' with my fellow patients? I dodged these questions like bullets, never giving a straight answer, infuriating everyone further with my seeming indifference, which was actually anything but.

'Are you signed up to treatment, Emma?' asked Brianne from her perch – she looked like a big red canary. 'Because it seems to me that you aren't?'

I didn't say anything, just cocked my head to the side and stared past her. 'I personally haven't seen any progression since you've been here,' chimed in Bernard.

Should I just walk out? What was the point in this slow, deliberate annihilation? Just as I was weighing up how much more shit I'd bring down on myself should I leave the room, Grant spoke out.

'I don't think that's entirely fair. I feel like Emma has built good relationships with the other residents since she has been here. And from what I hear she has begun being more candid in her small group.'

Not for the first time I wanted to hug him; for whatever reason Grant could see a part of me that a lot of the others couldn't.

'That may be correct, but being candid in small group doesn't help us in the wider forum to understand the bigger picture of what's going,' said Bernard.

I was sure he was supposed to be slithering about somewhere in a garden, offering apples to a woman in the throes of confusion. Suddenly the idea of sitting there for a moment longer appealed less to me than the idea of getting into even more trouble; I was already on a vote so I'd face that tomorrow and whatever else they wanted to throw at me. I got up and walked out, Grant calling for me to stay as the door swung shut against the sound of his voice.

*

That evening, Candace, who was on the new top three, came and found me. 'You're in for it, babe,' she said as she sat down next to me.

I looked at her, confused. 'What?'

She went on to tell me that Esther had been talking about me in the summit meeting. 'She put on this face and kept saying, "I am very concerned for Emma." It was obvious that she was trying to get you on the agenda, but Magda was buying it hook, line and sinker and was asking us if you were "signed up to treatment" and she was asking if we thought you should be here. The pair of them put you on the agenda for tomorrow.' Signed up to treatment; that fucking phrase seemed to be haunting me through the hospital.

*

I thought about the upcoming vote on Friday and tried to work out who would be for me staying and who would be against. It seemed, from my calculations and the staff-to-patient ratio, I might be out on my arse sooner that I thought, and as I hadn't heard from Dr Carter about temporary housing it was anyone's guess as to where I'd be going if I wasn't at the Henshaw.

Candace was right to warn me and in the morning I was again barraged with questions. Feeling more confident after having had the evening to go over my answers, I told them all that it felt as though none of the groups had any structure, and that everything was focused on the closure, an answer that, even if they were not satisfied with it, pacified them for the duration of the meeting. They weren't expecting me to talk at all so the fact that I had said anything, let alone something that seemed to come from a place of integrity, had shut them all up.

I felt a mild sense of triumph as I walked in to art after the 9/15. Everyone had now been merged as there were not enough patients to warrant two groups. Blanche started off by asking how people were, if there was anyone who needed to talk. Of course Lana began speaking at the first chance and kept going solidly for almost twenty minutes. Twenty minutes of listening to one voice exclusively can be a chore enough if you are friends with the person in question; if you don't like them it begins to feel like slow torture. She had no social conscience, no ability to look around the room and see that people were desperate for her to stop talking, she just went on and on and on. The only redeeming feature throughout the rambling diatribe was Mike rolling his eyes at me from across the room every time the twang of her accent grew louder or more emphatic, which seemed to be every few seconds.

'I was a heroin addict! I was on the streets! I've seen things you people couldn't even fathom!'

Eventually, and to everyone's great relief, Blanche managed to get a word in. 'Lana, you've been talking for some time now and we need to check in with the other people in the room.'

Furious, Lana folded her arms melodramatically over her chest like a disgruntled five-year-old. Blanche continued, 'I am very concerned for Emma and Esther at the moment. I think you both have things that you should be discussing with the group.'

That was a joke. *Concerned are you? You were the one telling me I would be chucked out if I wasn't careful.* As I thought about this for a few seconds Esther took the opportunity to start talking about herself. She, too, spoke continuously for twenty minutes until Blanche cut her off.

'It's almost time to finish and we haven't heard from Emma.'

Esther did her sad puppy face, her bottom lip beginning to tremble. The room fell silent as I was expected to start speaking. Instead, I looked blankly back at Blanche, as everyone else looked at me. I felt like once again I was an afterthought. Like Lana was given free rein to bombard us all with her tirade and then Esther had been allowed to use up the last twenty minutes and now, what? I was expected to encapsulate my feelings into the remaining four minutes of group time? Really? I was angry and I wasn't going to attempt to open up for the sake of 240 seconds of 'airtime'. I kept my mouth shut and stared at the floor.

Blanche sighed and said, 'Emma, I know you must think I am Nurse Ratchet...' but she didn't get any further as a roar of laughter boomed from Augusta and Mike. I heard Augusta say through her laughter 'Spot on,' and Blanche didn't even bother to finish her sentence.

When everyone had composed themselves I looked at Blanche and Mona – who as usual had been silent throughout the whole session, that constant gape of irritation on her face – and asked, 'Can one of you maybe look in the staffroom for a white bowl, it's gone missing and it's mine.'

This prompted a strange and indignant response from Mona. 'You think everyone is out to get you, don't you, Emma? You think that the staff are out for you. You seem to think we're conspiring against you and now are suggesting we're hiding your things from you.'

I did not try to mask my distaste for her and deliberately rudely said, 'Calm down, I just wondered if my bowl was in the staffroom. If it's going to give you that much of an issue to look for it, fuck it, I'll buy a new one.' I gave her the filthiest look I could muster, which to my surprise was mirrored back at me.

An hour passed and I was again in the art room. I had decided to go out to the supermarket and was sitting in there preparing myself to leave. Susie walked in and sat on the sofa next to me; she gently turned her body towards me.

'Are you okay, Em?'

To my astonishment, I burst into tears and began to incoherently mumble about suicide. I wasn't sure where it was coming from, when I had been perfectly composed just minutes before. The art door creaked open and Mike came in and began to tell me that everyone was worried about me but didn't want to piss me off by going to the staff.

There was a long pause, he took a heavy breath in and then asked, 'Are you still self-harming?' I hadn't ever bothered to conceal my talk of self-harm around Mike and thought he knew I was still doing it, so was slightly taken aback by this question and wondered if it was more for Susie's benefit than mine. I didn't say anything, just looked at the floor and nodded.

Losing the will to go out, I went back to my room. The mask had officially slipped, my composure had left me. I felt completely exposed and the voice in my head was using this to its advantage as it reminded me of every terrible, misery-evoking thought I could ever have. I picked up my phone and called Dr Khan, telling him that I had had enough, and that I wanted to die.

'I can't carry on any more. What's the point?' I sobbed.

Dr Khan's usually calm voice was more strained than usual. 'I want you to go and speak to the duty staff right now. Go and tell them how you feel. Or I can ring?'

Closing my eyes and regaining some sort of equanimity, I quietly replied, 'It's okay, I'll go and tell them.'

He then very sweetly, if not somewhat naively, said, 'You promise?'

I sighed, hating the lie before it had even come out of my mouth. 'Yes. I promise.' Before he hung up he said he would call me the next day. What I didn't say to him was that I didn't plan on being around that long.

I seemed to lose most of the day in my room and come midnight I was half suffocating in my own tears as I pined aloud in my room for my dog. I kept hearing myself gasp for her to come back. Lit by the glow of the television, I rolled up my sleeve and dragged my razor blade over my arms. It was that sort of detached cutting that happens when you can't even feel the blade on your skin. I saw my flesh open in white lines; my eyes would linger over them as they filled up with blood, bright red to the brim, then overran onto the floor and bed, spreading all over my bed sheets like red wine, but I couldn't stop. Every time I tried, I would lose myself again, plunging the blade deeper with each failed attempt to feel something. The image of her limp body on the vet's table invaded my brain like a sickness, tangling with the plague of my words: 'Are you *sure* she's dead?'

I stared at my skin in a trance, some distant voice in the background urging me that I should go and get someone to dress my arm. But I didn't want to be helped, and how could anyone possibly stop these images? I wanted to crawl into the hopelessness, I wanted to surrender.

*

When I woke up in the morning, I was still numb. I peeled my home-made bandage off my skin, cringing in pain as I did so; it was only halfway off and I saw the blood begin to gush again.

Patting it back down I decided to ignore it for the rest of the day. What I couldn't see didn't exist, and what didn't exist couldn't affect me. Of course the previous night hadn't just been about the dog. It was about everything. Coming to the Henshaw had never been an easy choice, committing yourself to going to live somewhere far away from your home with magnetic locks on the doors, going from seeing your friends every night to barely at all, coming off meds and giving up a huge chunk of your freedom were notions I had struggled with, but I did it because I wanted to get better. I hungered to understand my moods, the nightmarish lows and the wild highs. I wanted to stop self-harming, to get my food issues under control and to walk out of that hospital a brand new squeaky clean version of myself... But instead I was going to be emerging from there a shell of my previous self, not only had I not made any progress, I'd actually regressed. I'd become better at hiding things, I'd learned new tricks and new defence mechanisms. If the Henshaw had taught me anything, it was that I was almost one hundred per cent sure that this life was not for me.

The self-harm had bought me some time. Perhaps another few hours or days. It had served its long-standing purpose and gotten me through the night and deterred me from attempting something more final.

I spoke to no one during the 9/15, and proceeded to get through most of my small group doing the same. That is until the issue of Esther's epilepsy was brought up. There had been rumours circulating that she had not been taking her medication in order to induce her fits – there was even the suggestion that some were being faked. Fiona asked Esther how she felt about this accusation. Esther very quickly got away from the subject by 'raising concerns' for me. I stared blankly at her until in the meekest, most victim-like voice I presume she could muster, she squeaked, 'Emma, when you behave like this, not saying anything, it has an effect on other people, not just you.' She looked at Fiona like a dog looking at its owner expecting a treat when it sits on command.

My silence for a moment slipped away from me and I snapped back at her, 'Do you think I am so stupid that I don't know that? Don't be so fucking patronising.' The sound of my booming voice echoed around the room.

Esther looked at Fiona for reassurance, then wiping an invisible tear from her eye said, 'Okay, sorry, Emma.' Her behaviour was so manipulative and passive that it was infuriating to the rest of us that the staff could not see it. Esther had a habit of being your best friend at first; she would draw you into friendship under the pretence of being a sweet little Catholic girl in whose mouth butter wouldn't melt. She'd keep this up for about a week or two and then suddenly, and without warning, would turn on you – getting you in trouble with the staff repeatedly, and then expecting to still be your friend. She had done this with me, and with everyone else that had come into the hospital after her. It was the fraudulent victim act that got to me the most, that pushed my buttons – that and the fact that no one in a position of power could seem to see through her tricks or even begin to challenge her on some of her behaviours.

19

GO FUND ME

"I don't want any more of this try, try again stuff.
I just want out. I've had it. I am so tired.
I am twenty and I am already exhausted."

– ELIZABETH WURTZEL, *Prozac Nation*

Soon enough I was sitting with a coffee, a pen in my hand and a notebook on the table in front of me in a Starbucks not too far from the hospital; writing would sustain me when cutting could not. My phone beeped, flashing that I had a voicemail. With all the might it would take to lift a brick, I pulled it to my ear and listened to the voice of a secretary telling me I had an appointment at twelve o'clock that day to see Nicole at another hospital across town, the same Nicole who had been in my CPA meeting. Panic. It was already after eleven.

I frantically called trying to get another date or time, but the unapologetic receptionist said I wouldn't be seen again for at least a week. I needed this appointment, I couldn't miss it. I called the Henshaw and was rung back by the, yet again, new top three who were Mike, Esther and Magda. Magda who had had to step in as every other patient refused to be elected. It was

162

of course on loudspeaker and Esther proceeded to keep saying that I needed to come back and talk about going to the meeting before I went, that it should be rearranged and that I needed to take support with me.

As Esther said this I heard Magda saying in the background, 'She should come back here if she's *supposedly* suicidal.'

Keeping my voice calm I said, 'But this is a really important meeting, I can't afford to miss it!'

'I think you should come back and talk about it. One of us should go with you another day,' came Esther's reply. She was enjoying this. But there was no way I was going to let her or anyone else go with me. I closed my eyes for a second, taking a deep breath, and then redirected my question.

'Mike, what should I do?'

I imagined his expression as he breathed deeply into the phone and said, 'Do what you've gotta do, Em,' his way of telling me to go to the meeting. Knowing I had a vote coming anyway, knowing this would no doubt be the nail in the coffin, I said 'Thanks', hung up and caught the train across town.

As I got off my first train and waited for the second one I rang my mother. I explained I was worried about being on the vote but knew the meeting with Nicole was important. I exhaled, waiting for an answer to bring me some clarity, some guidance. Her voice was indifferent as she began to speak.

'I don't even *know* what's wrong with you, Emma. You haven't told me anything since you were thirteen… and now you want my help. You need to get a job, there is nothing wrong with you, that's my advice.'

Exasperated and unable to even think of an answer I hung up, texting her a moment later to say, 'Think my signal went, thanks for speaking, don't worry about it x'.

As the train rolled in a few minutes later and I stepped on, I received a message back from her that read:

'You will go into a council flat like the one you grew up in and despised. You will occasionally see your friends but they will grow up and go their ways. You will probably meet some ex-druggie, or mental patient, because those are the people you mix with now. You will perhaps have a baby, which will have a mother on benefits and with no aspirations in life, you will be the role model for this child, and so the whole ghastly process will start again. Why have you become such a dropout? You have broken my heart. Have the courage to face your fears and get on with your life before you get totally sucked into the system.'

Not blinking, I switched my phone off. If I couldn't see it, it couldn't affect me.

This mantra worked for me for about twenty minutes, and as I sat down in the waiting room of Queen Mary's, I began to sob. Dr Carter and Nicole called me in, and we spoke for some time about the Henshaw, about how it had been there since the CPA. I told them it was hell.

'I feel like it's a witch hunt and a lot of the staff are out to get me.'

They suggested again that when my funding for the Henshaw ran out I go into supported accommodation, adding to this that 'these types of places' often contained 'a range of people with a range of problems'. My answer was that as long as I had a lock on my door, I didn't care. The pair pushed for further inpatient treatment in the form of the Caddick, but I didn't want it, not yet anyway. Inpatient treatment thus far had, if anything, worsened my problems. The last thing I needed was another nuthouse. I was tired, so tired; we'd been talking for two hours.

Dr Carter looked at me, compassion all over his face, and said, 'I'd like to talk about your adolescence, and growing up. But not now, we've talked a lot today. Before we end, is there anything else you'd like to talk about?' Through my soaking wet face and smeared make-up I mumbled, 'I'd just like to say thank you, thank you for listening and trying to help, I really appreciate it.' They smiled and Nicole walked me to the door. I wasn't sure what had happened to Dr Carter over the last two years, why and how he had softened, but I was glad of the change.

I felt slightly more alive on the way back to the Henshaw. Perhaps the talking had helped; perhaps it was enough to know that two perfect strangers would help me where no one else would, or could.

It was grey and raining when I got back to the hospital. Mike was in the kitchen making a cup of coffee. Unprovoked, he gave me a hug when I walked in. Mike served the role of a somewhat uncomfortable dad; he wanted to let me know he cared but it didn't come naturally to him. He stirred his coffee. 'Esther talked about you non stop in handover.'

I hopped up on the kitchen counter. 'Oh yeah? What did she say?'

'She tried to fuck you over, big time – saying that you ignore the rules, don't take support, aren't 'signed up' to treatment. Her usual crap. Be careful Em,' he took a sip from his mug 'I don't know what she's up to, but whatever it is, it ain't good. You know I'll back you, but just be wary.'

Trying my best to ignore Esther's 'Get Emma' campaign, I spent the evening with Susie, Katie and Mike. Katie kept telling me how much I reminded her of her 'wee' sister, and she seemed to dote on me a bit – which I liked. Katie felt like an older sister to me, always coming and asking if I wanted to go for coffee, asking how I was or giving me little gifts and I really enjoyed the attention and moreover the feeling of closeness. I had noticed a spark between her and Mike; whenever she was around he seemed to brighten up and it was nice to see him happier, a lively change from his usual pessimistic self.

I sat next to Susie as we teased them about their budding 'relationship'. Augusta came in and sat with us for a while, but was used to getting most of Mike's attention (or at least sharing it equally with me) and in her usual blatantly honest fashion stared icily at the pair of them as they playfully mocked each other, not seeming to understand where this sudden affection had come from. She replied in one-word answers when I asked her how she was and after a few minutes she threw her hands dramatically up in the air saying, 'I have to go.' I think she expected me to follow her, but Augusta's petulant child routine was one I was now very used to and did not always have time for. Having said that, usually I would have gone after her, but I had had a long day and being curled up next to Susie as she played with my hair was more preferable to listening to Augusta squawk about Katie and Mike. Plus watching the pair of them flirt with each other somehow took me out of the hospital, and it was a welcome change from people screaming at each other.

*

I had it confirmed to me the following day that my funding would run out on 31 March. Almost four weeks to the day. Of course, the staff delivered this news to me in the packed 9/15 and then promptly asked me how I felt about it. I didn't give much of an answer, saying that I felt mixed about it – which was the truth. I didn't want to stay, but I didn't have anywhere to go.

I sat there after that as everyone around me continued to talk about my time in the Henshaw. It seemed beyond ridiculous that anyone could have thought that the last few months had done anything good for me. The whole thing seemed like some sort of joke, a social experiment gone horribly wrong.

My small group did nothing to dispel these feelings. Lana, or 'Le Gouble' as Mike and I had nicknamed her, meaning 'The Gob', was now fairly unbearable to be in a group with, or to be within ten miles of for that matter. Her roaring voice seemed to flatten everything in its path and there was no question she didn't have an answer for – it was especially hard to relate as she constantly put herself above everyone else, and according to her, her experiences were always *more* unique, *more* upsetting and *more* horrendous than anyone else's could have been. When Lana wasn't talking, Katie was. Although I liked Katie, she ranted like a woman possessed, making little sense in the process. Her voice was the constant backdrop for the room and trying to block it out was impossible – especially if she felt no one was listening, when she would get more and more aggressive with the way she spoke, eventually screaming her words across the room. Esther sat opposite me, glaring at them both, furious at not being able to have any of the limelight. In a way, this was the only time I felt any connection with her – she was the only other person in the hospital who had to endure listening to these two for three arduously long hours, twice a week.

Fiona was the only person who could interrupt without having too much hatred thrown her way, but even that was a push.

'I heard you put something very emotive down in art, Emma?' It took me a second to register a new voice in amongst the Irish/Scottish onslaught. I looked up to see Fiona gently smiling at me, waiting for an answer. I nodded as she continued, 'I was told it was very powerful and stirred up a lot in everyone?'

As I opened my mouth to answer her, Lana's voice sounded in place of mine. 'I thought it was very emotive. It reminded me of when I was sleeping rough and this pimp, I—'

Exasperated, Fiona butted in, 'I would like to hear from *Emma*, Lana.'

Lana folded her arms and began to tap her foot. I turned my head a fraction to the right to try and get her out of my peripheral vision. To my surprise I began to talk about the feelings behind the collage I had made. I had copied out the text my mother had sent me and surrounded it with photographs of images it had conjured in my mind – a heavily pregnant teenager with a beer in her hand, a guy shooting up in a doorway, a benefits office. I spoke for a few moments, which felt like a few hours, and stopped myself when it started to feel too exposing. And this, in a nutshell, was what my therapy was here: brief interludes of silence between the other patients where I would try and share something, spurred on by Fiona. But these moments were few and far between; the light they cast over the shadows in my mind was desperately needed, but always so fleeting.

*

That day I ate only what I could throw up. I spoke only when spoken to. And I cut my arms until I could feel again. *I am evil.* Cut, cut, cut. *I do not deserve love.* Purge, purge, purge. I put my music on as loudly as I could and sang along to the words, ignoring Augusta, Mike and Katie as one by one they knocked on the cheap wooden door of room twenty-six asking if I was all right.

Whilst I was wrapped up snug with my own despair, Susie was on the floor below me deciding to leave the Henshaw. When I spoke to her the following day she said it was becoming too damaging for her, that she couldn't bear it any more and that even more upsettingly, Carl was on his way to pick her up and take her home; he had agreed to let her come back to the family home if she 'behaved' herself. There was no stopping her, and to be honest I didn't want to. I knew, just as she did, that this hospital was becoming more toxic by the day. Carl was dangerous, but so was the Henshaw; she was at risk in both scenarios.

Reluctantly, I helped Tara, Augusta and Candace carry her belongings down to the front door. Carl arrived in his red BMW and it was a challenge not to tell him exactly what I thought of him. But for Susie's sake, I kept my mouth shut, saying hello and forcing a smile for fear of her suffering the repercussions if he sensed people were off with him. He got out and put her bags in the boot, waving to us as he did so, playing the role of the dutiful husband, not a clue that the people watching him knew exactly how much of a monster he was. Mike couldn't be there; his anger didn't allow it. He would have killed Carl if he had got close enough.

I stood in the doorway, half in and half out of the hospital, hugging Susie and wishing I could say something hopeful to her. She handed us a letter to read in the 9/15 and left. She had executed this whole thing much like Megan had, away from the prying eyes of the staff, and wanted a quick and silent exit. Augusta looked as though she might cry as the car drove off and quickly scuttled away down the hall. I stood and watched with Tara as our mutual maternal figure vanished. Susie didn't wave as the car turned; her face was devoid of emotion, her hair and make-up perfect as she stared blankly into the distance. Another one bites the dust.

*

As quickly as the staff had replaced Megan and Lyle, someone came to replace Susie. Brenda was eighteen, a five-foot-one peroxide-blonde beachball with a skin colour that could only be described as orange. She was obstinate and opinionated and I took an instant dislike to her, as did a lot of people. She blew into meetings telling us all we shouldn't be moaning about the closure, but rather should be thankful for the chance we'd been given. I can see in hindsight that she had a point, but she had not been dragged down into the ground with the slow, dying corpse of the Henshaw for what had been months at that point, watching your comrades get more ill, watching your chance at redemption slip away. I snapped savagely at her on several occasions, as did Mike, both of us telling her to shut up, saying that she did not have a clue what she was talking about. But I was only enraging myself; she didn't listen and if she did, her blind optimism would neutralise any acid that flew from my tongue.

My main issue with her was that she didn't seem to have any problems. Here I was ripping myself to shreds, throwing up on a constant basis, the voices in my head screaming at me twenty-four hours a day, and Brenda's issue was that she'd often run away from home. For no particular reason, she just constantly fled her house and disappeared for a few days at a time. There seemed to be no external forces encouraging this behaviour, no abuse, past or present, no horrific underlying mental health issue, she got on with her family, she was happy, so why was she here? Simply to bump up the numbers, it seemed.

'Here's an idea,' said Candace one afternoon in art therapy, 'Why don't you just not run away from home any more, then your mother wouldn't worry and call the police?' Brenda looked at her; her expression reminded me of a pigeon a lot of the time, a look of confusion at her own existence plaguing her face.

'Well, I get bored. I like people having to fuss and find me.'

My head was pounding; was she really admitting this? She liked terrifying her sixty-year-old mother who had only ever supported her?

'Why would you do that?' asked Tara staring at her with disdain.

'Well, why not? I get bored, I run off. I'm not hurting anyone.'

'But you are!' shouted Mike not able to control himself any more. 'You're hurting your family, and for no reason. It's just pure selfishness.' Brenda shrugged her shoulders as if the idea had never even occurred to her.

'Ah well,' she hummed.

'You're fucking ridiculous.' I couldn't help it, it just came out.

'Emma! That's not constructive,' said Blanche, scowling at me.

Brenda didn't even blink, had she even heard me?

Mike leaned over to me and whispered in my ear, 'Not constructive, but true.'

We sniggered like children as Brenda said, 'You can say what you like, all you want to do is be negative and moan anyway. You should try using this opportunity; you're all wasting it, like the wasters you are.'

Mike started screaming at her at that point, as did Augusta, Candace and just about everyone except me. I was too exasperated by her to even speak any more. Her very presence made my blood boil, and she was just more reason to leave.

20

LEAVING

"I hear a voice. Clear. Commanding. Unmistakable. It is my own voice, insecure and relentless. *You know you have to do this.* No, I don't. *Yes, you do. If you were better than this, you wouldn't be here.*"

— VANESSA VEGA, *Comes the Darkness, Comes the Light: A memoir of cutting, healing, and hope*

I couldn't hold anything down. Almost everyone I had started this journey with had left, been voted out or abandoned ship. The only thing that made any sense was bulimia. Eat. Feel guilty. Vomit. Every hour, every day. The outside world could go to shit for all I cared, I had my food, I had my blades, and if at any point either of those didn't work, I had that gleaming prize, that light at the end of the tunnel, the holy grail: suicide.

As I walked out of yet another crisis 9/15, Katie grabbed my arm and pulled me to the side of the kitchen. She lowered her voice and sank her head down to my level.

'I know what you've been doing.'

I cocked my head to the side, confused. 'Um, what have I been doing?'

'That!' she pointed to the Dalmatian red spots around my eyes. 'You've been throwin' up.'

I was torn somewhere between relief that someone had finally noticed (perhaps I wasn't invisible after all) and fear that she might tell the staff (and that they would try to make me stop). I spluttered over words and excuses before being cut off again by her.

'It's so obvious,' she continued, pointing to different parts of my face. 'Your skin's so dry, and those fuckin' great bags under your eyes. You look terrible, Emma.' I didn't have anything to say to the girl. She was the first person to have noticed in there. To have indicated aloud to me that I had some sort of problem. That something was not right. I literally felt my mind fragment into dozens of little bits as I tried to take in her words. *Was this a problem? But I'm still so fat, how can it be?*

I spoke to Katie for a while, trying to understand if there really was an issue with what I was doing, my main reasoning being that no one had noticed, therefore my logic told me everything was fine. It came to light that Katie was on a three-day 'starving' mission herself, so it was the blind leading the blind. She told me I must come and talk to her about it all. I said I would with no intention of following through. I couldn't; I was addicted. The thought of someone trying to take away my only reason for each day was a thought I couldn't bear. Every night I would stand in front of the plastic mirror above my sink, my pale arms covered in jagged cuts; I would hold up my top as I sucked in my stomach, almost forgetting to breathe as the lure of my exposed ribcage spurred me on. My bones seemed to get more defined every day. I had failed at so much, but I wasn't going to fail this; three more stone and I'll be acceptable, four more and I'll be thin, five more and I'll be perfect.

After I had been told about my leaving date I professed in front of everyone that this was 'absolutely fine' with me, but I needed more time 'to get my housing sorted out', so maybe I could apply for another few weeks? The staff seemed somewhat overjoyed at what they deemed a submission for help, and said they would see what they could do.

A few days passed and, though he said he'd tried, Andrew reported back that the primary care trust would only approve funding in three- to six-month blocks. I wasn't staying there that long, I wouldn't survive. The idea of three to six months in that place was more worrying than the idea of being homeless, so that was it. Eighteen days and I was out.

*

Small group was now completely unbearable. Lana just ranted and ranted, a constant slur of never-ending words, while Katie did the same but made even less sense with it, the only recognisable parts were the 'fuckings', 'fucks' and 'bastards'. Esther's only contribution came in quiet whines from the corner and I just sat there in stubborn, shackled silence hating them all, hating myself, and working out calories.

*

Whilst I was busy on my self-destruct mission drowning in my perceived notion that no one was helping me, Dr Carter, somewhere behind a desk in London, was in fact trying his best. I got a copy of the letter he sent to the housing association. I sat down and opened it.

It referred to me as having 'severe borderline personality disorder, co-morbid depression, deliberate self-harm, a panic disorder and having overdosed in the past.' And there I was.

Right there in black and white. I crumpled the paper up into a ball and threw it under my bed.

*

I had less than two weeks to go and I had begun to detach emotionally from the Henshaw. I stopped caring how much Le Gouble talked and ranted, or about Katie and Mike's now basically public romance. I spent more time at Jess's, or up in my room. My deep depression had not lifted; if anything it had permanently moved into my mind, but I was in some sort of transitional period. I knew soon none of this would mean much to me, and that it was just a case of keeping my head above water until the day of leaving came.

My room at the hospital was my sanctuary, much like it was at home, and it seemed to be a common understanding that my 'space' was off limits to most, the only exceptions being Katie, Augusta and Mike. Augusta took full advantage of this, and would frequently come tapping on my door.

One night, not too long after I had found out my leaving date, I heard her sparrow-like voice calling from outside. I was on my bed watching TV.

'Come in, Augusta.'

She peeped around my door. 'Are you sure? I just want to talk to you for a minute.'

'Yeah, it's fine, come in.' I motioned for her to join me in sitting on the bed, but instead she perched on the floor. I could tell she had something specific that she wanted to tell me, it was just a case of drawing it out of her. We spoke for a little while about the other patients and general menial things. She knew about my eating issues – she'd known from the start – and my ongoing self-harm, and kept hinting around these subjects. After twenty or so minutes came the confession that, in truth, I was not expecting.

'I've been cutting again.' I drew my eyes away from the television set and put them on her. She was cross-legged looking at the floor.

'*What?* For how long?'

She didn't look up.

'A few weeks. I didn't want to tell you because I knew you'd be angry with me.' Augusta lifted one of her sleeves to reveal a row of deep purple cuts precariously held together with Steri-Strips.

'Those need stitches,' I said, feeling myself wince a little.

'I know.' She covered her arm again, 'But I just couldn't tell anyone.'

I suppose it was the fact that when the militantly OCD rule-enforcer begins to break down, begins to break the rules, then you really do know that you are in deep shit. Of course, I wouldn't in a million years have been 'angry' with her, but that was obviously the narrative she had to tell herself to justify keeping it a secret. She urged me not to tell, but as opposed to Susie genuinely meaning for me not to tell anyone, I wasn't so sure this was what Augusta wanted. I think she wanted the staff to find out, just indirectly through me.

So I had established that I was very much up shit creek without a paddle with the Augusta situation. I didn't know if I should alert the staff, or keep it quiet. After all I had seen over the last couple of months, I still took Augusta's confession as a big red neon flashing sign that Henshaw truly was doomed; it was the cherry on top of the cake.

What came next was an overwhelming surge of paranoia from Mike's direction. He was now the last male patient in the hospital, with the majority of the women surrounding him having been beaten, raped or abused in some way or another by men. So in Mike's mind he had become some sort of pariah of hatred for the whole of his sex and a point of negative focus. And this seed, which in truth perhaps was not born of paranoia, and which in a safe therapeutic environment could and would have been explored, was now being watered and nourished by his own drug-damaged perception as well as the last rasping breaths from the dying hospital. Years of narcotic abuse were feeding into Mike's state of mind; he was a trembling, chain-smoking mess who was completely hypersensitive to any form of perceived criticism. He would talk to me, and a couple of the male staff, but that was it.

One afternoon I caught him in the garden smoking and drinking coffee.

'Hello.'

His hand was shaking as he drew his cigarette from his lips; he didn't look up.

'All right, Em.'

I patted him on his broad shoulder as I sat down on the bench next to him. 'You okay?'

'Na, not really.' He seemed like he wanted to talk, but just needed encouragement.

I softened my voice. 'What's up?'

He exhaled some of the smoke he had just taken in. 'I've got to get out of here. I can't take it. I'm leaving tonight for a couple of days, going on a forty-eight.' (A 'forty-eight' was the 'legal' amount of time a resident could leave the hospital for without being put on a serious vote and ultimately discharged.)

There was a short silence. 'Well, if you think it'll help.' I was quiet for a moment and then said, 'Have you told Katie?'

Sipping from his coffee cup he shook his head. 'Nope. Can't take her either.'

'Why? I thought you two were getting on really well?'

'She's too much. And Augusta's so jealous of me and her, they're always watching each other, watching me. I don't want all this. I came here to sort out my life, not become everyone's scapegoat. I've never hit a woman, I've never raped anyone, but

I feel like I'm getting blamed for all the fucking monsters out there.' Mike's eyes were frantic and wide; he took another long drag on his cigarette.

'I know. It's not all in your head, but the people who matter don't see you like that, you know?'

He nodded.

I sensed he'd had enough talking so I slowly stood up. 'All right, well, I didn't know about you going, if anyone asks. Try and chill out while you're at home, and…' I paused, 'don't do any drugs.'

For the first time in a while he chuckled, looking out onto the grounds and smiling. 'I won't.'

*

The Henshaw was a shell of what I had initially walked into six months ago. The garden was unkempt, the pond empty. (One cold day in January it had developed a leak; we discovered it at three in the afternoon, about five inches full of what little murky water was left. Completely horrified that the fish were going to be left to suffocate, I spent six hours single-handedly filling up the pond with buckets of water. I got in trouble for missing meetings and when I was asked to stop by the staff I refused, telling them it was murder if I walked away and condemning them for being able to do so. It was after nightfall, my back was aching, I was soaked from rain and pond water, but the fish were alive, swimming happily in their home. The next day, driven possibly by her feelings for me, or the fish – it is not quite clear which – Augusta went into town and bought a filter and repair kit and mended the pond. After I left the hospital she told me most of the fish had died due to another leak, but she had swept the last remaining dozen out and now had them in a tank in her sitting room, something I have always quietly adored her for.)

It was time to leave the Henshaw before the ground swallowed it up, taking me along with it. There was something about it that felt like leaving school. I fell into the same patterns, my father insisting that I buy the therapists and nurses chocolates, me snapping back that 'of course' I was going to.

I was due to leave on Saturday; it was Wednesday. I returned to the hospital with a bag full of chocolates in decorative boxes. In some attempt to differentiate the staff from patients I had bought the staff alcoholic truffles, something which (I was soon to learn) was a mistake. At 8pm on Wednesday evening a referred was called. I walked into it unassuming, wondering what we had all been disturbed for. I didn't stop to think that I was the reason.

Top three announced that the meeting had been called to establish if I had broken the rules by bringing alcohol onto the premises – in the form of the staff's box of truffles. Although it seemed ridiculous and rejecting, it felt familiar, like I somehow deserved this punishment, though I didn't know why, and equally it did not stop my rage taking over as I shouted, 'For fuck's sake! I was trying to do something nice. Forget it. Bin them! Just bin them! I don't care.'

Magda, who had initiated this meeting, was adamant in her resolve that I had done something wrong. I didn't understand her motives, it seemed like a last-ditch attempt to get me to 'talk' or to 'let them in', and if that's what she wanted she was going about it the wrong way. I am and as far as I am aware have always been a very untrusting creature; I need to believe a person means me no harm before I share even the smallest detail about myself and despite spending so many months with me it seemed Magda had not learned this. Her attempt to delve into my psyche was shut down by me within about four seconds. I refused to speak, or even acknowledge her when she spoke to me.

The others, my friends, patients, were for once, with the exception of Esther, a united front, all enveloping, all protecting, all as taken aback and angry as I was. Magda – I assume realising this had all been a bit of a mistake on her part – soon began waving her white flag and the meeting was drawn to a close. Before anyone could leave the room she said that we should all 'get together' and play some board games, and that everyone should be involved. The only game I wanted to play was the continual game of how deep I could rip into myself. How much can I punish myself for buying those fucking chocolates, for embarrassing myself, for being humiliated – yet again? How much can I hurt? I was fast fragmenting under the weight of my own anger.

Within seconds I was in my room, stamping on, pulling apart (for the hundredth time) a disposable orange and white razor. Routine had me laying out a T-shirt on the bed, my sleeve pulled up, my arm resting over the black material, still vigilant about not staining the bed sheets, razor in hand. There is often a pause before I cut, where I replay the reason I am doing it. The reason I deserve everything I am about to get. Blade to skin. Skin then parts. Reveals white gaping flesh. Flesh turns to blood. Rivers of self-punishment, tributaries of misplaced rejection running, pooling over my desert-white arms. I deserve this. I deserve this. I deserve this. I heard myself say aloud, 'Good, hurt. Fucking hurt,' a mantra that would engulf me in these moments, a soothing lullaby of self-loathing. I listened to my own words on repeat and believed it was okay that I was doing this, because I deserved it.

Time soon became unfrozen, and I flew back to myself with no concept of how long I had been away. Angry cutting is usually the worst, the one where I can do most damage without realising. I had open gashes lining my forearm, the white fat of my insides grinning at me, mocking, comforting. I thought of them all downstairs playing board games and curled around myself on my bed.

*

My last couple of days were the calm after the chocolate storm. I was adamant that I had to leave, that the hospital was toxic and that I was doing the right thing. In reality, I knew I was fucked. I was no better, my eating issues had gotten out of control since being admitted and my arms were now spending all day wrapped in makeshift bandages to stem the blood from dripping into public view. I was contemplating suicide hourly and my grand plan of action when it all got too much was to go to Amsterdam. It didn't matter that I had no future! I was going to Amsterdam! I could smoke myself into oblivion! Hooray, I'm saved! I was continually told by Tara, Candace, Augusta, Mike and Katie that they didn't want me to go, that it would not be the same without me. Augusta especially, who seemed to go through every spectrum of the borderline rainbow, ignoring me, obsessing over me, refusing to be near me, refusing to leave my side.

The Friday before I left I phoned the housing association and was told by one of the staff there that *unequivocally no*, I would not be given a flat or placed in housing of any sort. I spent my last day at the hospital not at the hospital, but in Starbucks suffocating in my own tears, lambasting the world and vomiting every time food or liquid touched my lips.

*

My mother had accepted the fact I was coming home, and thankfully I could fall back on the fact that my funding had run out and it wasn't just a case of me walking out.

My dad arrived in his big silver 4x4 smiling and saying hello to everyone as they helped me carry my things to the boot of his car. Mike was the closest to emotional I'd ever seen him, a gesture in itself that made my own eyes fill up. He told me to take care of myself. I hugged Augusta's stiff body next to mine and did not take offence as her arms remained by her sides. When I let go of her she apologised and looked as though she was about to break into a thousand pieces. I stood for a few moments reassuring her that we would remain friends and I would not forget her. She looked at me as though I were her mother telling her that Father Christmas was not only not real, but in fact a paedophile who carried dead children in his big red sack. In Augusta's mind I was leaving – not the hospital, not treatment, but her.

I didn't say goodbye to Brenda, Lana or Esther. But the others shuffled out of their rooms or off the sofa to hug me and wish me luck. As per my predecessors before me, I opted to leave on a Sunday, the day before I was officially due to go, which meant no staff to get in my way or question me, no 9/15 and no referred. I would slip out unseen.

As I got in the car and my dad uttered his 'Okay, Em,' (not a question) we began to drive away, and the last image I saw was Mike standing outside, a cigarette in one hand, and the other arm around Augusta.

No one whooped and cheered, or walked to the road to wave; the hospital I was leaving was not the one I had walked into.

21

A LONG SUMMER

"In the middle of the journey of our life I found myself within a
dark woods where the straight way was lost."

— DANTE ALIGHIERI, *Inferno*

The months after leaving the Henshaw were, to put it simply,
horrendous. I was soon back on my 60mg dose of prozac and the
decision was made quickly by my Community Mental Health
Team (CMHT) that I needed to be back in a hospital as soon as
possible. I began seeing Andrew from the Henshaw as part of
my outreach on a fortnightly basis again; he went far beyond the
call of duty to meet with me, always offering a safe place to talk
about how I was feeling. The leavers group had long since been
disbanded, so Andrew was my only form of support. He liaised
with the CMHT and together they referred me to the Caddick. I
once again, or rather *they* once again entered into a financial war
with the NHS, and so began another seemingly endless spate of
waiting for government funding.

In the days waiting for the money to come through, life
became almost unbearable. My mother was unhappy that I was
at home '*doing nothing again*' and could not bear the misery

that came along with me, although I tried hard to hide it in her presence. My days seemed endless. I woke every morning lying in bed trying to summon the energy to get up, to get myself washed and dressed and get out of the house. The daily goal was to try and stay out as long as possible; which, with hardly any money, no dog to walk, and all my friends at work or away travelling, was no easy feat. Filling the days was a tiresome battle that seemed to have no end in sight.

Two months after leaving the Henshaw I received my discharge summary. I reluctantly opened it and began to read what had been written about me:

It is difficult to ascertain what progress Emma made during her stay here. She was in the first cohort of residents who had been offered less than the customary year of treatment at this unit. This significantly impacted on her ability to attach to the community, compromised by the announcement of the planned closure of the Henshaw hospital just a few weeks after her arrival here. In her mind the announcement impacted on any attachment she might develop to the unit, engagement with the programme and work on herself.

There was a sense that fellow patients had an idea of what was going on in Emma's life that was affecting her, which however was largely kept from staff, maybe because she didn't feel safe with them. Emma seemed quite instrumental in fostering an 'us and them' attitude, by not being forthcoming with information, by adopting a sarcastic, aggressive attitude directed at staff and by standing up for others who she perhaps perceived as being unduly challenged by staff. This in part seemed to be a defensive manoeuvre. For though Emma was well liked by her peers, they seemed to lack confidence that they had something to offer her in the formal groups in terms of thoughts about her life and challenges to her, which no doubt reflected her own mistrust. By contrast, when Emma did allow herself to reflect on the direct attention of staff members, her protective shell of indifference would rapidly melt away and she would become quite tearful, about what she felt she had not received and what she felt worried about not being able to create for her future.

All in all there was an ambivalence in her and mixed messages conveyed about not being affected and being untouchable on the one hand but very interested and committed and indirectly revealing vulnerability on the other hand.

Although self-harm and her disordered eating were issues for work identified for her referral to residential treatment, particularly the latter did not come much to the fore in the Henshaw hospital; whilst it became known that she had engaged in self-harming on some occasions, and there was a general sense that this was continuing 'underground', the disordered eating stayed out of the public realm, e.g. as Emma seemed to prefer to have meals up in her room, ate at different times than other residents and typically away from them. Similarly there was a general acknowledgement that Emma has got body issues, e.g. always wearing baggy clothes which seemed to be hiding her figure to a significant degree, and being uncomfortable and irritable without make-up, it appears that this was not explored in any of the groups.

Given that Emma's attachment to the Henshaw was curtailed, and her stay was affected by

the announcement of the planned closure of
the unit, there was a sense that Emma felt
she needed to continue with coping behaviours
such as self-harm (cutting and overdosing),
possible use of illicit drugs, with disordered
eating behaviour suspected but not addressed
or spoken about. Around the middle of her
stay, she admitted in a review meeting that
she had self-harmed on a number of occasions,
and there were suspicions that this may have
continued until she left.

PROGNOSIS
It is difficult to give a prognosis given the
extraordinary circumstance of Emma's stay in
residential treatment, namely the threat to
the service. Emma did engage to some extent
with the service, and has some capacity to
reflect and change her behaviour, even in the
difficult environment of the Henshaw hospital in
transition, which impeded her fully attaching
to the service. It is to her credit that she
has made some impact whilst being here, and
she may well benefit from more therapy in a
residential service that could allow her to
further explore her relationship with her
mother, which seems a model, or pattern,
repeated in other relationships.

Susan Meister
Social Therapist
15th May 2008

It was an eight-page dissertation but those were the highlights. I
was annoyed that a woman whom I had almost no contact with
at the hospital had been able to write this 'paper' on me. Susan,
the whole time I was there, probably said good morning to me

once if that and I didn't see why she was in a significant enough position to talk about my 'sarcastic, aggressive' behaviour, or that I was instrumental in fostering an 'us and them' attitude. It *was* us and them. I hadn't felt there was one therapist there who was on my side, or really knew me; of course I was going to be defensive.

Reading the discharge summary bothered me tremendously. I didn't want to think about it or acknowledge it. I shoved it back in its envelope and buried it in one of my bedside drawers. They just didn't know me, that's all it came down to.

*

It was a June morning and I was in Starbucks having coffee and writing when my mother rang me. Someone had hacked into the Amazon account I had set up for her and spent £20. She screamed down the phone at me for what felt like forever, telling me I would have to pay her back and saying she had never wanted the account and it was me who had set it up. The usual stuff, that I had no job, no work ethic and therefore no understanding of money also came flooding out in a tsunami of built-up agitation. As she hung up, the anger I felt began to spiral inside me creating a hurricane of rage. The thought of her being at home, waiting for me to arrive there, further spiked my adrenalin; how could I placate her? How could I undo what I had done? Fight, flight, freeze, all my traffic lights flashing at once. I couldn't think. I just knew I needed to hurt. My feet were trying to weigh me down as seconds later I was on my way to the nearest pharmacy, my mind and my body already splitting into two separate beings. I stood in the queue with a packet of razor blades clasped like gold in my hands and didn't look at the cashier as he served me, though I felt his eyes burning into my face. I desperately wanted him to ask me why I needed the razors. To ID me. To try and stop me. But of course he didn't. I walked out in the same militant way I had walked in, the voices in my head the only thing I was able to hear.

Useless. You're useless. You're fucked now, Emma. You've fucked everything up again. You should be dead. In fact why don't you kill yourself? That's it! Kill yourself! But you won't will you, chicken shit? So you better cut instead. Cut it all out. Cut it away. Cut because you're a huge obese failure. Cut because you're good for fucking nothing. Cut because it's all you have.

I wasn't even fighting the sounds. I just let them scream at me as I half ran into the nearby park. The only voice I felt I had any control over repeated, 'I have the blades, I have them, I can make this stop now.' I sat on the nearest bench I could find, hands shaking. Same old. The park was empty, deserted for a hot summer's day. I opened the plastic packet, slid the first paper-covered razor out of its shell, rolled up my sleeve and let the fear and the self-hatred fall out of me and into the edge of the blade. I pulled it over my forearm, again and again. Ten cuts. Twenty cuts. Thirty. Time holds no place in these moments, but through the darkness I came sprinting out, and as if I were swimming to the surface of myself, my neck snapped upward, my face to the sky and I took in a long deep breath, desperate, gasping. The warm fluid coming from my skin felt like someone pouring hot water over me. I looked down. Blood had pooled around my trainers. I held my gushing arm up and cringed at the sight of so much exposed flesh. But there it was, the silence. No voice telling me to kill myself or hissing at me that I was useless or obese or a failure. My head was light, my body weightless, my thoughts were made of bubbles each and every one all trying to float away. I pulled a bandage out of my bag and wrapped my arm as best I could. When I walked through my front door my mother was not there waiting to shout at me. And by the time she got home she had seemingly forgotten about the whole incident. Once again, I had waged war on myself for no reason at all.

*

It was seven months from leaving the Henshaw to entering the Caddick. And in that time I managed to entangle myself with six or so different men. I needed constant distractions, constant affirmation, and they served that purpose for me. Firstly, there was Tom, who I met a week out of the Henshaw. Tom approached me in Camden while I was out buying hair dye and asked me to go on a date. Completely taken aback by this I agreed. We went on a few dates, each more painful than the last. He was younger than me, and I was trying to find my feet in a pool with no bottom. On our third date we went to a salsa club. I sat there next to Tom, who fired questions at me about myself. I had long forgotten the principles of good etiquette when it came to dating, so I told him everything. My disorder and depression was all I felt I had to offer, so that was what he got. 'So, what medication are you on?' he asked, leaning into me as a couple whooshed past us spinning each other round in circles. I leaned back.

'Um. Fluoxetine.' I used the generic name hoping it made me sound more exotic somehow.

'Isn't that Prozac?' he said. Busted.

I forced a smile, 'Yeah.'

Tom went on to tell me he was doing a drug study for a pharmaceutical company trialling Fluoxetine. They paid big bucks to stick him on the drugs for a few months, studying him like a serotonin-filled rat and of course, twenty-year-old Tom, with no problems whatsoever and the world at his feet, didn't mind this at all. He knew more about the drug than I did and his cocky, know-it-all attitude annoyed me. Still, when he suggested we leave and walk to Primrose Hill I didn't say no. Tom may have liked the sound of his own voice, but I hated the sound of mine, so it seemed like a good arrangement. He talked throughout the whole forty minute hike. I was so out of breath from starving myself and my general anxiety that by the time we got to the top of Primrose Hill I couldn't have contributed to the conversation even if I had wanted to. Thankfully he sat down on a bench and as I sat next to him; the tightness in my chest began to loosen and I could breathe again. I realised in that moment that I shouldn't have agreed to this little jaunt, and as he lunged toward me a sinking feeling of powerlessness washed over the scene. His sloppy wet mouth wrapped around my face. His tongue forced itself into my mouth. I closed my eyes and tried to vanish.

'Kiss him back, and soon it'll be over and you can leave,' came the little voice in my head. His hands found their way to my half-exposed chest. His fingers felt imposing and clumsy as they touched my cold skin, pulling at me, ripping the fragile seams of my chiffon dress. And as the minutes dragged on that's all I could think about: my dress. It was a size fourteen. After all the starving and vomiting I was still fitting snugly into a size fourteen. I smiled at the idea of Tom – trendy, cool, indie Tom, Tom from Cornwall who played the guitar, Tom who was going to travel across east Asia, Tom who was clearly used to getting what he wanted – sitting here with this mess of a size fourteen girl.

He leaned back huffing, dejected, and stood up. 'I'm going, are you coming?' I rose to my feet and followed him. As we walked back towards the street lights he asked if I wanted to come back to his hostel with him (*of course* he was staying in a hostel). I said no. Outraged by my audacity he shouted, 'Jesus, Emma I'm only asking if you want a nightcap, I'm not asking to marry you.'

Needless to say I never heard from Tom again. And I was relieved. I had been sacked without needing to resign.

Unfortunately, though, my escape was not as easy as it sounds and over the next few days the feelings of being a whore crept in all over me like a fog you don't realise is there until you can't see where you're going. The answer to this? Cut myself! Of course. I shredded my chest with a blade. In my mind I needed to make myself even more repulsive – that would surely keep the next Tom away.

But it didn't. I was at the slimmest I had been in a long while, but in my head I was still eighteen stone. Despite my plus-size clothing my body wore me well and I didn't look big. Male attention continued to baffle me to the point where I assumed that every man who looked, talked or dated me had something horribly wrong with him. But these thoughts did not stop me. I passively went along with whatever each Tom wanted. But I refused to shed even a layer of clothing. That was my deal-breaker. That would have involved them seeing me for what I really was: scarred, fat and damaged. This, of course, meant that a lot of the Toms didn't stick around for long. The minute they sniffed out the immovable frigidity that wafted around me, they lost interest. Or even if they ploughed on regardless, letting me keep my material boundaries, they would become frustrated with my dissociation and disinterest during moments of intimacy.

'Do you even want to be here?' was their usual fallback line. I'd look at them with disdain and boredom and they would huff, puff and walk out. But I didn't care and had usually set my sights on the next boy who was sure to save me. Obviously all my choices were completely wrong. Want what you cannot have, love the abuser, trust the adulterer, date the Lothario. And of course, the little aperitif to this meal of bullshit I was serving up? I didn't actually want to be saved, not by them, not by me, not by anyone.

I was doing a lot of drugs, cocaine mainly, and smoking weed every day. On top of that I was necking a zopiclone most nights – a sleeping pill which did not agree with me at all and caused me to self-harm badly when I took it – which is exactly *why* I took it. I was obsessed with my body and how ugly I was. I had a strong feeling that I needed to be 'dipped in acid and started again'. And every cut I made was in part to reflect how ugly and untouchable I felt. The abundance of male attention was confusing me horribly.

As the months outside the hospital passed with no one to watch me, I shrank. I had gone from eighteen stone to twelve stone, but I felt bigger than ever. And no matter how little I ate, how much I exercised or how long I spent with my head down the toilet, I was not losing the weight fast enough. I wanted to disappear. I spent the evenings on website after website coveting anorexic girls, measuring my stomach, thighs, and arms. And when the calories hadn't taken over my long nights, I was on self-harm websites, looking at pictures of damaged, hurt people, comparing my scars to theirs and lusting after the marks they had made. I was always trying to cut deeply – to need stitches – it felt like the only way my pain could be heard. The deeper the cut, the more justified the emotional pain. I was in a terrifying underworld of my own making during those months, from which it seemed there was no way out. I only sank further and further down into the murkiness of my own disordered mind. I struggled through each day, arguing with my mother, then trying to avoid her, writing in coffee shops, talking to my friends about whichever boy liked me and whom I did not like but was insatiably preoccupied with. I would stay out until everyone had gone to bed, then come home stoned, where the crippling fear of getting through the night alone would dig its claws into me – I tried to relieve this with the anorexia and self-injury websites before ultimately taking a sleeping pill and cutting.

I found comfort in the online forums; whether they were telling me not to eat, or not to cut, I felt I had allies. 'Pro-ana' websites were at their height; at the flick of a switch I could have twenty girls messaging me telling me 'to be a winner you have to be thinner' or 'nothing tastes as good as being thin feels'. Or likewise on the other side of the coin was a community of self-harmers telling me to 'stay strong' and that I 'could get through it'. And this is how it went. Day after day, week after week, month after month. Whilst I waited for funding. Whilst I tried not to kill myself.

*

Andrew was still my light in those dark days. My meetings with him kept me going, though his insights plagued me for days at a time. 'Your feelings about your mother have colonised your brain. I don't know where you stop and she starts, Emma.'

Not being able to give my parents a date for my impending second hospitalisation infuriated and frustrated them, as I'm sure it would any parent. But my mother in particular took it as a personal attack: 'You know when you're going in, don't you?' she would say, to which I would say no and it would prompt her to call me a liar. 'You just don't want to get a job, Emma. That's what this is!'

*

By the end of July I could not take any more of hearing that I was lazy and needed to get a job. It seemed easier to just find work than have to contemplate how much of a failure I was on a daily basis. I didn't care about money, or what I was doing, so I began to trawl the local charity shops and started to volunteer my time at the British Heart Foundation. I hated it. I hated summoning the energy to go in, I hated trying to learn how to operate the fucking till, I hated answering questions about my life and lying about why I wanted to volunteer there. But it shut my mother up. It gave her something to tell my grandmother, and my father's family and her friends when they asked about what I was doing. Though, so very predictably, it only kept everyone happy for a short time and soon I was back to the place I knew so well.

'You only work three days a week, Emma! That's nothing! *Nothing!* You should be there every day!' So instead of arguing, I lied and said I was going every day. Of course she caught me out by going there to check up on me.

July dwindled into August and August to September. I was going out still, still seeing my friends but mostly I would meet them in the evenings and an hour later we would be stoned or ordering coke from the various dealers we knew. I missed having a real connection with someone who understood the feelings, who understood the need to self-destruct. I hadn't seen or heard from Landon for a few weeks, he hadn't been answering my texts and I was starting to get worried. One night I asked his brother where he was. 'Oh, he got sectioned, Emma. They took his phone away so that's why you probably haven't heard from him.'

'How long is he going to be in there?' I asked, feeling suddenly upset that I couldn't talk to him even if wanted... needed to.

'A while I think... he stopped taking his meds and it all went a bit pear-shaped so... yeah... probably a while.'

22

THE DAY VISIT

"But I don't want to go among mad people," Alice remarked.
"Oh, you can't help that," said the Cat: "we're all mad here. I'm
mad. You're mad."
"How do you know I'm mad?" said Alice.
"You must be," said the Cat, "or you wouldn't have come here."

— *LEWIS CARROLL, Alice in Wonderland*

I dragged my feet off the 89 bus and eventually found the
Caddick hospital. It was a cold October day and I was nervous.
I was going there on a day visit to meet the staff and patients
and get an idea of the place and what they did. The Henshaw
had finally given up and officially closed in April not long after
I'd left and Katie had been transferred to the Caddick, so I felt a
slight relief knowing at least I would know one person there. The
Caddick was big, much bigger and grander than the Henshaw.
It looked like an old stately mansion. The hospital was locked
up tight and I had to be buzzed in through two different sets of
doors. As I approached the reception area I took a mental note
that it would be tricky to get out should I need to. The woman
behind the desk asked for my name as she picked up a telephone.

'Okay, Emma, go and have a seat, I'll let them know you're here.' I sat in a blue armchair and waited as I'd been instructed. After a few moments another woman appeared from a nearby doorway.

'Hello Emma. I'm Judy, head nurse. You've got a meeting with Dr Finstard, follow me please.' I followed her up the stairs in silence, round corners, down corridors and finally to Dr Finstard's office. This was all starting to feel a bit too overwhelming and I wanted to run. Judy knocked once and then opened the door and gestured for me to sit down. She sat next to me, a little too close for my liking, and stared at me with fixed, unblinking eyes. Judy was short and slim, with a cloud of ginger hair and glasses. She was very conservative in her dress and I felt her eyes studying my pink braids, tattoos and piercings with more than a slight aversion.

Dr Finstard was probably most people's preconception of what a psychiatrist looks like: late fifties, glasses, grey hair, goatee and a tweed blazer with patches on the elbows. He spoke with an accent that seemed Russian, and pronounced his s's as z's. I sat in silence as they spoke. Should I be 'fortunate enough' to come to the Caddick, I would be put on the adolescent 'ESPD' unit as I was under twenty-four.

'What's ESPD?' I asked, feeling stupid.

Judy answered in her calmer-than-calm voice. 'Emerging and severe personality disorders.' Uch. Severe personality disorder. That's what people thought about me, my personality was severe. I got hung up on this and forgot to listen to them for the next five minutes. When I rejoined the conversation they were asking me why I wanted to be at the Caddick, why I believed it was right for me. I cleared my throat; it was time for me to give my spiel, my lines, stand back everyone, she's coming through with her election speech.

'I want to be here because...' *I want to be here because this is my last chance. I want to be here because I am slowly killing myself. I want to be here because I cannot survive out there any more.* Obviously I chucked in my usual: 'I smoke too much weed,' *(but I don't have a problem)*; 'I can't stop self-harming,' *(and I don't intend to)*; 'I've got what I think is a pretty serious eating disorder,' *(and I'm anticipating how far I can go with it)*; 'I find it hard to trust but I want to change,' *(you are going to need a wrecking ball to get through the wall I've built and even then I'll put up a fight)*. They nodded along, looking pleased with my answers and apparent honesty.

Dr Finstard shook my hand and said, 'Well, Emma, I will be seeing you again. Your funding was approved so you will no doubt be joining us here in due course.' He said it just like that, blink and you'd have missed it. So I guess that meant I'd passed my little interview, or test, or whatever the last hour had been. I felt like a contestant on a game show; was I supposed to jump up and down and hug them both whilst screaming thank you? Perhaps they were about to offer me the mystery envelope? I'd totally take it. Instead I opted for three or four tears and a handshake before Judy led me away.

'You're going to do chores now, Emma. Everyone here has a job that they do each morning. You'll be with Cynthia today.' She hurriedly led me through a big wooden door that came out onto a landing where a stocky woman with a jet-black crew cut was standing. 'I'll see you in firm,' said Judy swishing through another door. I watched her vanish down a grand carpeted staircase.

'So, Emma, I'm Cynthia and we're cleaning the toilets!'

'Oh good,' I said hoping to get a laugh (which I did). I helped Cynthia clean the toilets wondering what exactly I was doing here in another mental hospital with my *severe* personality disorder, Marigolds and disinfectant.

'You can put your bag in my room,' she said to me as she locked away the bleach in what might as well have been a safe, shoving a huge bunch of keys into her pocket.

'Oh, they're not mine,' she said as she noticed me looking, 'I'll be giving them back to Judy in firm.' This place was already very different to the Henshaw: they actually locked away things that could be used to harm yourself with. We walked up a small staircase with two doors at the top; Cynthia opened the one on the left. I felt nosy going into her bedroom and tried not to look like I was snooping as I peered around the room. It was huge, with three beds in it and giant windows looking out onto a plush green common opposite. As I put my bag down Katie burst through the door flinging her arms around me in a dramatic embrace.

'Hello pet! How are you, wee Em? Are you okay? How was Judy? She's all right, ya know, just need to get used to her. Is Cynthia being nice to you?' Good to know Katie still had the capacity to enter a room like a steam train mowing down everything (everyone) in her path. I let her talk, thankful that when she asked questions she was never really asking, and even if she was I wouldn't have time to answer before she asked the next one.

With Katie still jabbering away they began to lead me down to the 'firm' meeting; Katie said it was their version of a 9/15. My anxiety was beginning to smother me. 'Are there a lot of people in this meeting? Will I have to talk?' They didn't really do much to reassure me, I got two 'yesses' and a monotone 'You'll be fine' from Cynthia. I wished I had my bag, I needed something to put on my lap, something to separate me from the rest of the world. Behold! A bag! No one may come near me and my trusty bag! But my bag was lost somewhere in the Caddick's rabbit warren and I wouldn't have known which way to go to get back to it even if I wanted to.

We walked down the grand staircase and through a door that led to another large room with about fifteen or twenty chairs forming a circle inside it. Judy sat proudly near the top of the circle. Like a disinterested cat ignoring its cooing owner she didn't look at me as I came in. I sat nearest the door and tried not to panic as I drew my head up and looked around. There was a boy who looked about my age in there.

'Dan!' Katie went and sat next to him and they began to chatter excitedly. Next another man came in; he was painfully thin and walking hunched over like he was about to crumble to dust at any second; he was followed closely by a young boy who was draped in dark clothes with thick black eyeliner. The young boy was Aaron; he was fifteen and also on a day visit. He would have to wait until he turned sixteen to be allowed to come to the hospital but they were letting him have a day visit nonetheless. The thin man was Kane. Kane was chewing aggressively on gum to the point where he looked like he was coming up on ecstasy. He stared at the floor, his eyes occasionally flicking up only to do a sort of roll in his head then go back down again. Oh God. They're all going to be mental. A few more came in, nurses, therapists, patients, I couldn't really distinguish. A moody-looking girl called Sylvia sat next to Dan in the two chairs at the head of the circle; they started looking through a big book together. She had long red hair down to her bum and a figure that I was already jealous of.

'Okay, let's start,' said Dan. 'On the agenda today...' Oh no, not another agenda meeting, was I going to have to vote here too? 'We'd like to say hello to Emma and Aaron who are on a day visit, and we'll be getting to know them, obviously...' Aaron and I looked at each other, the desperate, reassuring sort of smile of two people facing each other in electric chairs. 'But first we are going to talk about what happened yesterday with you, Adaline.' Everyone looked at me. I'm not Adaline, why are they all looking at me? But then I saw the person in the chair next to me move. Ah, Adaline.

Adaline, or Slime as I would come to know her, was a walking skeleton. She seemed to be around my age and had strawberry-blonde hair scraped back against her skull, wore glasses and, more pressingly, was in a neon shell suit. It was bright green and pink; I'd only ever seen photos of them from the eighties.

Adaline began to talk and throughout the next five minutes I learned that she had self-harmed fairly badly the previous day. I found myself taken aback and somewhat horrified by the telling off she got from everyone.

'I just don't know why you did it, when you could have asked any one of us for help. It was very, very manipulative,' said Sylvia as she flicked her red hair behind her.

'I agree,' said Kane, he took a long, slow inhale, so slow it was like he was eating the air, which looked like maybe it was the first thing he *had* eaten in months. 'You knew how badly your cutting would trigger everyone off, but you still did it, it was incredibly selfish.' He looked down at the floor again chewing his gum.

Adaline sat next to me crying, trying to defend herself as person after person chimed in. I wanted to push my chair next to hers and tell them all to fuck off, to leave her and her ridiculous shell suit alone. But instead I sat quietly, resolving that if I self-harmed here I couldn't tell anyone – obviously, a truly great way to start off.

Eventually, the meeting moved on to me and Aaron. Who would like to introduce themselves first? Aaron stared at the floor – great.

'Hi. I'm Emma. I'm twenty-three. I live about half an hour away.' It wasn't as in-depth as my 'selection' at the Henshaw, something I was deeply grateful for, as after seeing Adaline being destroyed I was in a less-than-sharing mood with these people. I stumbled over the trivial details of my life all the while feeling the all-seeing eyes of Judy hammering into me.

*

The day passed slowly after that. I had another meeting with Judy, who told me I would be expected to have family therapy, which I refused point-blank. We argued over this for some time and I ended with my standard response of 'I'll think about it'. Of course there was no way in hell I was going to ever agree to it. I was growing quickly agitated by Judy – she was treating me like a child and it was beginning to grate.

At the end of the meeting she ordered me to go down to lunch. I instantly panicked. 'Oh, I'm not really that hungry, Judy, I was thinking that perhaps...'

She was having none of it. 'Emma you need to go to lunch.' She emphasised the 'e' in need: I neeeeded to go to lunch. Before I could think of anything to say she continued, 'I'll be down there in a few minutes – go on.'

I got up and slowly walked down four flights of narrow wooden steps trying to remember the way to the dining room. I walked through heavy double doors and into the alcove where Katie, Aaron, Kane and a few others sat. I sat next to Kane, thinking, *Please save me from having to eat. Please pick up on something and help me out of this mess.*

He turned to me; his deep Irish accent came out like a hum, low and soft. 'How's it going? Scared off yet?'

I was all smiles, like someone at the bus stop had just asked me the time. 'Ha! No, I'm okay.' I lowered my voice to match his. 'Do we have to have lunch? I'm not really good with big groups of people.'

'Or food,' he said laughing to himself. It seemed to be a statement rather than a question. *Oh dear, was I that transparent?* I assumed from my deer-in-the-headlights expression he had got his answer. 'Yeah, we have to. Come on.' He got up waiting for me to follow. *Shit, shit, shit.* The room was huge, it seated about sixty people and it was filling up with them fast.

Lots of young children were running up and down chasing each one another, talking to the other patients as they excitedly queued up for lunch. I looked at Kane. 'Why are there kids, I thought you had to be sixteen to come here?'

He didn't look at me but answered, 'They're from the family unit, it's in another part of the building. But we all eat here, together, like one big happy fucking family.' He turned the corner and stood in the queue. Once you entered the queue, you couldn't really get out of it. It led into a small confining hallway with a buffet. The food and chefs were on one side and there was a wall on the other. I was trapped. Kane handed me a tray and said something, but I couldn't hear him over the voices who were now shouting inside me: 'OH MY GOD! EVERYONE IS WATCHING YOU! YOU HAVE TO LOOK NORMAL! DON'T BLOW YOUR COVER! BUT DON'T EAT! DON'T YOU DARE EAT!'

I wanted to slam my tray down and run, but there were at least twenty people behind me that I could see before the queue curved off out of the door and around the corner. My hands were shaking as I slid the tray onto the buffet table. I felt like I was going to pass out. The chef looked at me with a big smile, his kind eyes peeping out from behind his glasses.

'Hello, I'm Ken. What would you like?' I opened my mouth but nothing came out. I tried again, nothing. Fuck. Don't be this obvious, Emma.

'Um, salad?' He put a spoonful of couscous on my plate (forty-four calories), then another (eighty-eight). I pointed at the salad leaves trying to look convincing; he heaped some iceberg lettuce on. 'Thanks.'

But Ken was onto me, 'You need more than that!' Thankfully a space in front of me that led back to the dining room had opened up and I hurried away calling, 'No that's great, thanks,' over my shoulder. A massive sigh of relief had not yet left my mouth as I turned the corner into the now-heaving dining room. I saw Katie and planted myself next to her, quickly throwing my plate in the bin as I did.

23

WELCOME TO THE CADDICK

"This is not really me. I am not like this. I am like you.
I am not a patient from a mental hospital.
I am just an ordinary woman whose mind has gone
temporarily wrong."

— SALLY BRAMPTON, *Shoot the Damn Dog,*
a memoir of depression

It was 31 October, Halloween and the day of my admission to
the Caddick. The date couldn't have been more comically timed
if I had tried. In keeping with tradition I told my parents I was
getting a lift there, and went on the bus dragging my suitcase
behind me. I had 'goodbye' drinks with my friends, ended it
with the Tom I had been hanging on a hook for a few weeks, and
starved and vomited my way down to an almost-pleasing ten
stone. I was ready to be an inpatient again.

As I walked up the road that led to the hospital I saw, to
my absolute horror, Esther. She was standing outside in a green
hoodie frantically pacing up and down the drive. I couldn't
believe my eyes; after the Henshaw I never thought I'd have to
see her again, but oh no, here she was. I walked past her, 'Hi

203

Esther.' She looked like she was having an episode. Curiosity got the better of me and I paused a few feet away from her. 'Everything okay?' She didn't stop pacing but stared at me.

'No. This place is awful. Run, Emma. Run now.' Good start. I didn't bother to respond and went in.

I sat in reception once again as I had been told to do by the woman behind the desk and waited for my allocated nurse to come and get me. I could hear Katie in the distance shouting about something. Her voice grew louder and soon enough she was in the same room, still ranting and raving.

'Wee Em!' She broke away from the woman she was with to give me a hug. She pulled back and held me firmly by the shoulders, bending down to look in my eyes. 'You all right, pet?' I nodded. 'I heard about your house visit, we all did actually, apparently you were fucked? That's why it was so short, they thought you were off your face, we all laughed about it, well not the staff!' Katie didn't wait for a response, just cackled maniacally and wandered back to the woman who was waiting for her; they vanished down a nearby hallway, Katie talking the whole way. Oh, so everyone thought I was fucked during the house visit? That's embarrassing.

It had happened a couple of weeks previously. I had carefully orchestrated the whole thing so that the house was empty and my parents were at work. Two nurses, Derron and Poppy, had come over along with a patient called Sandra. The house visit was something they did with every patient, and yes I *was* fucked, extremely so. I had been up doing lines of coke with my friends until eight in the morning and they had come over at ten. In all honesty I didn't remember much from it, just the feeling of intense anxiety as I continually offered them 'drinks', couldn't sit still and sweated a delightful concoction of skunk, Valium and cocaine through my pores. Poppy was an attractive thirty-something nurse, blonde and petite, well-spoken, very Princess Diana-esque. Derron was from the Caribbean, he was short, stocky, younger then Poppy and seemed nice enough; he told me that he was going to be my nurse and main point of contact once I arrived at the hospital. And Sandra was the patient who had been sent with them. She told me we would be sharing a room along with another girl called Ellie. Sandra didn't know me, but I knew Sandra, knew of her at least. Strangely enough she had been an inpatient with one of my close friends at another psychiatric hospital some years earlier. The stories I had heard of her were that she was a five-and-a-half-stone anorexic who self-harmed extremely badly; I think there was even talk of a meat cleaver at some point.

Poor Sandra had obviously spent the last few years being pumped full of meds, anti-psychotics no doubt, and had ballooned up as most people do who find themselves on those drugs; she was very smiley, sweet and I felt better knowing I'd be sharing a room with her. And so that had been my house visit; if you imagine a terrifying mix of Johnny Depp in *Fear and Loathing in Las Vegas* and Julia Child, yep, that was me. No wonder they'd left after twenty minutes.

'Emma?' I looked up to see Derron standing over me. 'Hi, shall I take you to your room?'

We walked through the servery, the dining room and up the spiral staircase I remembered from before. My room was opposite Cynthia and Katie's. Derron knocked and waited for a second. 'I think everyone's downstairs but just in case.' After deciding it was safe Derron pushed open the door. The room was big, too big. Such a stark comparison to the Henshaw. 'That's your bed over there.' He pointed at the bed in the corner, a large window over it that looked out on to the grounds. 'I just need to check your suitcase, okay?' He seemed almost nervous at having to ask. I nodded and he bent down and unzipped my bag, rummaging through my clothes, opening my toiletry bag, examining each item and checking all along the lining of the case. This was certainly more thorough then Augusta's search had been. 'That's all fine,' he said, zipping it back up. 'I'll leave you to get settled, Emma, come and find me when you're ready.'

I rolled my suitcase over to what would be my little corner of the room. I sat down on the bed and opened the top drawer of the bedside table. I don't know what I was expecting to find but it was empty. I looked around. The bed opposite mine was neatly made, with a couple of photos stuck on the wall above it. The bed on my left was a mess, the duvet was on the floor and the sheets were dirty, the curtains above the bed were drawn, casting a shadow over that part of the room. I stood up and peered out of the window; the grounds were huge, beautiful. I didn't want to unpack, I felt out of place and anxious. The Henshaw was fairly big but in comparison this hospital was huge. Feeling like if I were left to my own devices I might make an attempt to leave, I decided I'd go and find Derron.

*

I had arrived at the Caddick on a day where things were not in their normal routine. There was a bonfire and fireworks taking place in the grounds that evening. Friends and family of patients were invited, and so everyone was busy rushing around putting on Halloween costumes, doing each other's make-up and helping set things up. The two people who were supposed to be points of contact for me were nowhere to be seen. So I spent the afternoon milling around being introduced to everybody by Derron, like some sort of monosyllabic child on its first day at a new school.

The least enjoyable of those meetings was with the on-site doctor who told me that I would need to supply urine samples for drug-testing. I nodded compliantly at her as I debated which of my teetotal friends would be best to ask for piss from. Sara.

Definitely Sara, but then they know I don't drink alcohol, so would alcohol show up in it? Sara likes a drink and...

'Okay Emma?'

Whoops, I looked up.

'Sorry?'

'I'll need to weigh you.' The doctor, Derron and Judy were all looking at me; absolute panic began to course through my body.

'Why's that?' I asked, trying to seem casual.

The doctor shot a look at Judy that I couldn't make out, then said, 'So we know whether you lose or gain any weight.'

I smiled at them as though I had smelt soured milk. 'Mhmm.'

'The scales are in the sluice room, that's where you get your meds. So if we're finished here?' She looked at Judy for confirmation; Judy nodded. 'Great, then let's go.'

I smiled like a shoplifter who has just been stopped outside the store and asked by the security guard to come back inside for a bag check, but not wanting to alert the hawk-eyed Judy I got up and followed the doctor. As soon as we were out of earshot of Judy and Derron I cleared my throat.

'Sorry, doctor, I'm absolutely desperate for a wee, can I just nip to the toilet?' She stopped walking and faced me.

'Yes that's fine. I'll be waiting for you in the sluice room.'

'Sure, see you in a minute.' I walked away with no intention of going back – weigh me? – was she mad? There was no way in hell they were getting me on the scales. I'd just tell her I got lost and was 'overwhelmed' if she asked why I never turned up. The one good thing about being in a nuthouse, you can blame everything on anxiety.

*

Night closed in and inevitably feeding time rolled around. My dinner-time habits were a finely tuned ritual of measuring, weighing, restricting and if necessary throwing up. I had got even more severe within my boundaries where food was concerned over the last few months and I was dreading this next bit. I had to show my face for dinner, especially on the first night, I couldn't let them onto me so quickly, so I again stood in the queue with what felt like hundreds of people, tray in hand.

My throat felt constricted, as if I couldn't breathe. *I hate this, I hate this, I hate this*, I thought over and over again. I felt my whole body begin to shake as I adamantly resolved to myself that I would not eat *anything* that I didn't know the calorie content of. I realised quickly that Ken the chef wasn't there in the evenings and it was patients running the kitchen, which made everything seem much worse – I'd been able to thwart Ken last time with a big smile; the patients might not be so easy to get past.

A pretty blonde in a grey hoodie stood in front of me with a long serving spoon.

'Hi! What would you like?' I looked down. Beige. All beige. Giant beige baked potatoes. Grease-dipped sausages. Beige chips. Festering cold beans. Jesus Christ, the calories didn't bear thinking about. And then, as I was expecting it would, that adamant voice inside me quickly transformed into a loud shrieking: *NO! Get out, get out, get out!*

I half slammed my tray down and squawked, 'I don't like potato.' She began to say something but I bolted from the kitchen like a wild animal across a motorway and scampered up to my room. I was not in the business of missing my evening meal. This, of course, would have been the simplest notion: just don't eat; but that didn't fit into my routine or calorie count. I knew the surrounding area, I knew there was a supermarket within walking distance. Outside my window the bonfire was starting, people were making their way out to the garden. I grabbed my bag and as inconspicuously as I could made my way down several corridors and flights of stairs, getting lost along the way.

After what felt like forever I got to the front desk. The woman from earlier had gone and there was a man sitting there now. I floated past him as silently as I could and tried to push open the first door that led to the exit. It was locked. I turned around; a familiar feeling washed over me, the sort of one I used to get as I was walking past a bouncer at a club I was too young to get into, praying he didn't ID me. *Don't arouse suspicion, Emma, just look casual.* I smiled, 'Can you open the door please?' The man looked at me over the top of his glasses.

'Why?'

I tried not to break character. 'I just need to go to the shop.'

'You're new, aren't you?'

I felt my nostrils flare in annoyance. 'Yes. I'm Emma.'

He pushed back his glasses as he picked up the phone. 'I'm Len, Emma. You shouldn't be going out at this time of night.' I glanced up at the clock on the wall behind him: 7:35. *Seriously?*

'Poppy, it's Len, can you come down to reception please, we've got a problem.'

Have we got a problem? Why's that exactly, Len?

'Take a seat,' he said sternly. I wasn't giving up, I smiled an even bigger smile.

'I just need to go to the shop, I'll only be a minute, if you could just... open the door.' I pushed at it again hoping it might open.

He didn't look up this time, just repeated, 'Take a seat.' Len was not impressed with me. I wanted to cry out of frustration and began cursing myself for not having used the alarmed exit I'd noticed at the other end of the hospital. I could have gone through it and said I didn't know, I'd have been gone before they'd even worked out I was missing. Poppy came rushing down a nearby staircase as if there were a fire, Sandra padding behind her. They sat down and began talking to me as if they were talking to someone with severe learning difficulties. Slow, calm tones, enunciating every word like English wasn't my first language.

'Emma. It's *very* late. We are *very* concerned. It's really *not safe* for you to go out. This is *against the rules* for a new patient.'

This went on for about ten minutes. Manipulation is a colour of the borderline spectrum that I have always kicked against; I do not like to be thought of as clinically manipulative, but I, like most other people in the waking world, can of course be manipulative when it's needed, and it was definitely needed. In my calmest, most rational voice I managed to talk them into letting me go out *unchaperoned* for *one hour*. 'I know the area very well. I would like to go for a walk to the shop. I'm feeling fine. People have been lovely. There is a lot of excitement here tonight and I would just like an hour to unwind.'

'But... but... you at least have to take someone with you,' said Poppy, flustered – it was as if she had never been in this position before and didn't know what to do.

'Every one is enjoying the bonfire, it would be selfish to ask them to leave. I will be absolutely fine. I'll take my phone and call if I need to.' She ran her hand through her hair and sighed loudly; she wasn't going to get me to back down and she knew it, so she was weighing it up, choosing whether or not to let me win this battle. The most beautiful sound in the world came as Len pushed a button and the door buzzed open. *And breathe Emma, breathe.*

24

I'M NOT LIKE THEM

"Because all the monsters have been let out of their cages
tonight, no matter what court they belong to. So I may roam
wherever I wish until the dawn."

— SARAH J. MAAS, *A Court of Thorns and Roses*

That first week at the Caddick was slow and painful. A lot of the patients either did not like me or were too wrapped up in their own misery to speak to me, so I floated around the building like a ghost, feeling invisible and alone. I met Ellie, my other room-mate.

'I'm Ellie Rose. Rose was my working name, but I liked it, so I kept it. It's pretty isn't it?' She was an eighteen-year-old prostitute from Yorkshire; loud and full of life, she giggled her way around the hospital as if it were a summer camp. Sandra was nice but she didn't really get out of bed; they would rouse her for group and her individual therapy but that was it, she lay under the covers snoring all day. It was obviously an issue because they would talk about it in firm, and every morning a nurse and patient would go up to try and pry her away from the mattress; occasionally it worked, but mostly she would scream at them to fuck off.

I was in adolescent group therapy twice a week with Ellie, Sandra and Dan. The group was run by two therapists, Johanna and Mr Newman. 'Group therapy' had always been an issue for me, but after being at the Henshaw I had officially washed my hands of it, so I wasn't expecting anything from these sessions. It made me anxious having to sit in a small room with both the girls I shared a bedroom with and a guy I didn't know. During the first group I sat in silence whilst they talked about a patient called Ashley who had recently killed herself. It had only been a few weeks since it had happened and they were all still understandably in shock. Apparently she had gone home for weekend leave and hung herself, just like that, no warning, no big red flags. I felt sad for her, and for all of them, but I didn't want to hear about it. The Henshaw was supposed to fix me, instead it sent me spiralling out of control then booted me back out into the world worse off than when I'd gone in. The Caddick really was my last chance and hearing that one of its patients had just killed herself terrified me – because if this hospital didn't work I feared that was what was going to happen to me too.

The size of the Caddick worked in my favour and in that first week it was easy to stay hidden. I kept my head down as much as I could, trying not to draw attention to myself. I fought the demon inside me that screamed at every available opportunity 'CUT, CUT, CUT!' I went to the meetings. I listened to the patients' stories. I listened to them scream. I listened to rape. And sexual abuse. And violence. I listened to them cry. I watched the staff cry. And I thought over and over again, *I shouldn't be here. I do not belong here. I am not like these people.*

Each day followed the same routine: I was woken up by 'checks' every morning at 7am – the nurses sticking their heads in the door to make sure we were all still alive. After that came work group; I was put in the servery where I pretended to sweep the floor and look busy. At 9am was the firm meeting, where they would ask how I was doing. I gave my usual robotic answer – truth draped in lies, with a sprinkle of comedy: make them laugh, they leave you alone. And they did.

*

I had been there for eight days now. It was a Tuesday morning, which meant it was time for the 'community' meeting. The community meeting meant all the ESPD patients, all of the family unit (bar the children) and most of the staff, so about sixty people in total. The community meeting took place in a huge room where all the hot topics of the week were brought up.

Cynthia was soon to be leaving the hospital. She was in her forties and had been on the search for her birth mother for the last twenty-something years. She had finally found her and had brought to the meeting a photograph her mother had sent of Cynthia when she was a baby. She clung to it and cried. I dug my nails into my hands as I sat in the armchair closest to the door with Johanna (my group therapist) sitting next to me, trying as best as I could to control my oncoming panic attack. I can't really give you the specifics of why my body and mind had begun to go into flight mode – I suppose it was the intimacy of it all. The raw, compounding, agonising emotion in the room was digging its claws into me and I couldn't get out. I closed my eyes for what I thought was a second then felt someone gently squeeze my arm. I opened them to see Johanna. She had a look of concern on her face as she whispered, 'Are you okay?'

I felt my cheeks flush, embarrassed that someone had caught me out, seen my true face as the mask slipped. I nodded my head and whispered back, 'Yeah, thanks.' I glanced around to see if anyone was watching us but no one was.

Before she let go of my arm she softly said, 'It's okay if you're not.' She smiled at me then looked away; it was a small gesture but meant so much.

Cynthia was now reading aloud a letter her mother had sent her: 'Dear Cynthia. I thought you would like this photo of yourself as a baby. You were only with me for a few weeks but I have so many of you, and us together. I look at them all the time.'

Cynthia paused, pinching the top of her nose with her fingers and, keeping her eyes closed, she said, 'I asked my foster mother once why she and my foster father only had one photo of me as a baby, but loads of their other adopted daughter, Mary. She said to me "You were such an ugly baby. We thought you might have been retarded for a few months. Mary was so beautiful, so we put the photos of her up instead."'

The entire room seemed to break apart with her at hearing that. Patients were crying, staff were crying. But all I could feel was anger. Anger at her being told that. Anger for how ugly she had been made to feel. I was still sitting there teeth clenched when Cynthia mentioned that she was going out for a meal on her last night and we were all invited. Oh shit. Restaurants were my worst nightmare, no control, no calorie content. A nurse called Alison butted in, 'Who's going? Raise your hands.'

For some stupid reason, I didn't raise my hand. And of course, she honed in.

'Are you going, Emma?'

My knuckles were white against the dark wood of the chair. 'Um, I think it's just a bit much, too soon for me. I don't really like big groups of people. Sorry Cynthia.'

Cynthia smiled kindly. 'Don't worry, that's fine.'

Alison was a tall, thin woman, curly brown hair surrounding pointed, angular features and a high-pitched voice. She looked stonily at me and coldly said, 'Half six on a Monday, it won't be busy, in fact our dining room is busier, so your argument doesn't stand for much.'

I wanted to cry. But there was no way in hell I would. Not in front of all these people. Thankfully, and to my complete surprise, a lot of the patients rushed to my defence saying they agreed it was a lot for me, and I'd only been there a week. I silently thanked them all in my mind, praying that the conversation would move on. But Alison ignored them and looked back at me. 'I think you should make the effort to go. You need to work on it.'

I wasn't about to be told that I needed to work on anything, and mirroring the flat tone that she had used I responded, 'I agree. But not in the space of one week.' She huffed, and to my great relief the meeting came to an end. I sat still, staring at the floor and waiting for everyone to file out.

'I really like you!'

I looked up. 'Huh?' It was Prue. I hadn't talked to her since running away from her as she tried to serve me food in the dining room and still felt embarrassed about the whole thing.

'You have a great way of saying things and responding to shitty questions!' She laughed and handed me a piece of paper with her number on it, telling me to text over the weekend if I felt low. I didn't know much about her, but in the meetings and from off-the-cuff comments a few of the patients had made, I knew there was a bad story there. She disappeared around the corner as I put the piece of paper in my pocket.

*

It was pitch black outside and I was sitting in the TV room alone when all of a sudden I heard the most gut-wrenching, blood-curdling scream, the type of noise that makes everything inside you tense up. And then it came again, worse this time and louder. I stepped out of the room and followed the noise towards reception. Ellie, seemingly drunk out of her mind, was lying on the floor screaming, punching herself in the stomach and cracking her head repeatedly on the wooden floor with a frenetic-looking Sandra and Prue trying to stop her as the night nurses flapped around like startled pigeons. I had never seen anything like it. SMACK went her head again against the floor as Prue screamed at her to stop. Ellie kept shouting, 'I want it dead! I want it dead!' I shrank out of the room in shock and started back along the hallway where I bumped into a talking-to-herself, mid-episode Katie.

'What's going on?' I asked.

'Ellie's gone ape shit. Don't tell anyone I told you,' Katie lowered her voice, 'she's pregnant.' I thought back to Ellie punching her stomach and opened my mouth to ask another question but Katie was already going again, whirring off towards the noise. I got myself a glass of water from the kitchen and quietly skulked back to the TV room.

The screaming didn't stop, it went on for what felt like hours. I heard Ellie being dragged upstairs by a group of people where she lay on the floor above me and slammed her body against the ceiling so hard I thought it might cave in. I wondered how her throat wasn't hoarse, how she hadn't completely lost her voice. The banging and hollering continued long into the night and of course I couldn't go into my room because this is where it was all taking place, so I lay on the sofa with a blanket around me assuming this is where I'd have to sleep. At one point I heard what sounded like Katie also start to scream – I later learned that Ellie, whilst hallucinating, had attacked her, punching her three times in the face and ripping out a handful of her hair. As I sat watching the television there was another loud bang; this one didn't sound like it had come from above me but rather from the next room. I wondered if I had got it wrong but then once again, bang. Reluctantly I got up and headed for the door. The firm room was next to the TV room, so as gently as I could I pushed the firm door open with my fingertips, a tiny way, just enough to see inside. I hadn't spoken to Angela yet. She shared a room with Katie and Cynthia and was in her fifties. Whenever I had tried to sheepishly smile at her she would scowl at me so I had avoided her as much as I could. I peered through the crack in the door and watched as, shrieking, she picked up one of the chairs and threw it full force against the window. The glass shattered into hundreds of pieces all over the carpet. She picked up another chair, this time throwing it at the wall. I watched the wood splinter and come apart as she moved onto the next one. One of the night nurses came rushing through the hall towards the noise and I quickly ran back to the TV room. I switched off the lights, hoping to create a shield around me in the darkness. I sat back down and began praying quietly to myself that if I stayed invisible the storm would surely bypass me.

The banging and screaming coming from both above me and the firm room went on and on. My ears ached with the noise, as my whole body tensed with worry. The door to the TV room creaked open; I held my breath waiting to see who it would be. It was Dan.

'What the fuck is going on?' he said looking bewildered and laughing. I looked at him, still in slight shock, and shrugged my shoulders. He sat down next to me on the sofa, a smell of alcohol strong on his breath as he exhaled. 'Fuck.'

I scrunched up my nose and turned to look at him. 'Are you drunk, Dan?' I suddenly felt like an idiot for asking.

'Um, sort of. I was! Not so much now. I thought I would walk in and everybody would be all over me for being like this, calling the staff, askin' about my day and that,' he paused, 'but they don't give a fuck!' He started laughing again, an infectious, manic laugh that I couldn't help but join in with. He looked handsome, smartly dressed in a dark red shirt and black jeans.

I smiled, 'Well, you can tell me, if you want?' I had barely spoken to him since I had been there, but here we were being thrown together and I desperately needed the distraction and company, so Dan began to tell me about his hideous day of family therapy. He was from a big family in a small town in Ireland where anything mental health-related was deeply taboo and still viewed as incredibly shameful to the families of the people involved. Dan's family were no exception to this when he started showing signs of being unwell – they had pretended it wasn't happening, which just made matters worse. 'So, as it turns out, my dad hid my suicide note from everyone,' he said undoing the top button of his shirt. I looked at him bewildered, 'Why would he do that?' He smiled at me. 'To save the rest of my family from the embarrassment. For the longest time I was in an acute unit wondering why no one had come to see me, why they'd all just abandoned me... He told me today it was because he'd forbidden any of them from visiting... Apparently I was "better left to it"...' He looked away, shaking his head.

'Did the acute unit help at all?' I asked coyly.

He looked back at me and laughed. 'Well, if you mean did they pump me full of lithium, strap me to a gurney and give me electroshock therapy for months on end then yes, yes it did!' I grimaced at the thought. I'd never met anyone who had had electroshock; I didn't even realise it was something that was still used... I thought it had been banished long ago with leech baths and lobotomies.

We talked for a while longer before heading into the kitchen because Dan wanted to make a coffee. Through the window that led out to the car park we saw Ellie being dragged (still screaming) by a group of police into an ambulance.

We watched in silence as they tethered her to a fold-out bed and one of the paramedics jammed a needle into her arm. A few minutes later she wasn't struggling as much, but despite whatever they had given her, she was still screeching when they pulled away. It was pretty horrific to watch. Dan turned to face me, 'Well I guess the show's over, until next time of course… da da daaa!' He looked at me grinning, I tried not to smile at his flippancy. He put his empty mug in the sink and yawned. 'I better go to bed, pet, try and sleep off this drink.' He held out his arms and ordered, 'Right, hug me!' He smelled like whisky and cologne. As he let me go he said, 'I wanted to ask you for one earlier but thought it might be a trigger to have a drunk man asking for a hug!' I didn't say anything, just smiled and shook my head.

*

I hadn't been asleep for long when I was woken up by Ellie returning from A&E. I looked at the clock – 4:45am. Brazenly and loudly she marched into the bedroom followed by a nurse called Claire. Ellie switched on all the lights and began rummaging through her things; she pulled something small out of a drawer and pointedly put it in her pocket. I lay up on my elbow in bed watching her.

'Ellie, *what* are you doing?' said Claire, looking exasperated.

'Getting my razor so I can cut my fucking wrists open,' came Ellie's completely monotone response. I felt my eyebrow arch and couldn't help but smirk at how facetious she was being. Claire stood in the doorway with her hand on her forehead and let out a long 'Ooh God,' followed by, 'I need to go and get help.' She disappeared off to find another nurse. Ellie stood listlessly in the centre of the room suddenly not knowing what to do without an audience. Realising she would not get any attention from me or a loudly snoring Sandra she began to shout for Claire and trotted off after her.

*

'I'm really sorry.' The sun was shining on Ellie's face as she sat on the end of my bed. She'd opened my curtains. I looked at the clock again; it was 8am. I pulled myself up to face her.

'Okay?'

'I was really fucked. I'm not a bad person, I'm just struggling at the moment.'

I ran my hand through my hair. 'Yeah, I get that. It's fine, sort of. Thanks for apologising.'

She looked down at her bandaged hands. 'I can't remember anything. Is everyone angry at me? I think I punched Katie or something, that's what Claire said.' She stood up and walked over to her full-length mirror and examined herself. 'I look fat.' I remembered what Katie had told me about her being pregnant and glanced at her stomach; you couldn't tell. 'I'm still pretty though, aren't I?'

She looked at me wanting an answer; this was a bit weird but I felt I had to say something.

'Yeah, of course,' I said, feeling awkward and put on the spot.

She smiled at me. 'I know I am! Fuck 'em if they're angry. I don't care anyway.' She sprayed a generous amount of perfume onto her neck and chest and walked out.

*

The rest of the day passed uneventfully. Whenever I found myself alone my mind wandered back to Dan. The obsession inside me was brewing, I could feel it creeping in.

As the afternoon rolled around I sat in another community meeting with about forty people in it; I thought I was going to die from anxiety. I huddled in an armchair in the corner of the room by the door and watched in horror as it filled up. I stared at the floor the entire time feeling as though a twenty stone man was sitting on my chest. Judy sat opposite, watching me. She was the all-seeing eye of the Caddick, and for some reason that eye always seemed to be fixed on me.

There were more staff than usual in the room and I wondered why, but as the meeting began it soon became clear: they were there as reinforcements. 'We have a new family coming this week.' Judy looked uncharacteristically sheepish as she spoke. 'Laura and Ben will be joining us, as well as their very young baby.' She cleared her throat. 'They have their difficulties just like everyone else and we are hoping you will all be welcoming. We take everyone's safety here very seriously and if we thought there was a great threat we wouldn't allow them into the hospital.' It was all feeling very convoluted, like we were being told half a story, and it wasn't just me who was feeling as if something wasn't being said.

'Why are you telling us this, Judy?' asked Jen, one of the mothers on the family unit. Alison took over from Judy at that point. 'We are telling you because there is a point of concern that we need to share with the wider community before Laura and Ben get here; it's regarding the sex offenders register, you all have a right to know the situation.'

Oh God, was he a rapist? Or a paedophile? How was that going to work? How could they let him on the family unit around the children? What had he done?

Alison went on, 'Laura was involved with something some years ago and is on the sex offenders list and must be monitored around children; she has served her time in prison and is coming here to help her rehabilitation.'

Laura? The woman? The woman's on the sex offenders list? I didn't even have time to process it before there was an uproar in the room. The family unit was mainly made up of single mothers with children under five. There were four single mums and one couple and they were all losing their heads.

'She's a fucking paedophile?' shouted Jen, completely bewildered.

'No,' said Judy in her calm, even tone, 'we are not going to go into details about what happened because it is not for us to say, but—' she was cut off by Sheila, one of the other mothers.

'You're letting a predator in here? Around our kids? How will they be safe? She shouldn't be allowed to come here, Judy, this is disgusting!'

Alison spoke up again, 'She has served her time in prison and it was decided that she no longer poses a threat.'

'Are you fucking joking? This is a joke! Is this a fucking joke?!' Jen was standing up now, beside herself, screaming at them.

'It's very important that you are able to say how you're feeling, Jen,' said Alison, but Jen was now storming out of the room, Sheila following her, both shouting about paedophiles as they did. The room fell silent for a short time after that until Kane spoke.

'I understand why they're so angry. I wouldn't be happy.'

'Can you say more on that, Kane?' asked Johanna.

'Not really, what's there to say? In their eyes you're putting their children at risk from a predator, that's about all there is to it.' A few more of the ESPD patients aired their concerns, saying they weren't happy with Laura coming, that it triggered them and their own abuse histories. But regardless of everyone's feelings, the date was set, the funding agreed and Laura and Ben would be moving in at the end of the week.

*

It was my second session with Nora, my individual psychotherapist. I had now only seen her for a few hours in total but she seemed to already have an understanding of me that I both appreciated and disliked.

'I think you really want to cry right now. I think all you

want to do is break down and cry.' She stared at me as I shifted uncomfortably in my blue chair opposite her. She was right, but I wasn't about to tell her that.

'I cry in front of people all the time. I don't have a problem crying. I cried in front of you the first time I met you,' I said, my tone a little too defensive.

'Yes, but you desperately tried to stop yourself.' She was so poised, and right again.

'I don't like crying because it makes my face red and puffy and even more disgusting!'

There was a long pause.

'When you were little, Emma, your emotions showed all over your face – when you were upset, when you were angry, but now you have your make-up to be the perfect mask. No one would ever know what was going on underneath.'

'Some people can see through it,' I said, feeling defeated. I wanted to start trying to be honest with her, and so went out on a limb. 'I was going to cut last night. I was set on it. I had it all planned out.'

'And you didn't because of what was going on with Ellie?'

I nodded.

'Because everyone would have been taken up with her and no one would have been there to see you and what you were going through?'

'What? No! Not at all! What sort of attention-seeker would that make me? Of course that's not the reason!' I tried to balance myself before going on. 'I didn't do it because there was no privacy. Everyone was in my room because of Ellie. The bathrooms here are disgusting, there's nowhere to sit and they're freezing so I didn't want to go in there.'

'I think, Emma, you either feel you are in the centre of the room, like the community room, or the firm room, or you are right outside it. You are never on the periphery. You desperately want to trust me. You desperately want to break down in here, right now, in front of me and tell me why you wanted to self-harm. But you won't let yourself.'

I folded my arms and looked at the clock. 'It's time, Nora.'

25

DAN

"A borderline suffers a kind of emotional hemophilia;
[s]he lacks the clotting mechanism needed to moderate [his or
her] spurts of feeling. Stimulate a passion, and the borderline
emotionally bleeds to death."

— JEROLD KREISMAN & HAL STRAUS, *I Hate You, Don't Leave
Me: Understanding the Borderline Personality*

It was a few nights after the community meeting about Laura
when I broke into pieces and cried uncontrollably about missing
my dog and the last awful, haunting moments of her life. It had
been almost a year since she had been put to sleep but I still
missed her badly. I sat on the floor of my bedroom rocking and
digging my nails into my hands, small blood bubbles rising up
underneath them. Katie was the only person I could and would
talk to about this memory, and she came in and sat with me as I
cried, trying to comfort me as best she could. Katie had her own
little dog back in Ireland which she adored and I felt like she
understood my grief, and wouldn't judge me for mourning like
this for an animal.

As I began to calm down she started to talk about Dan.

'He's been trying to impress you,' she said sniggering.
'Why?' I said, looking up through my blurry eyes.
'Oh because he thinks you're all clever and mysterious!'
I tried to fight my smile.

*

Over the next few days Dan and I spent each waking moment together.
'You're so easy to talk to, pet. I haven't spoken to anyone here in a year as much as I've talked to you in the last week.' He gave me the words, and I made the songs, which I sang all day, all night and every second I had to spare. Perhaps *this* was it! Was Daniel Stone the cure I had been looking for all along? He wasn't like all the Toms, *he* was different. Who needed hospital? Who needed therapy and nurses and group? I had him, maybe that's all that was really missing from my life?

*

Another community meeting and the family unit were out for Laura's blood; she looked like a frightened animal. She had only been at the Caddick for a few days now. I'd passed by her the day before in the dining room and said hi. She seemed nice, very quiet and pretty – incredibly pale, with huge bright blue eyes and yellow, cracked teeth that gave away a drug-addled past. Ben was the total opposite of Laura: he was loud and chatty, broad, tall, hard to miss, and their tiny baby Sam was absolutely beautiful.
We had not been told exactly what she had done to go to prison, only that she was currently nineteen and 'it' had happened when she was sixteen, whatever 'it' was. Mostly there was hearsay, gossip, although Jen and a couple of the others on the family unit said they knew; apparently they had found out her surname and

226

looked her up on the Internet. Whatever they had found out had horrified them all so much that they openly felt they could tell her to her face she was 'disgusting' and should be 'dead or still in prison'. It was true I didn't know what she'd done, I had avoided the stories and whispering in the halls, but still, I didn't feel the same as the others. She was here, wasn't she? She was trying to change. She sat there in the community meeting quiet as a mouse as they systematically took it in turns to shout at her.

'Your baby needs to be taken away from you. God knows what you're doing to him alone in your room,' Karen, one of the 'elders' of the family unit screamed. She'd been there the longest. 'You should be dead, if this was America they'd put you in the chair.' The staff attempted to interject but it fell on deaf ears. Laura did not respond to them, she just sat there, shaking and staring at the floor.

As the meeting was being drawn to a close, words began to bubble up in me and before I knew it I was speaking for the first time in the community room of my own accord.

'Well done for sitting through all this, Laura. If I were you I'd have wanted to run out a hundred times over and it's really good you managed to stay.' The words tumbled out of me before I had a chance to think about the impact they would have on my place in the 'community'.

It was a big gamble, but I seemed to reap rewards as Alison said, 'Emma, now I want to say well done, for saying well done!' My fellow ESPD patients smiled at me, no doubt amazed I had actually spoken out. Laura whispered 'Thank you' three times, raising her eyes off the floor to look at me for the last one. In turn I tried to avoid the eyes of the family unit that bored into me screaming that I was scum – right along with the paedophile they thought I was protecting.

*

'What are you thinking?' Dan looked at me across the round wooden table in Starbucks, a wary smile spreading across his face.

'Nothing. Why? What are *you* thinking?'

We had been here for two hours and I had lost all control over my feelings for him and what he might feel for me, to the point where it was actually making me physically sick to try and work it out. I know I had only known him for a short time, but I felt a connection with him that I hadn't experienced with another person in years. It felt exciting and also dangerous, which made it that much more enticing. I rooted around in my bag pulling out my make-up and mirror and glanced at myself in the small reflection as I re-applied my eyeliner. He was watching me with a strange look of scrutiny.

'You're a girly girl,' he said in a disappointed tone. My eyes flicked up at him as though he were Nora accusing me of not wanting to self-harm in case I had not got enough attention.

'I don't like my face,' I snapped back, agitated but trying to keep my voice from revealing my annoyance at his comment. 'I'm paranoid that I look bad, which is why I constantly look in my mirror, or any mirror I walk in front of. I don't think I look fucking nice. I'm just trying not to look *so* ugly that people stare.'

He looked at me realising he'd got it wrong and an expression came over his face that I hadn't seen before.

'But you're very attractive.' I looked down and started shoving my make-up back in my bag. 'It's make-up, Dan. Anyone can look good with make-up on. It's all bullshit, a façade.'

He interrupted again, 'No, you're really, really attractive, Emma.'

Signed, sealed, delivered, Stone, I'm yours.

*

Back at the hospital I sat in the alcove with Annie and Angela staring out onto the grounds as the sun went down on another day. Angela still hadn't said so much as a word to me and Annie always seemed hopelessly lost in her own little world. I hadn't really had much interaction with her, she was around forty, plump, with blond curly hair and had deep, mauve scars on either wrist which she tried, in vain to cover with dozens of brightly coloured bracelets. She kept to herself most of the time but was always polite on the rare occasions she'd spoken to me. Annie shared a room with Esther and the two seemed quite close, often chatting about religion and seemingly not much else. Dan appeared in the doorway. I tried to wrestle the smile off my face as he came over.

'Will you come with me, pet?'

I pretended to be reading something on my phone. 'Where?'

He glanced at Angela and Annie to see if they were listening then said more quietly, 'I've got photos I want to show. Pictures I've taken, I want your opinion.'

I thought I caught a look exchanged between the two women but got up and followed him to his bedroom, panicking that one of the night staff would see, or that Annie or Angela might tell someone.

His room was long and rectangular with a large bay window at the end of it. Because the male-to-female ratio in the hospital was so one-sided he and Kane didn't have to share, and he had the large space all to himself. I sat on his bed, feeling nervous and excited as he showed me his photography. Amazing black-and-white images of an abandoned mental asylum in Ireland. I flicked through them.

'They're so good, Dan,' I said, genuinely meaning it.

'I wanted to show you some of the poetry I wrote as well, because you said you write a lot. I wanted you to see if they are any good. But...' he pulled a notebook out from under his bed,

'I'm embarrassed. Just take them back to your room and read them.'

I smiled, 'Okay.'

I sat on my bed reading his poetry and berating myself. Why have I done this *again*? As usual? Same fucking old. I become consumed. He, whoever *he* may be, becomes my whole world. My reason to get up; my reason to function. My reason to fucking breathe. And for what? For another Tom? For a guy who's leaving in four weeks? Who's fucked up himself? *What* am I doing? *Why* am I doing this? Letting myself get so ridiculously carried away? Was it at all real, any of it? Or just an obsession as usual? I liked him, sure I did – but I knew it was wrong. And I knew, deep down inside me, that I was going to get hurt, but still I couldn't stop. I wanted to. But I couldn't pull myself away. The internal back and forth went on all night, the continual, neverending head fuck.

26

STEAK AND BLOW JOB NIGHT

"The problem with the world is that the intelligent people are
full of doubts, while the stupid ones are full of confidence."

— CHARLES BUKOWSKI

The community meetings were becoming too much for me. I
spent all week dreading Tuesday morning. The biggest gathering
of them all, the horrifying sixty-people hell-fest. The meeting
where someone might say something to me and I'd have to talk
in front of all of them. I sat there every time, staring out of the
window, trying to count the bricks along the adjacent wall. But
this particular morning, I would have to get up and leave halfway
through as my session with Nora had been moved to a different
time. I clock-watched, hoping for a fight or an argument to
break out so that they would all be at least slightly distracted.
My heart was thudding in my chest. It was only five or six steps
to the door but I knew that when I stood up, they would all look
at me. They would all notice how fat I was. They would all judge
and wonder what Dan saw in me. My eyes fixed on the door, it
opened a crack and Nora, standing back and unseen from the
rest of the room, motioned for me to leave.

I rose to my feet the voice in my head booming, *THEY ARE ALL LOOKING AT YOU. YOU FAT PIG! NOW THEY ALL KNOW! THEY ALL KNOW HOW FAT YOU ARE!! DAN IS LOOKING, LOOKING AT YOU WOBBLING ABOUT LIKE A JELLY.*

Just. Get. To. The. Fucking. Door. My feet began to move as if they were weighted to the ground, invisible shackles around both my ankles.

'Emma, can you stay?' Alison's shrill words seeped through the noise, saturated by the voices in my head.

'Session,' I blurted out as I stumbled out into the hall, my legs threatening to buckle under me. I followed Nora up the staircase with my breathing getting steadily worse. She was walking ahead of me, not talking – that would have been deeply 'unboundaried', we only actually spoke inside her office. *Breathe, just breathe*, I thought over and over again – but I couldn't, my chest was shrinking, my lungs were failing, and before we got to her room, I was hyperventilating, clinging to the wall with tears streaming down my face as I heard Nora's distant voice telling me I was safe. I tried to listen to her over my gasps for air.

'Okay, Emma. Just breathe. It's okay. Just breathe, don't try and talk.' She eventually got me to walk to her office where I sat hunched and foetal, bawling like a child.

'What brought this on?' she said, sounding more alarmed than I had heard her sound before.

'People… staring at me. I'm so disgusting. I'm so fat. Now they all know.' I burst into tears again.

'That's not the reality, Emma.'

'You have to say that! You're lying!' I was shouting now. 'Of course I'm fat! Look at me! I'm obese! I'm vile! I'm surprised *you* can even look at me without feeling sick, and those meetings, those fucking meetings! My God! I can't bear it! All week, all week I dread it.'

I shoved my face in my hands struggling again for breath and whining out loud like a cat in pain.

'Have you told anyone about how those meetings make you feel?'

'*No!* If I speak out they'll all ask questions about what's wrong with me, so I don't say anything, which just makes it worse.' I reached for the box of tissues next to me, knocking over some of the toy soldiers she had on the table.

'So, you are in a catch-22. If you talk, you feel that people will see a weakness and pounce, but if you remain silent, you think they will grow angry with you?'

I nodded.

'Why do you think you will be met with such hostility? Why do you feel no one will be on your side?'

I took a deep breath and started again. 'I don't know.' Finally my voice had reached a normal volume.

'I think you feel that you are manipulating people into liking you. You think that, right now, I am being nice to you because of something you have done to me, that I am not aware of. Perhaps you think because of your panic attack I am being forced into having to be nice to you?'

'I probably am doing something manipulative,' I said, looking at her for the first time since I had been in the room.

'I hope you will be able to share this with the community.'

I wanted to change the subject, and so began to tell her I was becoming close with Dan and really enjoyed his company.

She smiled, relaxing into her chair. 'So, you like him?' And, stupidly, I thought she meant I *like*-like him, so, not pausing for breath, I went into a ludicrous confession for five minutes straight.

'He's just so lovely. And tells me I'm attractive and we laugh and joke and it's so wonderful. He feels like someone I could actually trust. I know I'll be over it soon, please don't tell anybody, oh God, you will, won't you? Oh don't please. I don't even *like him*! Please don't tell Judy.' I looked at her baffled face, and my stomach turned. 'And I just did that to myself, didn't I? You hadn't even said it, had you? Oh fuck,' to which she looked thoroughly bemused and like she was fighting laughing at my frantic, unneeded admission. So yes, that was that, the cat was out of the bag.

Her response was to say, 'So? You like Dan. Why should anyone else have to know that? Only him, if you plan on telling him, or others if you choose to tell them.'

I sighed loudly and fought leaning over to hug her. My secret was still safe, for the time being at least.

*

After an hour of talking to Nora about Dan I tried to be away from him – I felt somehow my defences were down and if prompted I would spill my guts to him about my feelings in an instant. The problem was that in a hospital, albeit a big one, there are only so many places to hide and, as was the emerging pattern, when the sun went down, my obsession awoke.

We were joined at the hip all night. He gave me his chair outside and sat next to me, cross-legged on the floor smoking. 'So there's this little hideaway out there.' Dan pointed into the black night. I looked out onto the grounds, silent other than the sound of the leaves moving gently in the breeze.

'Out where?' I asked.

'There,' he motioned with his head. 'Out amongst the trees. The kids from the family unit built it I'm guessing, probably a few years ago. It's hidden away... I don't know if anyone else knows it's there.'

I smiled excitedly. 'Show me?'

Dan took a last drag on his cigarette and rising to his feet stubbed it out. 'Okay, come on.'

We walked down the steps into the grounds, giggling and checking behind us as we crossed the lawn into a thicket of brambles that led to a small wooded area. I squeaked with excitement as a badger bounded past us in the dark. Without asking he took my phone out of my hand and used it as a torch to lead us through the night. And through the trees, there it was it. He was right, it was such an adorable little place, safe, secret, untouched. A perfect hideout. The kids had dragged a little table and chairs into a clearing amid the dense trees; there were colouring books, picnic blankets and dolls, all safe and dry under the canopy of leaves above us. And all of a sudden, standing there in the dark, I wanted to kiss him. I wanted him all around me, like ice, like fire, burning and soothing the emotions that swam inside me. After a few moments, maybe feeling as flooded as I was by the intimacy of the situation, he led me out, walking backwards but facing me, using his coat as a shield against the branches that wanted so much to scratch us.

Back on the steps he started showing me constellations, teaching me the difference between stars and satellites. And sitting there in the bright moonlight looking up at the night sky I felt calm and serene, like the world was finally smiling back at me.

*

The next night Dan and I stayed up watching *Silence of the Lambs*, relaxed in each other's company and hysterically laughing. He persisted in begging me throughout the film, and for the next two days, to do the voices… I would make my voice as low and deep as I could and say, 'It rubs the lotion on its skin…' And he would throw his head back and laugh until tears streamed down his face. He was lying on the sofa as I sat in front of him painting my nails and trying to look halfway decent while I batted my

STORM IN A TEA CUP

eyelashes. The banter with him was a lot of fun. Just the constant playing, the tireless back and forth. He would ask, 'What are you thinking?'

I would stare off and pretend I hadn't heard him. 'Hmm?'

He would get frustrated. 'What, Emma? What are you thinking?'

'Oh, nothing...'

We became a walking satire of ourselves. He would hold doors open for me in front of everyone and nod for me to go through behind him, as I did he would loudly say, 'Why are you following me?' then would laugh hysterically, as would I. It was becoming a constant battle of wills. Who will break first, who will confess their feelings?

Of course, people were talking, to us, and behind our backs, Katie seeming to be the main contender for both.

'I don't want you to get hurt, sweetie, I don't want your heart to break. Yous are both messed up. I don't want you to mess him up even more, or him to mess you up even more.' I ignored her, after all she didn't understand. This wasn't some passing fancy, this was the real thing and Dan wasn't going to abandon or hurt me, how could he?

*

'You're only content when you're in his space.' Nora stared hard at my face watching my reaction before going on. 'You cannot take even the idea of separation because the minute it happens you start getting very anxious about the whole relationship. It starts to curdle in you when you're away from him, it churns into something very poisonous and the only way to make that feeling go away and to make the feelings real again is to be next to him, or any him for that matter.'

I felt like a famine victim receiving a food package, give me more, Nora, keep feeding me, tell me what's wrong with me, I need this.

'So when you are with that person, Emma, you push and push and *push* for affirmation, until eventually, they've had enough.' She leaned in, slowly, purposely. 'Your need for love is *so* great that it's all-encompassing. All you do is crave and long for love and affection.' She paused, leaning out again and crossing her legs, relaxing back into her chair. 'Let me ask you something. Are you getting jealous of other women around Dan?'

I didn't know whether to tell her the truth, worried in case my admission would warrant flagging up with the staff. I sighed aloud, giving in without a fight. 'Yes. I'm jealous. I'm a very jealous person, I always have been.'

'I think you are also a very critical person. Of yourself, obviously, and also subconsciously of others.'

I rubbed my temple with my fingers. 'Yes but I never look at another girl and think "you bitch", I'm looking at them thinking "you are so much prettier than me".'

She mused on that for a second before going on, 'Whether that is the case or not, I think the internal critic inside you is raging more than you care to admit, or perhaps are even aware of.'

I left the session feeling like a total idiot, and completely over exposed. Was my need for love really so great? Was I jealous? And horribly critical of others? I walked out and bumped straight into Dan.

'Did you talk to Nora? You seemed down before, did it help?'

I just kept laughing, uncontrollably, neurotically, putting my head in my hands as I thought, *I've just spent the last hour talking about you.*

Not long after my session I was sitting in the alcove still thinking about what Nora had said. The little alcove, with its yellow walls and blue armchairs, was the social hub of the ESPD unit and everyone would migrate there throughout the day.

Adaline was sewing, Kane was strumming on his guitar, and Annie and Esther were quietly chatting amongst themselves. Dan appeared through the doorway with a suitcase; he was going home to Ireland for the weekend. The closer you got to your leaving date the more you had to go home for the weekends, to try and reintegrate yourself back into your normal environment. He walked over to me and set his case down.

'Well, I'm off. I just wanted to say goodbye.' He seemed a little stressed.

'Okay,' I said looking up at him. I didn't want him to go; in the fortnight we had spent together we had been glued at the hip and the concept of four days in the hospital without him felt like a lifetime.

'Are you going to hug me?' he asked stretching out his arms. I got up and let his body envelope mine. As he left I turned back around to see everyone gawping at me.

'What?' I was worried I'd done something wrong. Kane smiled at me then went back to strumming slowly on his guitar. I said it again feeling a little irritated. 'What? Why are you all staring?'

Esther and Annie laughed, bemused. Esther looked at me. 'We're laughing because Dan never says goodbye to anyone! Let alone hugs them!'

I felt my face redden and said, 'Oh,' quickly looking down at my phone screen hoping that they wouldn't see. I stared at the blank screen, biting my lip to stop from smiling.

*

'Trev wants to rip a new hole in Emma!'

Ian Stanton's words were on repeat like a bad record I didn't remember putting on. I made the fatal mistake of meeting Natalie in the pub on Saturday night to watch the rugby with some of her boyfriend's friends, the majority of whom I had been to college with. I wasn't at all interested in rugby, but Dan was gone and I wasn't friendly with anyone else at the hospital. Prue was nice but I hadn't spent any time with her, Ellie was never around, and Sandra was always in bed, so I needed a distraction.

'Tuesday is steak and blow job night at my house,' announced Ian, laughing, slapping his friends on the back and winking at me, like it was some sort of joke I was in on.

I don't know why I ever bothered to spend any more than five minutes surrounded by these boys. I liked Natalie's boyfriend Chris, he was always kind to me, protective even, but without fail every time I was near the rest of them they managed to ruin any faith in men I may have gathered – quashed it, burned it, and destroyed it within minutes.

I overheard Trev saying, 'Yeah, I'd nail Emma.' Ian delighted in this and of course telling me it, over and over and over again. I was quiet when I was out in these groups, timid and nervous most of the time, constantly trying to be invisible. But of course the more you try to be invisible the more you're often just inadvertently shining a spotlight on yourself. Ian wanted to embarrass me, he wanted to pull away my walls and boundaries and watch me squirm uncomfortably in front of him. He enjoyed it, it made him feel like a big man in front of his brain-dead friends. When I turned my back and ignored him as you'd do to a bad-mannered dog who keeps jumping up at you, he went outside and told Natalie, Chris and the rest of the group repeatedly, 'Trev wants to nail Emma! Trev wants to rip a new hole in Emma.'

I was mortified and furious. Women here, men over there. Tits, cunt, a whore. Is that all we're good for, being objectified? Being fucked? I was so confused. Losing the weight meant I was now being seen, I couldn't shrink back into my rolls of fat and hide there any more, I was completely exposed. How can you want to be desired and want to repel equally? Just like Irfan, just like all the Toms, I was somehow doing this, inviting it, causing it. Trev wanted to rip a new hole in me, and it was my fault. I didn't know how to hide; how could I go back to being invisible? I couldn't stand myself.

The music in the pub was too loud, the chattering, the clinking of glasses, the smell of beer, the roar of noise every time someone scored on the TV, and yet amid it all the only thing I could hear was that voice louder than ever, telling me, 'You need to cut.' In what seemed like a flash I was back at home in my parents' house, sitting on my bed with my sleeves rolled up, a razor blade glinting in the light of *Fight Club*, which was playing on the TV.

I am so disgusting. Rank. Obese. Ugly. Pathetic. Needy. So, so needy. I am hopelessly persistent in my patheticness. *I am Emma's flailing sense of rejection.* I am, I am. *I am fucking bored of wanting. Waiting. Coveting. Lusting. Steak and fucking blow job night. Rip a new hole in me, boys, I am all yours.* Or let me do it to myself. It's all the fucking same.

'You decide your own level of involvement, Emma,' Nora had said to me in our session. I certainly fucking do. The room and the voices spun me in a circle until the sun was on its way up and my bed sheets were dirty red and soaking.

27

THEY ALWAYS BLAME
THE WOMAN

"One ought to hold on to one's heart; for if one lets it go, one
soon loses control of the head too."

— FRIEDRICH NIETZSCHE

I was lying on the sofa in the alcove when Dan returned to
the hospital. I couldn't mask how happy I was to see him and
thankfully he beamed my smile right back at me; he came over
and asked for a hug but I was already going for one.

'Come outside with me, I need a smoke,' he said. I sat on the
floor in front of him as he lit up a cigarette. Saturday night had
taken its toll on me; my arms and legs were covered in hundreds
of fresh cuts, my whole body was aching and I felt insecure about
being around him. The trust we had been building had been
shattered by Ian over the weekend and I felt guarded and nervous.

'What's wrong, pet?' he asked looking concerned.

'Nothing. It's nothing. It's not important.' I shook my head as
I yanked at my sleeves , worrying they would rise up and expose
the new cuts.

He sat down. 'If it's bothering you, I want to know. Tell me.'

And so, going against the urge to keep my secret, I told him what had happened.

'That must have been really horrible. Why were you with those men? Why didn't you just leave, or you could have called me?'

I didn't answer his questions, just quietly said, 'I'm disgusting.' The words slipped out of my mouth without me meaning them to.

'Stop it, Emma.' He gently nudged at me with his elbow. 'Name one thing you don't like about yourself.'

With my face planted on my knees I mumbled, 'The way I look.' I stared up at him as he lit another cigarette.

'I don't think that you really see what is looking at you in the mirror. I know it won't make any difference, but I think you're very pretty, more than pretty, actually.' His words, which had felt so nice the week before, now felt like a knife twisting inside me, sharp and painful. He was lying, he must be.

We escaped up to his room so he could write his final review, managing to dodge the staff and other patients as we went. I lay on the empty bed on the other side of the bedroom, hugging the abandoned teddy bear that sat there, quiet, still, content to be near him again. There was a knock at the door. Petrice, a social worker who did most of the night shifts, came in and asked Dan if he knew where I was.

'She's right there,' he said pointing at me.

'Ah, Emma, I was worried. I couldn't find you.'

'Well, I've been right here,' I said smiling at her. Petrice eyed me suspiciously then left.

A few more minutes of comfortable silence passed.

'Emma?'

I looked at him. 'Yes, Dan?'

'Do you think *I'm* attractive?'

Feeling my cheeks turn pink I squealed, 'Why are you asking

me *that*?' I rolled over and faced the window. Another moment of silence, this time not as comfortable. 'Dan?'

'Yes, pet?'

'Yes, I think you're attractive.'

*

I woke up feeling happy the next morning, always short-lived in a mental hospital. I sat in firm, bored, listening to the morning announcements. Esther was chairing the meeting with Dan.

'So first on the agenda is Ellie,' said Esther. She was harder at the Caddick; I couldn't quite put my finger on it but the sad little teary-eyed girl I'd grown to loathe had vanished and instead Esther just seemed really pissed off all the time – I think the staff at the Caddick challenged her much more than they ever had at the Henshaw and not in the way she wanted.

'Why am I on the agenda?' said Ellie in her strong northern accent.

Judy sighed loudly. 'You know why, Ellie. You need to tell your fellow patients what you told the staff.'

Ellie stared at her, belligerent. 'What? That I'm pregnant?' She smirked at Judy's disapproving pursing of her lips. 'Yeah, I'm having a baby for those of you who don't know, so you all have to be really nice to me or I might miscarry.'

'How far gone are you?' asked Annie.

'Two months,' said Ellie. 'The dad and me aren't together, obviously, but he's gonna help with the baby, and no, for those of you wondering, he's not a punter.'

We all congratulated her and she seemed happy with the attention. Katie looked smug throughout, pleased that she'd known the secret all along. I noticed Prue didn't look surprised either and guessed Ellie must have told her too.

Esther carried on down the agenda list landing on Dan, and

began talking about his impending leaving date. I sat there trying to ignore them all as they asked him how he was feeling about it. I was floating in and out of listening when, like an atom bomb, Judy looked straight at me and said, 'This is going to sound like a telling off but it was handed over that Emma was in Dan's bedroom in the early hours of the morning. Apparently 3am.'

Judy turned her whole body towards me, 'Can you say what that is about, Emma? Why were you in a male patient's bedroom unaccompanied; what were you doing in there?'

Everyone in the room was looking at me, the staff, the patients. I felt my chest start to get tight, the embarrassment pouring over me like cold water. More defensively than I meant to, I said, 'I was stressed out and we were talking… and it wasn't 3am, it wasn't even nine!'

Everyone stared at me, no one looked once at Dan. I instantly felt like a whore, because that was what she was accusing me of surely? That I was in there for something sexual? Judy sighed heavily. 'Emma, it would be helpful if you could tell the truth and admit you were in his bedroom at 3am. Why would the staff lie? You need to be honest and tell us why you did that?'

'It was eight thirty, Judy, I'm not fucking lying.' I glared at her, she looked away shaking her head in indignation. After the boys at the weekend, this was the last thing I wanted to hear. As we left firm, Dan joked, 'Come to my bedroom!' I tried to smile as the tears began brimming in my eyes.

I quickly turned and started up the stairs to my room when I heard, 'Are you okay?' I glanced behind me, it was Prue. She followed me up the stairs as I began to cry. 'It's bullshit, hon, if you weren't in there at three they should have believed you. You're not a slut and you shouldn't have been made to feel like that.'

I nodded as I wiped my eyes. 'Thanks. I want to be by myself for a bit.' I knew if I didn't break eye contact quickly she would know exactly what wanting to be 'by myself' meant. I turned and ran up the rest of the stairs. Ellie had her one-to-one session straight after firm so I knew she'd be in with Nora, and Sandra was, as usual, comatose under her duvet. I stood in front of Ellie's huge mirror with the bedroom door closed.

'Whore,' I jibed at my reflection. 'Not him, *you*. You are a slut.' I took off my T-shirt, quickly glancing behind me to make sure the mound under the duvet still hadn't moved. Satisfied Sandra was still totally was out of it I looked back at the mirror image of the razor blade in my hand. I began pulling it across my chest over and over again. With every cut the anger inside me shrank, not the disgust though, which just grew.

*

Forty-five minutes into my session with Nora, I had covered just about everything. The weekend with the boys at the pub, sitting in Dan's room, the firm meeting.

'You expect this from men,' she said.

'What do you mean, I expect it?'

'You have this opinion of men, that all they want is sex, that it's all you're good for.'

I didn't want to hear any more, I wasn't in the mood for it and so bluntly said, 'I've cut my chest. I did it after firm.'

That changed the thread of the conversation. Nora's calm demeanour quickly melted away, and sternly she said, 'You have to go to your nurse now and tell him. Right now, okay?'

I obediently nodded.

I walked down the hallway by the nurse's office but I couldn't find Derron or anyone else for that matter; the hospital seemed desolate. Annoyingly, and just typical of my luck, Judy poked her head around the staffroom door as I knocked. I stood in the meds room with her and pulled down the neck of my T-shirt. She winced, scrunching up her face.

'Oh Emma. That's horrible.' I tilted my head, exasperated.

'Cheers Judy, that's just what I wanted to hear.'

She ignored me, adding, 'It's superficial though.' I thought of cutting off my arm and wondered how superficial that would be for her. It has always baffled me to hear the word 'superficial' directed at me by certain physicians as they reach for the Steri-Strips. Do they actually think that hearing that is at all helpful? It has always felt more like a dare to me if anything. I left Judy and went back to my room where I stayed for most of the day.

*

It was time for afternoon teas; every day at 4pm both units and all the staff would gather together in the community room for tea and biscuits. As much as I didn't want to go it was frowned upon if you missed out on it, so I started making my way down to the community room. As I began to push open the community room doors I heard someone calling me.

'Emma, wait.' I turned around to see Derron jogging towards me. 'Hi! Sorry, I wanted to tell you that handover got it wrong, it wasn't you in Dan's bedroom, apparently it was Katie in there. I was in Dan's review this afternoon and he stood up for you saying you shouldn't have been made to feel like a liar when you were telling the truth. And, I just saw Petrice and asked her and she said it wasn't you. So everyone knows the truth now!' He was smiling at me sympathetically. 'I'll come to teas with you,' he said, holding open the door for me. As I walked through he added, 'I think it's good you're forming a friendship with Dan. And I'm glad everyone knows you weren't lying.' I looked at the floor, the wounds on my chest stinging under my clothes. Redemption, but too late.

*

As I shovelled salad into my mouth sitting alone in the kitchen that night, Judy parked herself in front of me.

'We must stop meeting like this,' I said as I stabbed another lettuce leaf onto my fork, looking up just in time to see her sarcastic smile. 'Shouldn't you be gone by now, Judy?' I noticed she had her coat in her hand and wondered why she'd stopped to see me.

'Dan told us it wasn't you in his room and Katie confirmed it was her.'

I wiped my mouth with my napkin. 'So I heard.' I looked at her. 'Do you hate me, Judy?'

She cocked her head to the side. 'No, Emma, I don't hate you. But I'm keeping my eye on you.'

'Goody,' I said as I stood up, walking out of the kitchen. Heading back up to my room I wondered why I found myself silently seeking her approval.

*

It was the next morning and I was sitting in group therapy, no one speaking as usual. Ellie, true to form, walked out after five minutes muttering 'Fuckin' freaks', slamming the door behind her. After thirty-five minutes of silence I gave up on being asked how I was and asked Dan how his review the previous day had been. He was reluctant to talk about it at first, but I managed to coax it out of him, and aided by my encouragement he spoke openly for half an hour about how he felt the whole thing had gone. At 3:20 I decided to steal the last ten minutes. I hadn't yet spoken about myself in group and ten minutes seemed like just the right amount of time to allocate for my first confession. I took a deep breath.

'I had a bad day yesterday.' Dan asked why. 'Being made to feel like a liar in firm, in front of everyone, and what's more not only made to feel like a liar but like some kind of slut; it upset me. My

247

weekend had basically been more of the same, being made to feel like some kind of whore… The combination was just too much. And…' I didn't want to say it, but I needed to tell them, I needed to tell Dan. 'I cut. A lot. I cut my chest.' Silence. Confession met with silence. Three minutes slowly ticked by on the clock.

Mr Newman looked over at me clearing his throat. 'It must make you feel very shut down and vulnerable, Emma, that no one is responding.' I bored holes in Sandra's expressionless face; she was blank, listless. I looked at Dan as he bored his own holes into the floor; he looked furious, or upset, some variation of an expression I couldn't quite make out. 'This is your first time really sharing anything in group, so I would think this feels very difficult,' said Johanna as she stared hopefully at Sandra and Dan. Nothing. I did feel vulnerable, and exposed, so not knowing what else to do I began ranting.

'No one ever responds. People don't know what to say to me. No one can help me apart from myself, so why talk about it? It's unfair on everyone else. I should have kept my mouth shut.' Another minute of silence. You'll never experience the feeling of time stretching out in front of you like a never-ending landscape of doom as you do in therapy. Dead silence in a room full of people feels deeply unnatural, it makes every second tick by like an hour, every moment feeling more agonising then the last. It was 3:27. I didn't want to find out if no one was going to say anything in the next three minutes, I couldn't bear the feeling of rejection, so got up and walked out. I climbed down the stairs slowly, listening for the group door, hoping Dan would come after me, or even Johanna or Mr Newman, but it remained shut.

As I reached the kitchen I heard someone screaming, the wailing shooting up the walls and down the corridors. I didn't want to know, I went to my room, got my bag and left. I sat in Starbucks terrified that Dan hated me because of what I'd done, which in turn just made me want to cut myself again.

It had only been a short while, but my feelings for him were giant and all-consuming. I had never met someone like Dan before, he was a live wire that could catch fire at any second and his energy, his pain, in turn, lit a fire in me. I sat there staring at my hundred-calorie coffee trying to self-soothe and calm down; cutting again would be completely counterproductive and if he wasn't pissed off with me already for self-harming, he would be if I did it a second time. It was the frustration of it all – I felt like a worm on a hook, wriggling to get away, knowing it was my own greediness that had got me stuck on there in the first place. And the worst thing? The horrible twisted truth was that I had wanted Petrice to see me in his room. Perhaps because that would have made it real – I just hadn't wanted her to tell anyone.

As I sat in the coffee shop lost in my own thoughts I felt someone come up behind me. Before I could turn around I heard, 'Boo!' Katie sat down next to me. 'Did I make you jump, wee Em?'

'Yes. What are you doing here?'

'Well, two things. I knew you'd be here because you are deeply predictable,' she chuckled to herself licking the cream off the top of the drink she'd bought on her way in, 'and Sandra said you were upset in group; people were worried so I wanted to make sure you were okay.' She took another lick of cream.

'And two?' I said impatiently.

'And two, I have a date! But you can't tell anyone, Judy would freak! I'm sorry I wasn't in firm, I would have told them it was me in Dan's room and not you.' She took a glug of her drink. 'I was only in there nattering by the way, I couldn't sleep and Dan's always up for a chat.' Katie stayed and talked to me for a while before skipping off to her secret date. As much as she drove me mad sometimes I really appreciated that she would always come and find me when I needed a friend.

*

249

After a few hours more of trying to give myself a reality check, I stealthily got back to my room in the Caddick without being seen by anyone, and as I sat under my duvet reading, my phone rang. It was Dan. Seconds after I told him where I was he appeared in the doorway. 'Can I come in?' he tentatively asked. I sat up and nodded. He perched on the edge of the bed. 'Are you okay, Em?' Before I could answer a shrill, bloodthirsty scream escaped from Katie's bedroom, but it wasn't her, it was Angela. We heard her smashing things and shouting as people began to rush into the room. Here we go again. Dan's eyes flashed wide and excited and much to my surprise he whispered, 'We should get out of here.' He stood up and held out his hand. I bit my lip, worried we'd get in trouble. 'C'mon, pet,' he said again. I took his hand and within twenty minutes we were sitting in a beer garden in town far away from the storm that was raging inside the Caddick's walls.

As we talked, the week's events kept catching up with me. I was happy to be with him but I kept feeling overwhelmed; it was coming over me in waves of anxiety. I put my face in my hands. 'Why do you do that, Emma? Cover your face all the time?' I groaned into my palms.

'Because it's rank, Dan.'

I didn't look up but could visualise his face as he said, 'Stop it.'

We got back to the hospital at 10pm, sneaking in unseen as if we'd been there the whole time to stand in the queue with everyone else and wait for meds. As I sat cross-legged on the floor flicking Dan's leg like a thirteen-year-old girl who doesn't know how to flirt, Adaline stepped over me to the window where Nurse Brian was handing out pills. She had on pyjamas with a T-shirt and no shoes. I couldn't help but gawp as I peered at her mutilated anorexic feet; they were cut to shreds. She was like a skeleton and I wondered how she could actually cut herself that deeply without hitting bone. Usually Adaline would wear slippers so I couldn't help but wonder if this was intended as a show for everyone.

'Emma.' I stood up taking the tablets Brian gave to me, swallowing them with water in front of him. Dan and I were told that the screaming we had heard before had signalled Angela having taken an overdose of paracetamol and cutting herself deeply enough to warrant stitches. It had taken the staff this long to calm her down and she needed to go to A&E to get patched up. Dan was asked to accompany her with a couple of nurses.

I sat patiently in the alcove as I waited the three hours for him to get back, Katie at my side going on about the effect Angela's breakdown had had on her. 'I mean, there is blood all over the fecking room. I've put the sheets in the wash but Jesus, I'm not a housekeeper! I come back from my date all happy, walk in to my bedroom and that's what I find! Imagine that, slicing open your fecking arms all over someone else's things, disgusting! I hope I don't catch anything!'

At midnight Dan came through the door and I soon found myself sitting in the kitchen with him, Angela, and her bandaged wrists. It was the first time she and I had spoken since I'd been there – I had just started to assume she hated me, but tonight she seemed warmer, so I jumped at the chance to make her some toast when she asked. Katie came in and we all sat together talking around the table. Katie joking about me and Dan being 'an item' as Angela ate her toast. Dan and I spent the time winding each other up, putting on a little show for our fellow patients.

'Dan, pass the milk,' I asked him, to which he'd reply, 'Can you just stop coming on to me Emma!' I rolled my eyes, 'I'm not coming onto you, I'm all whored out for the day.' He'd do a mock frustration tone, 'Jesus, just stop flirting with me!' They all laughed, and I couldn't help but smile with them and play along.

A little later and Dan and I were alone again sitting on the smokers' steps in the garden. Suddenly and without explanation his mood changed; one moment he was fine, the next he became shut down and cold. I kept talking regardless of the change in atmosphere, trying again and again to engage him before resorting to deliberately trying to annoy him, poking at him and asking inane questions. He didn't react and so, starting to feel a little redundant, I playfully said, 'Am I annoying you yet?' He looked at me, dark pupils swallowing his green irises and said, 'Do you think anything would change if I was angry with you?' I shrugged nervously like a child who has been pulling at a dog's tail for hours only to have the dog suddenly snap. He was almost shouting. 'Nothing would change between us. If I was angry with you I wouldn't stop talking to you, *do you know that*? It doesn't change anything.' It was a sentence I didn't know I needed to hear.

'I want to tell you something,' he said, calmer, lighting another cigarette, looking into the night that was laid out in front of us. 'When I was in A&E with Angela, all I wanted was to be with you. I didn't want to say this to you because I don't want to sound obsessive.' He must have seen the look of worry flash across my face because he went on to say, 'It's nothing manipulative you've done to me, it's nothing bad. I just really like being with you, near you. I can't stop thinking about you, Emma.' Oh God. Help me I'm drowning. Someone pull me out before I'm under forever.

28

PRUE

"In keeping silent about evil, in burying it so deep within us that no sign of it appears on the surface, we are implanting it, and it will rise up a thousand fold in the future."

— ALEKSANDR SOLZHENITSYN,
The Gulag Archipelago 1918–1956

The Caddick, unlike the Henshaw, liked to arrange day trips out for everyone. These types of group outings, whether I was fourteen or twenty-three, brought out the naughty child in me, and I couldn't help but play up whilst on them. It had been three days since Sylvia had finished her treatment and left the hospital. I had barely uttered a word to her and wasn't bothered by her leaving at all but the staff obviously wanted to give the people who had been living with her for the best part of a year a distraction. Added to that, there was a new patient, which always caused a bit of a disruption to everyone's routine. Aaron, the boy who had been with me on my day visit, had turned sixteen and was the latest person to be admitted to the ESPD unit.

We arrived at the Tate Modern on a Wednesday morning,

six staff and most of the ESPD. After an hour of getting frustrated with modern art I wanted to leave, as did Prue and Dan. Prue never left the hospital and it was proving too much for her being out in such a busy, public place. Dan and I offered to take her back to the hospital, not before assuring the staff we would go straight there making no stops along the way. We got on the train at Waterloo headed for the Caddick, but as we neared our stop, I realised something was wrong with Prue. She was anxious, hypervigilant the whole train ride, jumping at the slightest noise and looking around as if she suspected someone was following us. She kept jumbling up her words and falling over her own sentences. Alarm bells started ringing for me and sure enough as we walked back into the hospital she began to fall apart. I sat with her in her room as she screamed, and screamed, and screamed. After the screaming fits she would start trying to strangle herself, wrapping her own hands, or any clothes she could find around her throat and attempting to make a ligature with them, I'd shout her name trying to get her to stop but she was completely dissociated; it was as if she wasn't even there – I had never seen anything like it. But something in me took over and I stayed with her throughout.

Nurses came in and out trying to help, but her screaming would get worse with every new face; for some reason she could tolerate me being there with her. I wrapped my arms around her as she rocked and mumbled about things I didn't understand and more to the point wasn't sure if I wanted to. Dan sat next to us, quiet, at arm's reach, offering me a reassuring smile when I needed it. Every few minutes Prue would try to get up and I would pull her back down with all my might, not wanting her to get to the bathroom and be able to lock the door. The staff could easily unlock it but who knows what she could do to herself in the time it might take them to get in? It was on the third or fourth time she did this, and as I reached up to grab her, my sleeve slipped down and before I could pull it back up Dan saw a fresh line of raw cuts on my forearm.

*

'Are you angry with me?' I asked, not looking at him as we sat facing each other a few hours later in Starbucks.

'No. I just wish you would talk about it more. It upsets me that you feel you are alone with this. Please talk to Nora at least?'

I nodded, not wanting to lie out loud. He opened another packet of sugar and poured it into his coffee. 'Em, why do you like me?'

I felt the heat rise around my neck as I began to fiddle with my hair. 'Because you're funny. And, you make me happy.'

Arm in arm we walked alongside the river, the gentle hustle and bustle of the town providing our backdrop. He talked about Ashley (the patient who had killed herself), the day she had left the hospital only to go home and never come back. She had told everyone she was fine, she had seemed okay and none of them had suspected a thing. They got a call on the Monday from her brother saying he had found her swinging from her bathroom light fitting; she was nineteen. I stayed quiet, listening, trying not to imagine her dangling there.

Back in his room I sat on the floor as he playfully poked me. 'Why do you think you're ugly?' I buried my face into his bed sheet and groaned. 'You're not ugly.'

'Okay. Thanks, Dan.'

'You're not ugly.'

'Okay, Dan.'

'You're not.'

'*Okay*, Dan.'

He put on a CD by an ex-patient who used to be at the Caddick. Gentle acoustic guitar and a sweet lullaby voice – he talked about her as it played, saying he used to fancy her. My face perhaps gave me away and he quickly said, 'Sorry. Does it upset you when I talk about her?'

I looked at him blankly. 'No, why would it?' He didn't answer as he pressed stop on the player.

*

'They killed her. They killed my baby in front of me.' I looked at Dan, his head was down. As was Katie's, Esther's, Marie's, Ellie's, Aaron's, Adaline's, Kane's, Annie's, and Angela's. Judy caught my eye and gently smiled at me. I felt my whole body, from the inside out tremble. Heat rushed from my toes to the top of my head and I thought I might be sick. Prue's face was blurred through my tear-filled eyes. She had her knees drawn up to her chest, her hood pulled down and was rocking violently back and forth. As her mouth opened to speak again I silently begged her to stop. Please, no more.

'The next day they took me to a warehouse, there was a young boy there. I couldn't see him but I could hear him screaming, screaming from what they were all doing to him. They kept telling me that today was the day they would kill me. They had a knife.' She stopped to gasp for air through her tears. Everyone in the room sat frozen, it was like we were all made of glass and one badly thought out movement could shatter us all. Please no more Prue, please.

'After they had finished with me, I was in the corner of the room with my eyes closed. I heard the boy shout, "Please don't kill me." There was a commotion and then he stopped screaming, and it was silent.' I have never in my life wanted to leave a room as desperately as I did that day. But I couldn't do it to her. Annie had just walked out, followed by Adaline. So I forced myself to sit there. To listen. To stay with her and to be able to bear it. In the space of fifteen minutes I had learned that Prue had been one of the victims of a savage paedophile ring. The most horrendous part was that several people in her family played pivotal roles within the ring, and would take her regularly to be violated. At a very young age she had become pregnant, and those demons (I say demons because what can you call them, they are subhuman, they are beyond animal, or monster) had forced her to give birth and killed the baby in front of her as she floundered helpless and drugged, tied up and held down. To this day, it remains one of the most horrendous, disturbing and heartbreaking stories I have ever heard. The abuse she endured taught me about a depravity in my fellow man that up until that point I truly did not know could exist. How she survived it, I will never know. And the fact that she was here, still alive, still fighting to undo the damage that was done to her was nothing short of a miracle and only served as a testament to how strong she truly was.

But on that particular day, sitting in firm, hearing glimpses of her story for the first time was just too much for me. And when the meeting was drawn to a close, I had lost all ability to function. The horror of what I had heard was a long, unending shrieking in my ears that didn't stop as I left the hospital. Or as I sat in a local shopping centre's toilets and tried to cut some sense back into the shards of my thoughts. After an hour, with flecks of my blood all over the walls and floors, my head was back to something resembling quiet.

Though over the next few days, Prue's story once again grew in sound and momentum inside me; something had been awoken and I lost myself repeatedly in razor blades and toilet stalls trying to quieten the internal noise and imagery that had been catalysed in my mind. I attempted to convince myself that maybe it had all been a lie, that she was just an attention-seeker and had made everything up, but the umpteen court cases she had attended to bring her perpetrators to justice soon quashed that theory for me. It's not that I didn't believe her, I just didn't want to – some things are so awful that it's easier to pretend they aren't real rather than to face the truth that they did go on, and that evil like that really does exist in the world, although most people never have to see or experience it.

*

The following morning I had vanished into town as the sun came up, long before firm. I couldn't face them, any of them. I had sat in the shadows watching Len from the stairs, waiting until he left reception to make a cup of tea, and, hitting the buzzer behind his desk, quietly bolted out of the door. My phone rang a while later and as I answered I heard Alison's shrill voice, 'Emma, where are you? You weren't in firm, what's going on?'

'Coffee shop,' came my weak response.

She sounded annoyed. 'You need to come back, now!'

Every word felt like a tremendous effort for me. 'Can't,' I breathed into the phone and hung up. Twenty minutes later Katie and Ellie appeared and physically had to remove me from my seat. I hadn't even bothered to go into the toilets, I just sat there with my arm on my lap jamming a razor blade into myself. I wasn't making sense, all I wanted was to cut.

'Emma, are you okay?' Ellie had never really shown any concern for me before and I remember thinking it was sweet of her to have made the effort to be part of the 'search and rescue' party. I watched Katie's eyes look down at the blood on the floor.

'Right, we're going. C'mon, wee Em.' She ushered me up, took my hand and guided me back to the Caddick, Ellie trotting beside us in her stiletto heels, her little baby bump starting to show through her tight vest top.

I remained silent as Claire put gauze on my wrist and ended

up still applying it right up to the nape of my neck. 'Oh, Emma. You must talk to someone about all this, we're all here for you, please, please talk to someone.' I could hear her, but as much as I wanted to, I couldn't respond.

Dan avoided me. He seemed angry but I was too catatonic to care. On the fourth day of my leaving the hospital and being dragged back needing bandages, he found me in the kitchen staring out of the window at nothing and put his arm around me.

'Why didn't you call me?'

I shrugged. 'I couldn't, Dan. I'm sorry that I've upset you, made you angry.' I used my sleeve to blot the tears from around my eyes.

'Em, I'm not angry, I promise. It just hurts so much to think of you alone, doing that to yourself. I'm here.' He moved his head down slightly to meet my gaze. 'I'm right here! Please, call me, talk to me.' He wrapped both his arms around me and pulled me into him, and for the first time in days, I let him.

29

THE REVIEW

"They called me mad, and I called them mad,
and damn them, they outvoted me."

— NATHANIEL LEE

The week that followed was better. I spent most of my time with Dan, and we escaped from the walls of the hospital as much as we could. I got to know the real him, not the inpatient, not the mental-health-problems him.

As we sat in a sweet little café up on the hill in town one night, now only two weeks before he was due to leave, he said he wanted to ask me something. I looked at him as he stirred his tea, nervous of what was coming.

'What is it?'

He shook his head as if he had changed his mind. 'Oh nothing.'

'Dan! It's so annoying when people do that!'

He looked genuinely apologetic. 'I'm just not ready to ask.'

As frustrated as I was, I decided to let sleeping dogs lie.

Arriving back at the hospital that night we discovered Marie had run off. She was a thirty-six-year-old ex-psychiatrist who was seemingly sweet-natured but one of the most attention-seeking adults I had ever met. In the short few weeks I had been at the hospital we had been called into three separate meetings as she had told the staff she had taken an 'overdose'. It would always transpire that she had swallowed maybe two diazepam, three at best; often the amount wasn't even enough to be considered a full dose for most people. So, discovering that she had run off wasn't a major concern to anyone, but regardless a few people, including Dan, went to look for her. I sat under the moonlight on the swings, slowly moving back and forth in the breeze. The garden was peaceful, still. Alongside me was the family unit quiet as usual after dark, the only signs of life were a few lights still on in the bedrooms. I looked around, the grounds were so beautiful. It always struck me as deeply ironic that such a stunning place could house such pain and ugliness. I tilted my head back and let my hair fly behind me as I kicked my legs into the air. It was starting to get cold as I saw what I instantly knew was Dan's silhouette in the distance standing at the back door. It didn't take me long to jump off the swings and walk over.

'Did you find Marie?'

'Yeah, she was in Starbucks having a latte,' he said laughing as he lit his cigarette. I sat down, knowing what I was about to step into and continuing all the same.

'So back in the café, what were you going to ask me?'

He cut me off. 'It's not the right time.'

I couldn't help myself as I screeched, 'Dan! This is so fucking annoying, it's making me really anxious!'

He sighed heavily, almost exhaustedly. 'You know what I'm gonna ask anyway, Em.' And there it was, the moment stopped dead, that split second when you know everything is about to change and there is no going back. I suddenly wanted to run away, but it was too late as he stood up smiling a nervous sort of smile and theatrically shouted into the night sky, 'DO YOU HAVE FEELINGS FOR ME?'

Tugging at his leg for him to sit back down I quickly said, 'Yes. You know I do.' He asked why. 'I've told you. There are a lot of reasons. I feel happy when I'm with you, you make me laugh and you're interesting.'

He looked away. 'I'm so attracted to you, Emma. I think you're really sexy.'

We were holding hands, I didn't even remember it happening but I pressed my cold palm against his as I said, 'You drive me crazy carrying on and chatting with the other girls here. Why do you do it?'

'To irritate you.' He paused. 'That's *nothing* compared to how neurotic I get when you're out with Katie.'

'What? Why? I don't fancy her!'

'Because I get pissed off,' he paused and laughed before continuing, 'I want to be the one spending time with you. We've only got ten days left together.' I couldn't believe I was finally hearing the words I hadn't been sure were even real. 'Ten days, Em. What are we going to do? We have to leave each other. We're gonna get hurt.'

'Ten days left in the hospital, Dan, the world is right outside those doors.'

He looked at me again. 'Haven't you noticed I have to leave the room when we're alone sometimes? Don't you wonder why?' I shrugged, confused. 'It's because I can't handle it when we get too close. I worry I won't control myself, I want to touch you, kiss you.' He put his head in his hands, I didn't know if it was embarrassment or frustration, probably both.

'Why don't you then?'

He looked up. 'Why don't I what?'

'Kiss me?'

He laughed. 'Cue Esther to ruin the mood,' and then, sure

enough, she came wandering out of the back door and sat down next to us.

'Hi guys.'

We giggled like naughty schoolchildren as she stared at us baffled.

*

The reality of our confessions had seemed too much for Dan by the next morning and he left for Ireland without saying goodbye to me. I felt incredibly rejected and texted him saying, 'I wanted you to kiss me last night.' He didn't reply.

The weekend dragged, kicking its heels through Saturday and Sunday. Left alone without the constant distraction of Dan, my depression swaddled me as if I were a newborn baby. I didn't eat, I self-harmed and I cried relentlessly like a dog in the pound. By the time Monday rolled around I was virtually pathological. I needed to see him, be near him, touch him. I needed to know where I stood. Nora was right, constant affirmation, constant reassurance. When he finally walked in my heart threatened to leap out of my chest and swallow him whole. It took half an hour for him to approach me and tell me he had missed me. And then, completely out of the blue, he asked, 'Did you self-harm over the weekend?'

Perhaps I should have lied, I'm not sure why I didn't. 'Yeah.' He shook his head as if not wanting to register my words and walked away. I felt my chest crack and threaten to break. Thankfully, modern technology didn't have me longing for more than an hour as he texted me.

'Did you cut because I didn't contact you?'

I suddenly felt like he had been testing me, ignoring me deliberately to see if it would hurt me and then in turn to see what I would do with those feelings; it felt so controlling, how dare he do that to me? Toy with my emotions as if I were some doll he could pick and choose to take off the shelf and play with when it suited him?

'No Dan. I knew that's what you thought. I had a hard weekend, I didn't feel good. It was nothing to do with you.' Lies, of course, but I carried on. 'I wish you had just asked me instead of assuming. I don't regret anything of what I said, I like you, even if your feelings have changed.' I sent the message as I lay in bed and waited for his response. He didn't reply, and I didn't sleep.

*

I didn't have long to dwell on Dan's and my love games as in the morning I had my first review. Ten therapists, four nurses and me. All in a big circle. Absolutely terrifying. You were told to write a summary of yourself and all your issues – listing all your problems and saying what it was you wanted to work on and ultimately what you wanted to get out of therapy – which you then had to read aloud to them – nothing quite like listing all your horrible personality traits and faults down on a piece of paper then reading it to a room full of people. I stayed up the whole night writing my 'self-review'; it read like the world's worst dating profile, single white psycho. Derron came and got me and led me to a big room where everyone was waiting; I sat down surrounded on all sides. Even though I knew most of them, or had at least seen their faces around the building, I was anxiety-ridden and petrified of what was coming. Blind terror took over and something like endorphins began to rush through my body churning their own formula of Valium; everything slowed right down. I went in to LAMDA-exam mode. Relaxed, calm, in my role beautifully. I watched them talking with total detachment, as if I were being forced to watch a film I had little interest in; it felt as though they were dissecting someone else and the whole thing had nothing to do with me.

I read my review with almost perfect eloquence. No mistakes, no stuttering – in hindsight I probably should have at least tried to pretend I was taking the whole thing seriously but it felt so much easier to just joke through it. After I'd finished, Derron read his review about me. This was his first review too, he had only just begun working at the Caddick and he was more nervous than me, stumbling blindly over his words and stopping every so often to wipe the sweat off his forehead. His report was pretty basic but he got excitable in various places talking about drugs and my relationships, as well as referring time and time again to my 'gothic appearance.'

'Nora would you like to read your report?' said Judy; it felt like more of an order than a question. I sat back and breathed deep, worrying what Nora was about to reveal to everyone about me.

'Emma has been at the Caddick for a month now and has attended all sessions. In the first couple of weeks she presented as rather quiet and unassuming as though wishing to just blend into the background and not be noticed. Her style of dress and make-up...' Oh here we go, go on then, tell them all why I dress like this – it's going to be some cry for help isn't it? '... her many hidden tattoos and piercings on her skin are likely to have several meanings but one of which may simply be to act as a thin barrier between the external world where she can present as quite ordinary and her internal one, in which she can feel extremely disturbed and distressed. She is very preoccupied with what can be seen and known about and what must remain hidden and guarded. I have wondered whether the stairs and corridor to my consulting room, like her tattoos, also act as a boundary between the community public life downstairs and the more intimate and individual approach of her sessions, which at the moment, she says she prefers.'

Oh God, talk about diving right in. I needed this to stop, it already felt too exposing and she'd hardly started. I didn't want to let on though, so sat perfectly still with a smile on my face that suggested I was *absolutely fine* with everything that was going on. Nora kept reading.

'She is aware she is currently developing and forming a more trusting relationship with me whilst also forming a similar exclusive relationship with a male patient in the community.' I gritted my teeth and continued to smile though I felt Judy turn to look at me at that point. Please Nora, don't say anything else, don't give away my secrets. She carried on for some time talking about my attitude to my 'perceived' vulnerability and that I would become 'horrified' in sessions if I felt myself becoming upset or emotional – she said I'd go into a 'detached and withdrawn state' in those moments. I craved to know what Nora thought of me, I wanted to take in everything she was saying and really break it down in my mind, be able to work with it – but being in this room, with all of them, I felt like my clothes were being torn off layer by layer until I would eventually find myself sitting there naked. Yet for some reason, I couldn't drop the facade. I couldn't let them see that I was being affected by any of this. I sat there wondering why I couldn't just let them in; was I (as Nora repeatedly said) terrified of showing any vulnerability?

'In this more detached state of mind she can be very observant of me and voice any gesture that may indicate in her mind I am distracted, bored or uninterested in her. On the one hand I think she wants me to know what it feels like to be scrutinised, exposed, and to know something about humiliation, whilst on the other hand I think she is letting me know about an extreme underlying fragility regarding her sense of existence. I think she feels herself to be so insignificant and worries I can't keep her in mind. In recent sessions this has been somewhat validated when she has become preoccupied with separations, losses, deaths and impending deaths of people and her dog, whom she loved. The fear of a loss of something valued feels absolutely catastrophic to her, as though her own psychological existence can be so easily annihilated.'

I really didn't want to talk about annihilating my psychological existence, in fact, actually I think, *'Job done,'* I was feeling pretty annihilated. Thankfully she soon came to the end of her report. Judy looked at Mr Newman asking him to read his next. *Oh God, was this ever going to end?* Mr Newman began, 'I think I'd like to follow on from that actually – as it would seem Nora and I draw some parallels there.'

'Please, I'd like to hear your input,' said Nora.

Oh, great, don't worry about me then guys, you just fucking carry on, God forbid we stop if Nora wants to hear your fucking input...

'Yes, in group I've found that Emma seems to hold a very strong view of herself as harbouring something bad and corrupting...' I groaned internally, 'even when she has been able to describe this and has to a degree felt understood, this belief cannot be shaken. We have seen instances of when self-exposure has left her feeling enormously vulnerable to these feelings, completely isolated, and she has then needed to get out of the room, and even the hospital.' *Which is exactly what I was planning, you've hit the nail on the head there, Mr Newman old chap*, I thought to myself. The second this was over I was out of there and they wouldn't be seeing me again all day if I could help it.

When Mr Newman had finally finished I assumed that was it, then came *bloody* Selena's report, the dance teacher. Things like, 'Emma feels the games we play in dance drama are childish and does not want to revert back to being a child. Emma is adamant that she won't join in, but apologetic about it.' She wasn't as stupid as I thought she was. I absolutely loathed dance therapy, it was a horrific beast conjured from my worst nightmares. Selena was the bright-eyed, bushy-tailed, slim, attractive dance therapist. Her most favourite activity for us to do was the parachute game – give me strength. We would be given a big obnoxious multicoloured parachute and would have to hold it all around the edges and throw it up and down in the air so it inflated and deflated, eventually climaxing in it being thrown up in the air and they (Dan, Sandra, Aaron or Ellie) would crawl under it and lie down. They'd lie there for ages, with Selena sauntering around teaching them ways to be 'peaceful and mindful' or whatever the fuck she was doing. She was all about connecting with your body, I was all about destroying mine. It was a match made in hell. I honestly felt at times that the whole dance drama thing was just some ploy to break me. I would never, ever engage. I sat as far as I could from them all playing on my phone and giving Selena looks of absolute disgust if she suggested I join in. Dan even irritated me in these sessions, flouncing about, seeming to enjoy it. I usually left dance drama wanting to self-harm, and often would. It stirred up something so deeply unpleasant in me every time I was forced to attend and would stick to me like glue for days afterwards. Selena kept reading her report, I smiled sweetly at her imagining the sound of her head exploding as I slammed her against a concrete wall. Mr Newman broke through my thoughts with his reassuring, calm voice.

'I wouldn't take Emma at face value right now. She gives the impression of being detached but she's actually incredibly tuned in and listening to everything that's being said.' My expression didn't change but I felt almost like someone in the room knew me.

Nora added, 'Yes, Emma does this in her sessions, she likes to appear as though she is taking everything in her stride, but it's not the case.'

When I was finally told the review was over, I jumped up as if escaping from an ill-advised one-night stand's bed.

I hid in Starbucks all afternoon scribbling in my diary about what had transpired in the review, necking back coffee and dreading having to return for group a few hours later. When I eventually returned, over-caffeinated and enthused, I was told Sandra had been sent home to think about whether or not she actually wanted to be in treatment. She hadn't gotten out of bed for the last week and had missed every group session, dance drama, and her individual sessions. Ellie had gone back to Yorkshire for her monthly chaperoned visit with her birth mother and Aaron wasn't feeling well so had stayed in his room. So group basically turned into couples counselling with Dan and me. We both snapped and shouted at each other, I was pissed off that he'd seemingly been testing me by not contacting me while he'd been in Ireland and he was simultaneously annoyed that I'd self-harmed.

Mr Newman and Johanna looked like two people who had been brought into the cinema at the end of the film, confusion scrawled on their faces as they tried to work out what was happening. Finally Johanna, exasperated, said, 'What is going on? Why are you being so aggressive with each other?' The hostility was unbearable. He kept going on and on about me not telling anyone other than him that I'd cut so he had to 'carry it' on his own.

'I mean, how do you think that makes me feel? Knowing you're walking around with your fucking arms ripped open, and no one else knows? Can I go and tell someone – NO! Because then I'm betraying you! Will you talk to me about it? NO! Even though I tell you to all the time, so what the fuck am I supposed to do?' There was a pause until he continued. 'I'll tell you all what, something that will make this really simple for EVERYONE, when I leave this hospital that will be that, I'm done. Done with all of you. I'll walk out that door and none of you will hear from me again.'

It was at that point I lost my cool completely and my voice, which had been fairly level, began to boom across the room. 'I hope you understand how fucking scary and hurtful it is to have someone saying that the minute they walk out the door that's it. That we won't see you again, or hear from you. That *I* won't hear from you. It's fucking awful, Dan, what the fuck is wrong with you to say that? Seriously, tell me, what is wrong with you?'

He looked at the floor with his tail between his legs. Neither Dan nor Johanna nor Mr Newman had seen me get angry or upset like that and they all seemed a little taken aback. I started to cry angry, helpless tears. It was horrible. A horrible hour. It had all been made that much worse by the fact that a few nights before he'd left for Ireland, Dan had sent me a message saying, 'I think some part of you wants me to reject you and I can't do that', so his speech in group completely contradicted that, which felt like him rubbing salt in the wound – it was as if he wanted to get a strong reaction out of me, to watch me erupt, and for there to be a huge catastrophic fall out but I didn't really understand why. It was like he was pulling me in with one hand and pushing me away with the other, and it was incredibly confusing. I probably did want some part of him to reject me, to just turn his back and go; it would prove that I was worthless, prove that I was dispensable and prove that I truly did mean nothing to him.

*

The next morning, true to form, Dan was buzzing around me again. He was a roller coaster, up then down, round and round, and I was starting to struggle to know where I stood. I had opted to miss the community meeting and instead spend a couple of hours getting ready and trying to make myself look decent.

I went to my session with Nora and talked to her about how frustrating I was finding the whole relationship with Dan, and that I couldn't keep up. She said she felt there was a mother/child scenario going on with Dan and me, and that I should just talk to him about my feelings, rather than brushing everything under the carpet.

'Have you actually just asked him, Emma?'

I looked at her baffled. 'Asked him what?'

I was sure I saw a tiny smile at the corner of her mouth. 'Asked him why he is behaving like this? Maybe if you just laid your cards on the table and were honest with Dan, told him how his behaviour is affecting you, you will be able to find a solution with him and move forward.'

I felt like the village idiot. Such an obvious answer – just talk to him.

So later that night as Dan and I sat in the garden on the swings I told him I had found his behaviour confusing and hurtful. The honesty, as Nora predicted, seemed to do something positive and he apologised, saying that he had just been struggling, fraught with worry about leaving the hospital and in turn, leaving me. So, thankfully, through following her advice, we were back to our usual selves by late evening.

30

FAT BITCH

"THE EDGE, there is no honest way to explain it because the only people who really know where it is are the ones who have gone over."

— *HUNTER S. THOMSON*, Hell's Angel's;
A Strange and Terrible Saga

Thursday brought with it the promise of the weekend, but also, dance therapy. I fought and fought myself and for once stayed throughout the whole session and very begrudgingly managed to join in. Selena put postcards all over the floor and asked us to pick one, so I did, trying to ignore Ellie as she sat on the sofa behind us sniggering. We were supposed to pick two cards. One for mind, one for body. I picked just one card, for mind.

Ellie lay behind me. 'I'm getting fat! I don't want to be fat. Stupid baby!' She prodded at her stomach.

'Ellie, can you pick the next person to speak?' said Selena.

Ellie looked at Sandra, then back at me. 'Emma, how do *you* feel about your body?' She was poking at me, trying to rile me up.

Without looking at her I said, 'I'm not talking about that, I picked this card for my mind…'

After I finished talking Selena loudly proclaimed, 'Emma has only picked one card, we should all acknowledge that Emma doesn't want to talk about *her* body.'

Oh fuck off Selena. And so it began. The beating drum. I sat growing in size and ugliness by the second. Feeling more and more like I was going to cry. More and more *ugly*, the room grew smaller as I just grew.

Lunch came next. Me, eating, disgusting. Hating myself with every mouthful. But if I didn't show face and sit with everyone at least once a day Judy would be on to me. Dan sat opposite Ellie on the next table, I watched with envious eyes as she flirted mercilessly with him. She'd been doing it for a while now; since it became clear to most people that there was something going on between Dan and me, she had honed in. Ellie was used to getting all the male attention and that I was getting Dan's was not sitting well with her at all. Even pregnant, she would try to lure him into sleeping with her, but only ever in front of me.

'Dan, give me a massage, I'm so sore,' or, 'Look how big my boobs have gotten,' she would then heave her huge rack up in his face as he uncomfortably diverted his eyes. I'd brought it up with him, of course; he'd always said she didn't mean a thing and that he wasn't attracted to her. I wanted so much to believe him, but I never could.

*

I sat in the community meeting after lunch in a chair that was too far away from the door, willing myself not to run to the toilet and throw up the couscous and three lettuce leaves I had just consumed. The room filled up to almost full capacity, and that twenty-stone man was back on my chest. I'm not sure how the conversation had got round to it but Prue, Kane and Annie began talking, crying, shouting and hollering about sexual abuse, and then genital self-harm. It was something I had never put a label to; though I cut my chest, I had never self-harmed *down there*. But as I was to reluctantly learn in that room, it was quite a common practice. I heard the sort of stories that make the hairs on the back of your neck stand up, and although some part of me knew cutting, burning and bruising my skin was wrong, actually putting a knife up inside you seemed like a whole different ball game and one that, at the time, I would have been happier not knowing existed. I began to feel like I was going to faint as one of the women described a time when she had 'lost' a razor blade 'up inside' her…

'Every time I tried to reach up and find it, the razor would slash my fingertips and I'd just end up accidentally pushing it further inside, I had to get it surgically removed in the end.'

The walls were moving, swaying back and forth like I was on a ship; was I going to vomit? I definitely felt like I may be about to throw up. The blood was draining from my body as the wretched image of what I'd just heard played on a terrible loop in my head. I'd have left the room if I'd been able to feel my legs. As they stopped to draw breath, I was asked to talk about my review. My voice was shaky and I looked at the floor throughout but I managed to speak and tell them how it had gone, feeling proud of myself for saying anything at all, and sensing that a lot of people in the room were happy of the subject change.

As I stopped talking, Alison's voice thundered across the room, 'You're not saying anything, Emma! You're giving a report on a report. No one here knows you! I don't know you. Who here knows Emma?' She looked around the room expectantly.

Thankfully, and unexpectedly, Judy interrupted her and said, 'It must be terrifying for you having to speak in this room, Emma. I know it was brought up in the review that you get very panicked in large meetings.' Relieved at Judy standing up for me and hoping that this might have been the last word I took a long breath. I couldn't talk any more – I knew they wanted me to, I knew they had more questions, but there was no chance. I sat looking at the floor only to hear Alison start up yet again.

'Do you know how you're coming off right now, Emma?'

I shrugged. 'I don't know.' But I did know: fat, ugly, stupid, childish, grotesque. Again, to my relief some of the other patients butted in, telling her to back off me.

'Leave her alone, Alison, she is still new here and we all know she struggles in these meetings,' said Angela defensively, with Annie adding, 'You have no respect for people. Pick on someone your own size. Emma is doing her best.'

A part of me wanted to rush over and hug them, but the damage was done, done, done.

Alison wasn't giving up though. 'Why do you need to jump to her defence, why can't she speak up?' I wanted to get up and run out of the room, but my whole body was numb.

'Alison, will you just let the girl alone?' said Kane turning as he did to offer me a reassuring smile.

'I don't think we should keep skipping over the issue of Emma not talking.'

'Just leave it, Alison!' shouted Prue.

'So no one here agrees with me?' Alison looked indignant, like she was just pointing out the obvious, and maybe she was, but that was it – enough! Legs or no legs I got up and ran out of the room hearing Alison shout, 'You need to stay!'

No fucking way. The second the door of the community room closed behind me I couldn't breathe. There was no warning this time, I had to grab the wall to steady myself and slowly pulled my body along it until I got to the dining room. I kicked a chair out of my way, then another, then another, not watching as they slammed against the glass windows – some part of me enjoying the loud echoing thud they made. I climbed onto one of the tables and sat cross-legged in the centre of it, tears now streaming down my face. If I moved from that position, even for a second, I knew I would have lost it, kicking a few chairs would have been the least of my problems, it would have been a repeat of the squash room back at the Henshaw.

'What on earth's wrong, sweetheart?' Mena, one of the nurses had followed me out of the meeting. Her gentle tone was soothing, but not soothing enough.

'I'm DISGUSTING.'

She stood in front of me. 'What has brought this on, Emma, was it Alison?'

I shook my head. 'No, well yes her, but... I like someone here. I like them a lot. Him. I like him a lot. But there is another girl trying to get his attention... she's pretty, much prettier than me and thin. And he keeps reassuring me but it's just making me worse.' She spoke with me for some time, all the while keeping up the pretence that she didn't know who I was talking about – when in reality by this point even the cleaners in the hospital knew I was involved with Dan in some way or another. I left Mena, went upstairs and re-did my make-up.

It was a couple of hours later and I was sitting in the alcove with Sandra and Ellie. Whenever it was just women around Ellie she was funny and kind, with a sweetness about her; she sat talking and joking with Sandra and me. All the feelings of anger and jealousy I had that revolved around her melted away and she seemed like any normal girl. A few minutes later Dan came in and suddenly, dramatically, the atmosphere changed, Ellie changed.

'I want to go clubbing!' she said getting up, and before any of us knew what was happening she turned off the lights, put on dance music and began to grind the floor, her small, pregnant belly flopping out of her little pink top. 'Come and dance with me Dan?' she called, rubbing her hands seductively over her chest.

'No thanks Ellie,' he said smiling awkwardly. Ellie reached into her bag that was next to the sofa and pulled out a banana. She peeled it and put it in her mouth, staring at Dan as she did. She began to lick it, suck it and giggle to herself – I felt like my eyes were going to bulge out of my head. What the hell was this, what was I watching? I glanced at Sandra who looked as disturbed as I was. I didn't know how to make it stop, what to say or do. So I didn't say anything, instead I got up, disgusted and uncomfortable, and went and found Katie. I begged her to go and get coffee with me; she agreed, happy to get out of the hospital.

As we stood at the bus stop she began saying she was in terrible pain and needed to go to A&E. She had been fine just a few minutes before, drinking her macchiato and eating chocolate cake, but now I was worried. I put my arm around her. 'What's wrong Katie? What's going on?' She wouldn't answer.

'I have to lie down on the pavement!' she said, steadying herself on a nearby lamp post.

'Katie, there's a bench just there.' I pointed literally four feet away from us but she shook her head.

'No.' She crumpled onto the floor and lay face down on the cold pavement in the middle of rush hour, various members of the public around us growing more and more concerned by the second. I asked her what was wrong again – to which she couldn't give me an answer – just groaned – I asked if she would like me to get us a taxi back to the hospital, she refused.

'Katie, do you need an ambulance?' She shook her head again and, kneeling now, she began to howl in pain. I was mortified, maybe I shouldn't have been, but I was. I was happy to help but she didn't seem to want help, she just wanted to scream and shout and make a huge show of us in the middle of town. I was completely exhausted by her when we eventually got back to the hospital an hour later. As we stood outside with everyone in the smoking area she was laughing, joking, chain-smoking and chugging Diet Coke as if nothing had happened.

'So you're absolutely okay now?' I asked her, feeling irritated.

'Sure Em, must have been a passing thing!' She threw her head back cackling at the joke that had just been told. As much as I liked Katie I couldn't help but feel that the whole episode had been some weird grab for attention; it was clear she was absolutely fine now. I felt the frustration start to simmer in my gut. I tried to focus and listen to what the people around me were talking about but the anger was growing inside me. Why was it okay for Katie to have behaved like that when we were alone? To have put me through the emotional ringer for apparently no reason at all? I felt overwhelmed, like I was going to burst in to tears, so before anyone could notice I turned and ran up to my room.

As I pushed open my bedroom door I heard a soft voice behind me, 'What's wrong honey?' Prue had followed me. I couldn't keep it in any more, the secrecy and the feelings were killing me, so I told her about Dan, about my feelings for him and finally about Ellie's behaviour. 'Oh honey, Dan wouldn't touch her in a million years!'

'How do you know? She's really pretty...' I trailed off, wiping my eyes with my sleeve.

'Ellie's got a lot of issues and as much as I love her she's fucked up when it comes to guys. She doesn't want him, Emma, it's just a ploy to irritate you, and he certainly doesn't want her.' Prue got up to leave, exhaling loudly. 'I shouldn't tell you this...' she paused, 'but Dan has told me how much he likes spending time with you. That he loves the attention you give him, loves being with you. His feelings for you are mutual, Emma, so please, try not to be upset.' She smiled affectionately at me and left the room. With Prue's words now safely in my head my tears promptly dried up, and smiling again, I grabbed a tissue and blotted the smudged mascara from around my eyes. As I made my way back down the staircase Dan was standing at the bottom, a look of relief on his face when he saw me. 'I was coming to look for you,' he said racing up the stairs and hugging me before I could answer. And round and round we go.

*

Within the hour I was once again out of the Caddick and at the local corner shop with Dan. 'Do you want anything, pet?' he said paying for the cigarettes he had just bought. I shook my head. 'Kinder egg?' He held up the chocolate egg as he laughed.

'No thanks!'

'You haven't had dinner though… or breakfast… What have you had today?'

I huffed, 'Dan just buy the fags and let's go!' The shopkeeper held out his hand and Dan gave him the money.

As we headed back to the hospital, the cool night air felt comforting against my skin. It had been such a bad day, and finally it felt like it was calming down; maybe we could actually have a nice night together after all. As we began to cross the road a car slowed down alongside us; there were two men in the front, the one closer to us wound down his window. I thought they were going to ask us for directions, but instead the man in the passenger seat leaned his head out of the window and staring at me, a grin across his face, shouted, 'FAT BITCH!'

Oh no. No, no, no, no, no. Anything but that. Anything. The men roared with laughter as the car sped off.

'What the fuck was that?' shouted Dan after the car. My eyes started fill up again for what felt like the twentieth time that day. He tried to hug me but I pushed him away.

'Don't.'

'Pet, please, come here.'

I pushed him away again. 'Please, don't touch me. Well, now I can cut I guess! Guilt-free!'

'No, Em.'

But I wasn't there, I was in the back seat of that car. *Fat bitch, fat bitch, fat bitch.* As we got back to the hospital I raced upstairs, got my hidden blades from under my matress and locked myself in the bathroom. EVERYTHING DISAPPEARED FOR AN HOUR. Aggressive, angry, punishing cutting. They wouldn't have screamed that at Ellie and she was fucking pregnant! She was still slimmer than me at three months gone! As the minutes flicked past alongside the backdrop of my repeatedly slashing at my skin with the razorblade, I began to see the man in the car as some sort of prophet; after all, he wouldn't have said it if it wasn't true. I repeated this line to myself for what seemed like forever, kneeling on the floor with my arm hanging over the white porcelain as it quickly turned red. 'He wouldn't have said it if it wasn't true.' Drip. 'He wouldn't have said it if it wasn't true.' Drip, drip.

Although I could hear Dan calling my name outside the door, I didn't answer. I'd hear him and think, *Just one more cut and then I'll unlock it.* But the truth of it was that there wasn't a patch of uncut skin left on my forearm. I was cutting into cuts, the deep carmine gashes lining my pale skin like crimson paint on a white canvas. I was only a spectator here, moving in and out of my body and mind as if I belonged to neither, the tether between real and imaginary was as tenuous as it had ever been. It was like watching a film, total disengagement; I couldn't feel the blade, I couldn't control the action, and I couldn't have cared less how it ended. The sound of Dan's voice eventually faded away and was replaced by a different one that took me a moment to place.

'Honey, please let me in?' It was Prue. I don't know how long she pleaded with me to open the door, but eventually it worked. She came in, carefully shutting it behind her and crouching on the floor next to me. I had rolled down the sleeves of my hoodie but the blood was still gushing down in between my fingers, staining the tiled floor. 'Can you show me what you've done?' she asked trying to keep her poker face as she glanced over the bucket spill of blood in the bath.

'No.' It was the first time I'd heard my voice in what felt like hours.

'What happened Emma? Dan wouldn't tell us.' My heartbeat softened at hearing that. *Thank you, Dan.* Not looking away from the white chrome in front of me, I told her. She began to cry, though I got the distinct impression it was for a memory of her own. It took some persuading but Prue walked me to the nurse's office where Claire bandaged my arm. I was coming around, ever so slowly. Claire kept asking what had happened, I told her someone shouted something at me, but wouldn't tell her what. You see, logic dictated that if I didn't tell them they might remain under the spell of not seeing me for what I was. I truly thought that if I told them someone had called me fat that I would lift the veil, break the spell, and they would see it too, if they didn't already.

I went downstairs a little after 2am, eyes bright red, face blotchy, once again smeared mascara down my cheeks. Dan and Sandra were in the kitchen making a cake for some bizarre reason. I sat on the work counter and watched, hiding my bandaged arm as best I could. Dan wouldn't leave my side; he kept finding excuses to touch me, a reassuring hand on my leg, a squeeze of my shoulder. As Sandra pulled the cake out of the oven Dan ordered me up to bed. I refused to go. 'I'm not tired.' He grabbed me and hugged me. 'You are so! You need some sleep pet, go on.'

The next morning after two hours of sleep I was a wreck, though of course I managed to wash my hair and put on my make-up. Despite my emotional and physical exhaustion I had a productive session with Nora. We talked about the events of the last few days, and about my weight loss over the last year.

She said it had been so quick that the mental hadn't caught up with the physical, that my image of myself was still 'completely distorted'. She also said something needed to be said about Ellie's behaviour. 'It's deeply inappropriate and unhealthy for everyone, including Ellie, and I will be bringing it up in the staff meeting later on.' Though I didn't agree with Nora about my apparently 'distorted image' (unless I was actually morbidly obese instead of just obese?) I was glad to hear she thought Ellie's behaviour warranted flagging up, and felt better that I had told someone, and moreover that something was hopefully going to be done.

*

Friday crept up like an unwelcome gift. I cried when I woke up, but other than that my mood seemed to stabilise itself – aided in its improvement by Dan and me flirting for the majority of the day. At 1pm I crept out of the hospital to go and see my tattooist, Jim. He was a six-foot, twenty-stone South African guy who was tattooed from head to toe. When I watched Jim with other clients he was brash and straight to the point, but whenever he was working on me his demeanour changed; he was soft, calm, gentle. I had met Jim a couple of years earlier and he'd been doing all my artwork since. I felt safe with him and he often felt like more of a friend than someone I was paying. I got the words 'I carry your heart' written in script on the left side of my chest. It was 5 December, the anniversary of my dog's death, and I wanted to honour her memory and to prove I hadn't forgotten her. Jim retouched the swallow on my wrist and told me he wanted to do a big piece on my arm for free – for his portfolio. I said I'd think about it, knowing already what my answer was. One more thing to hide from the hospital staff, how hard could it be?

31

FINAL WHISTLE

"You have to crawl into your wounds to discover where your fears are. Once the bleeding starts, the cleansing can begin."

— TORI AMOS

An hour later I was in a pub with Ben and Dan. They consumed jug after jug of some awful-looking blue cocktail and Ben (who had been told he would be discharged from the hospital should they find him gambling again) showed me how to play the fruit machines. Back at the hospital I watched them play pool in the games room, trying not to laugh too much as Laura stormed in screaming at Ben for being drunk. Hearing the commotion, Ellie's head poked around one of the wooden doors. Her eyes immediately fixed on me 'I thought *you* were going home for the weekend.'

I tried not to smirk at her blatant annoyance, 'I was, but I stayed.'

She made a little 'humph' noise, smiled sweetly at Dan, stuck her tongue out at me and left.

At 8pm Dan and I felt 'restless leg syndrome' kick in and we left the hospital again. Len was on reception and glared at

STORM IN A TEA CUP

us as we said we were going out; he tried to protest, refusing to buzz open the doors, but thankfully enough one of the staff was walking back in from a cigarette break, so we took the opportunity and escaped as she came in.

We found a quiet pub by the river and sat in a dark corner out of the way. A girl came by selling roses; she stopped in front of us. 'Would you like one?' Her smile was met with my abrupt 'No thanks', but Dan was on his feet reaching into his pocket. He bought me a plump red rose and although I felt the whole world stop and stare at me thinking I was not worthy, some part of me, some cynical part, softened. I clung to my beautiful rose and held his hand tighter under the table. As I began to feel like a normal girl, on a normal date, Dan's phone rang. It was the duty staff at the Caddick telling Dan he needed to be back. No one knew I was with him; they all thought I had gone home for the weekend. He laughed about his misbehaviour while he walked me to the bus stop.

'Why don't you come back with me?' he said.

'Because they'll tell us off, and I'll get whore-gated again, the terrible slut who made Dan stay out "all night"… I'm gonna go see my friends.' He huffed, disappointed.

It was standing there, waiting for the bus, that I felt it begin. Time slowed down to a heavy beat. His breath and his body, moving in, as my body in turn went stiff. He started laughing, I smiled nervously. I looked away from him, trying to delay what I knew was happening. I pulled back.

'I'm sorry… I'm a pain in the arse, Dan.'

He pulled me into him as he said, 'You aren't.'

His eyes burned into mine for a few seconds and then he did it, he kissed me. And kissed me. And kissed me. I rose up, out of the scene, and floated away.

*

Saturday and Sunday away from the hospital dragged, brought back into real time only for a moment when I got a text from Dan which said, 'When are you coming back? Missing you loads.'

I almost ran to the train station. I envisaged me running back into his open arms and being embraced by a long, lingering kiss. The reality was me sloping back into the hospital and perching opposite him on an armchair in the alcove, answering other patients as they asked me how my weekend had been. He looked ridiculously handsome, strumming on a guitar and giving me the occasional knowing smile. It was driving me mad: look but don't touch. At 4pm everyone began to move into the community room for afternoon tea, and the second the last of them disappeared through the doors, we were all over each other.

That night we sat alone in the TV room, wrapped around one another watching a film. Before we could untangle ourselves the door creaked open and the duty staff came in doing their night rounds; it was too late to move and they didn't seem to care, so we stayed there. He was so close to leaving now that I wasn't bothered what Judy or any of the other staff would say; I was protected by his feelings for me and that's all that mattered.

On Dan's last full day the wolves of insanity were baying at my door, but I held it together, the morning slip-sliding past me in a tirade of fake smiles and answers designed to pacify. They did the opposite as nurses forgot their body language and eyes squeezed into angry, black tunnels as over and over again I told them all I was 'fine'.

I censored myself like a professional con woman. Like a liar who believes her own lies. Like *me*. A big smile, which never once gave way to the anger which was bubbling just under the surface of my skin. But no matter how they fired questions, I stood firm in my resolve. *Don't give it away, Emma. Don't say a word. Don't break.*

*

As the sun vanished the December night vastly improved the backdrop of our final evening. Dan had also been frenetic all day, shell-shocked about leaving and going home. Eventually, and thankfully, he calmed down, I calmed down and our last night came good. He gave me a book he'd brought me to write in and presented me with a card; inside it he had written things like 'I feel like I've known you for years' and 'I feel at ease when I'm with you, I'll miss you so much'. It wasn't exactly the declaration of love I had hoped for, but I clung onto it like a life raft.

We sat in the kitchen listening to music. Angela was with us. I put my arms around him and when she looked away he kissed my hand. He went to bed earlier than usual and I stayed up until 2am talking to Petrice about how much I was going to miss him. Petrice I could trust, I knew this because three days previously she had knocked on his door to do checks long after everyone else had gone to bed. I jumped up and scrambled behind the wardrobe and hid. As I sat with Petrice she said, 'I knew you were there, behind the wardrobe. But I would never tell on you. Since you came, Dan has been so happy. I'm glad you're here.' I got up to hug her before going to bed.

In the morning reality began to hit, and Dan resembled a lamb on his way to slaughter. After my session with Nora, I perched outside the hospital on the wall where all the smokers went. I heard someone walking up the path behind me, and then a voice that in its deep Irish familiarity soothed my soul.

'I'm going to miss you so much, Emma.' Dan sat down next to me. 'I want you to come to the station with me to see me off, but I don't want you to come alone. I'd be worried about you afterwards.'

I looked at him. 'Why?'

He lit up his cigarette. 'I wouldn't want you to feel upset and be alone. I'd fret about you.' He gently put his hand on my knee.

'Okay,' I said trying to think of who I could bear to be there with us, 'perhaps Katie should come?' He nodded.

Dan went inside to begin the farewell ritual – saying goodbye to the other patients with a hug or handshake and them telling him how far he had come since they had first met him. Usually everyone was expected to be around for this, but I just couldn't stomach it so I stayed outside sitting on the wall alone.

Katie was happy to come with us, which also pacified the staff who obviously had the same concerns as Dan about me going with him alone.

When we got to town, in true Katie style she announced she was meeting someone and hopped on another train without giving us so much as a second to respond. Dan grabbed my hand with such a force that I jumped.

'Are you okay, Dan?'

He looked ahead as he said, 'For fuck's sake! She was supposed to come with us, I didn't want you to be alone.'

I tried to believe myself as I replied, 'I'll be okay, Dan, I'll be *fine*.' We arrived at platform two, with four minutes stretching out in front of us like a death sentence. I stared at him, my mind, which up until this point had been so full, began emptying of all words.

Two minutes.

He looked at me. 'I'm going to miss you so fucking much, you don't know what you mean to me, Emma, I've not felt, I just don't know how to tell you...'

One minute left. I took his other hand in mine. 'You're only a few hours away; it's not that expensive, I'll come and see you, and you can come here.'

Thirty seconds.

'Be good, Dan. Don't drink too much.'

'Of course not, pet. Will you be good?'

'Yes. It'll be hard, but yes.'

His train pulled in. He pulled me in. The word hug is not

287

appropriate here. He held me, he did not hug me. I kissed his lips and when we pulled apart his eyes were glassy. I looked away.

'Go.' I said it as if I were giving him permission. He got on the train. I took a few steps down the platform, wiped my eyes quickly, and held my breath.

Final whistle.

The train pulled out. His face was so full of concern until he spotted me, and that warm, loving smile swept across him as he waved.

I turned around and walked away, my feet feeling as though they each had a brick tied to them, the tears now cascading down my cheeks, the hopelessness already settling in. He said he'd text when he got home.

At ten thirty that night there was still no word. I sat with Laura and Ben on the family unit, hugging baby Sam to my chest and imagining Dan on his journey. The feeling of Sam's little head resting in the groove of my throat was the only thing to bring me any comfort.

'He'll call, Em, don't worry,' Ben said patting me on the shoulder; he paused then added 'Do you want a spliff?'

Laura hit him. 'Ben! Do you want some chocolate is what my idiot boyfriend means?'

I laughed and thanked them. 'No guys, I'm okay.' I genuinely thought if I said it enough it would be true.

*

I lay in a hot bath in the early hours of the morning terrified of my loneliness and wondering how I ever coped in this place without him. It was 3am when I finally found my bed; he still had not contacted me.

*

My eyes fixed on the ceiling at 7am as and Mena stuck her head in our bedroom door. 'Checks' she said softly, looking from Sandra's bed to mine, then in Ellie's direction. I turned over to see Ellie quietly putting her make-up on and reached for my phone. Nothing. I switched off my alarm and went back to sleep. I wasn't going to the community meeting, I wasn't going to any of it. It was Friday; they would be going around the room telling each other their concerns for the weekend. I knew my concerns for myself, I didn't need theirs too.

Finally dragging myself out of bed at twelve, I went shopping. Then I went to my parents' house, put on my five-inch heels, dress, make-up, and staggered to a local pub for Natalie's birthday. Every call I made to Dan went to voicemail.

At 2:30am my phone beeped. 'Hi Em, thanks for your calls, sorry I missed them. Today after my meeting with my CPA I realise that I don't have a fucking clue what I want or need and I'm so scared. Thanks for your letter and present it was lovely. I miss you so much. I'll call you tomorrow for a wee chat.'

Tomorrow arrived, his call didn't.

32

EVERYTHING IS FINE

"I looked over the boat at my reflection in the water.
I looked kind of happy
for someone who was drowning."

— MARY LAMBERT, *Shame Is an Ocean I Swim Across*

Four o'clock saw me sipping coffee on a very seasonal Sunday in December, listening to Christmas carols and watching people buzz around me with excited children and a multitude of shopping bags. The sun had just begun to disappear and I should have been back at the hospital two hours ago.

No texts. No calls. No emails. I rang him. No answer. Oh Dan, what are you doing? I stuck my head in his room when I got back. Just to smell him. His aftershave still lingered in the air, the only part of him that let me in. I spent the rest of the evening checking flight prices to Ireland. Maybe he just needed to see me, maybe I should just turn up? Okay I didn't know his address or anything but I could figure all that out when I got there, couldn't I?

I missed having a reason to get up, to look forward to getting through the day so that we could have our night together, I missed spending time with someone who actually seemed to understand me. Someone who *wanted* to spend time with me. Me for being me. Me being me.

The urge to cut was unbearable, but I knew it would get back to him. I wanted to see blood and gashes and scars. I wanted evidence of a pain I couldn't see, but knew was there.

It had been seven days since Dan had left and I was not 'managing' as well as I'd hoped. I wasn't actually 'fine' after all. I couldn't get out of bed. I'd set my alarm every morning, but I just couldn't. I didn't want to. Everything seemed to be made all that much worse by Nora being off sick just when I needed her the most. I didn't know what was wrong with her, only that my session was cancelled. So without the promise of seeing her, I left on Wednesday night and didn't come back until Thursday afternoon. I didn't tell any of them. I ignored their calls and voicemails and smoked and snorted myself into a blind, unfeeling stupor. At 11am on Friday morning as I lay face down in my bed at the hospital, a psycho social aid called Elisa came in saying I had a management meeting. I hadn't had one before but knew you got them when you were in trouble. I pulled the duvet over my head and told her to get out of my room.

*

At twelve fifteen I met with Judy and a psychiatrist named Dr Tan in a strange room in the rabbit warren of the Caddick that I had never been in before.

Doctor Tan was slim, and incredibly tall at around seven foot. He seemed painfully intimidated by me, which only spurred me on as I sat there like a petulant child, my arms folded over my chest, glaring at him. Judy looked at me, 'Emma, we're here today because there has been a lot of concern about you this week. Your level of engagement. You've not attended firm, or work group, or group therapy, and I hear you're even planning to go home for two weeks over Christmas, which just isn't acceptable.'

Before I could respond Dr Tan interjected, 'You keep saying everything is *fine*, Emma, but I think you are just wanting to present in that way when actually there is a lot more going on.'

I continually dismissed them, every attempt at a question or a connection was batted away by me as if they were mosquitos on a hot summer's night. I was watching myself from the corner of the room thinking, *Stop this! Just stop! Talk to them! Tell them you're struggling*, but I wouldn't, couldn't.

'This is just how I am, how I've always been.'

Dr Tan cocked his head to the side. 'What do you mean, Emma?'

'I don't run around here getting attention, causing a fuss like a needy four-year-old, like other people…' I let the suggestion in my voice trail off.

Judy shifted in her chair. 'You seem very angry, Emma.'

'Is that a question or a statement, Judy?' She didn't answer. I was being massively difficult. I was pissing them off, they were pissing me off and this was getting none of us anywhere. 'I have to leave, my mother has locked herself out of the house and I have to go and let her in.' They knew I was lying, they challenged me but were met with my unyielding, unapologetic denial. I left the hospital and didn't come back until the evening.

I'd wasted the day walking to town and hanging out in the park by myself. My phone rang; it was Katie saying Dan was on instant chat. My phone didn't have 3G so like a fool I rushed to the nearest Internet café, throwing £3 down at the man behind the counter. I logged on and as Katie had said, I saw Dan there. I waited a couple of minutes to see if he would say hello. He didn't. My fingers hit the keypad harder than I intended them to.

'Hi Dan.' And there followed a very strained three-and-a-half-minute interaction.

'Hi.'

'You've been shit with your phone.'

'Thanks. It's been hard. I haven't really felt like talking, Emma.'

'I was worried about you, that's all.'

'Okay. My battery is low, so I'll speak to you soon. Hope you're okay.'

The rage of rejection swelled inside me like someone inflating a balloon in my gut. That fucking bastard. Why is he doing this to me? What is wrong with him? My anger of course was only directed at him for a few minutes until my internal dialogue swept in. *Well done, Emma, YOU SURE KNOW HOW TO PICK THEM. You are so fucking stupid. Did you really think he liked you? You stupid fat bitch. Who would?* As the voice inside my head laughed hysterically at me, I left the café and walked back through the town's churchyard. I didn't get far before I slumped down on the floor, and took out a not-so-old friend who promised to make everything better. *Come on, you know I can help. Use me, let's make this stop.* They weren't deep, minor even. I cut seven times. Seven minor reasons to feel differently. And with the blood came relief, and with the relief came the pain.

*

'He's pushing you away because he likes you,' said Katie as she got into her bed. She had asked me to stay in her room that night as she didn't want to be alone. Angela had been sent to an acute unit after taking an overdose the day before. I sat with my phone on my lap looking at her, trying to smile.

'Thank you, Katie.'

As she sat up to turn off the light her tone changed. 'But don't be surprised if it now goes the other way.'

I looked at her, confused. 'What do you mean?'

She shrugged, 'Well, he might just kill you off totally.' With that she turned off the light. 'Night, Em.'

Thank you, Katie. After that comment she fell into a deep sleep and I was left imitating a washing machine, lying there until the early hours of the morning with the same soiled things revolving around my head.

*

As I walked past the reception desk the next morning the receptionist called my name. I walked over and was handed a letter. I turned the manila envelope over in my hand. 'What's this?'

'Dr Finstard left it for you, it's a summary of your review.' I sat outside on the wall alone and reluctantly opened it.

Dear Emma,

I am writing to you following your first review on the 1st December 2008.

You had brought a thoughtful contribution in which you described your main difficulties. You spoke of your self-harm since the age of 12, your rapidly changing mood and your drug taking in the past which you no longer see as an issue. You also spoke about your difficulties in relationships, for example how easily you expect to be hated. You also spoke about how you can shut yourself off and how you can keep people, including those who try to help you, away with a flippant attitude or in other ways.

It was very noticeable in the review how for some time you adopted an attitude that you yourself described as detached but that could

294

be experienced as quite superior. This seemed to reflect an important state in which you can look from a distance and probably with some contempt, at other people and their attempts to help you. In other areas we have often seen you as very quiet and difficult to make contact with. These different ways of withdrawing seem to protect you from thoughts and feelings that otherwise can be very disturbing and overwhelming.

In some ways, I think you are quite aware of disturbing feelings in yourself. You can for example, be very worried of making a terrible mess and of disturbing or even damaging other people with what's inside you and so you can be very worried of what others think of you.

In the way you communicate, it can at times be difficult to judge you correctly. For example, it is not clear whether we would be wrong if we accepted your view that drugs are no longer an issue or if we thought it still needed to be taken seriously. Or, when you are quiet, we may think you are withdrawn and detached, but sometimes you are very engaged in a quiet way, yet at other times, you clearly are disengaged or even refusing any contact, in a worrying way.

In the days since your review, we have, to our concern, actually seen more withdrawal, leading to you leaving treatment this week, not making any contact and causing significant concern. I'm sure the leaving of another patient you were very close to and your therapist's sickness played a part in this, but it is another example of your difficulty in facing disturbing feelings, like a sense of loss or sadness, and instead shutting yourself off from other people and from your own mind.

295

It seems to me extremely important that both you and we take your tendency to withdraw seriously and make an effort to keep you engaged, with patients and staff and with what goes on in yourself.

With best wishes,
Yours sincerely,
Dr Erik Finstard.
Consultant Psychiatrist in Psychotherapy
Caddick ESPD service

With best wishes? Are you sure? You just described me as 'superior' and said I treat other people with contempt? The whole thing made me sound like a head case, a confused, angry little girl who didn't know whether she was coming or going, and the worst part of it was, that was pretty much exactly how I felt.

33

LAURA

"We make our own monsters, then fear them for what they
show us about ourselves."

— MIKE CAREY & PETER GROSS,
The Unwritten, Vol. 1: Tommy Taylor and the Bogus Identity

I was spending the days babysitting Sam for Laura and Ben as
they remembered what it was to be a couple. I was growing
much closer to Laura and she was becoming a friend, a person I
could talk to; it felt good to have that bond with someone again.

One evening she came in to collect Sam from me. Her pale
blue eyes were spotted red and her cheeks were puffy. 'What's
wrong, Laura?' She took Sam off my lap and sat down, tears
spilling from her eyes.

'I bought one of the kids on the unit a birthday present. But
they wouldn't give it to her, they left it outside our bedroom
door, still wrapped with the card torn up.' Before she could finish
speaking a couple of the mums from the family unit walked past
the window; they didn't look at Laura but gave me a look filled
with so much hatred that I felt my cheeks flush. 'I can't take this,
Em,' she whispered, 'I'm not strong enough.'

I put my arm around her. 'You are strong, and you can take this.'

She shook her head. 'No matter what I do, they'll judge me for my past. "Laura Tate, convict", that's all they hear.' She had never mentioned her surname before, in fact it had been somewhat of a closely guarded secret. I knew the second it had left her lips I would use it to find out what she'd done.

'Kane, can I borrow your computer?'

'Sure, Em.' I knew I should stop, I knew that when you go digging around for truths you discover secrets that were best kept buried, but armed with her real name, I typed it into the search engine, and there it was, her picture.

'A 12-year-old girl was raped and tortured by a dangerous paedophile and his demented teenage girlfriend. Brian Ford, 26, and his lover Laura Tate are now behind bars for carrying out a horrendous sexual attack on the 12-year-old girl who they kidnapped, handcuffed and threatened to kill. Police were told that the attack was part of a fantasy to torture a virgin which the couple had planned and which Tate had written about in her diary. After choosing their target, Tate then helped Ford to rape their victim.'

My hand cupped over my mouth as I felt tremors of horror run through me; he had got twelve years in jail, Laura three. I felt sick. And suddenly despised myself for googling her.

I had hugged her! I told her how strong she was and how the parents on the family unit were bullies and beneath her. Three years is a fairly long time, and there was no doubt that she was under his control – I mean, he had groomed her for years, abused her, she was a child herself... Oh God, was I advocating? That poor twelve-year-old girl would now be a teenager, her life probably still in pieces, as I tell her abuser to 'be strong', buy her presents, look after her baby and alienate myself from a whole community who aren't prepared to 'live and let live'. Were the family unit right? Was she let off too lightly?

Not an hour after finding out about Laura's horrendous past I was told that my session for the next day had been cancelled again as Nora was still ill; this was the second week in a row. I was up until it got light outside, eyes wide and wired, being haunted by the demons I alone had summoned.

The following day stretched out in front of me like a vast expanse of emptiness, there was nothing to do. No one to talk to. No one to trust. I couldn't face Laura and avoided the family unit like a plague. The isolation caused my mood to drop rapidly and dangerously. Without Dan there, and looking after Sam not feeling like an option, the days began to tick by like hours. Endless time filling endless minutes. Seconds, fucking seconds, creating parts of seconds.

*

It was 17 December. I spent the day like a shadow, moving quietly in and out of rooms unnoticed, until Ben came rushing into the alcove with Sam. 'Em, me and Laura have couples therapy, can you watch him?' I smiled, relieved it was Ben asking me and not Laura, and popped Sam onto my lap. I sat bouncing him on my knee for a few moments until Judy appeared, sitting next to me on the sofa. She tilted her head to the side.

'Are you feeling low, Emma?'

I didn't bother to look at her. 'Yes, Judy.'

She looked at Sam who was happily gurgling. 'Why do you think that is?'

I sighed, debating whether to tell her the truth or just give an answer that would mean she would leave the room. 'I just feel down all the time. Nothing is getting better, and having nothing to do is not helping.' I turned Sam around to face me, his cheery smile threatening to lift my mood. 'He's really the only thing that makes me happy.'

'You need to try and mingle with people, with the other patients.'

I thought of Adaline and Esther... Why would I want to spend time with people like that? I made an 'Mhmm' noise.

'Well if you want to talk, Emma, you can come and find me.' She got up and sauntered out of the room.

With no more interruptions from anyone, that's how I spent the next few hours – Laura was roped into setting up the Christmas meal with the other staff and patients so I got to look after Sam for most of the day; it gave me a purpose and for that I was so grateful.

Angela was still on the acute unit, so Katie begged me to stay in her room again that night saying she couldn't bear to be alone. Reluctantly, I agreed. I managed to get to sleep after a two-hour non-stop tirade of her talking *at* me. She didn't mean any harm, talking was her therapy, her way to exorcise her demons, but the problem was that I was not her therapist, and had never agreed to be. She filled my mind with images of her ex-fiancée jumping off the cliffs at Beachy Head, his mangled body lying undiscovered for days and then telling me about how, in her mourning she had refused to eat for almost three weeks which resulted in her having to be sectioned and tube fed. I lay in the dark long after she had dozed off, imaging what his body must have looked like when they eventually found him.

I'd asked Katie to wake me up at 8am. At 7am she switched on the radio turning it up to full volume, opened the curtains, bounced on me, and then ripped off my duvet. I could have gone for her, the anger swallowed me so violently that I couldn't speak. She was laughing and I was raging. I had barely slept after her 'bedtime' stories and I was beyond exhausted. She walked out of the room and I lay in the bed shaking with anger, a familiar feeling of exposure and vulnerability rising. Humiliation and no control. I lay there thinking the most graphically violent thoughts, which swayed from attacking Katie to ripping parts of my own flesh off. *Cut, cut, cut.* The thoughts of self-harm grew with fierce momentum and I couldn't seem to make them stop. They crawled inside the mess within me and nestled in amongst the dirt. I got up, the rage searing, anger swelling and rising inside my lungs like a thick black smoke.

I stormed into firm with a face like thunder, my jaw clenched so tight that I couldn't have spoken even if I had wanted to. Dr Finstard didn't take long to say that Ellie and me leaving the next day to begin our Christmas break was 'unacceptable.' Most of the other patients would be staying for at least another week. He asked me to comment. I stared resolutely at the floor, no one could say or do anything to make me speak. After a long, heavy silence, Judy said to Adaline, who was chairing, that I was on the agenda 'anyway' and she wanted me to go first.

Adaline (or rather Slime, as some of the others called her) had recently begun a rumour that I was making myself sick. I hadn't heard it from her directly; Katie had told me. Obviously, I *was* making myself sick but Adaline hadn't seen or heard me; there was no way she could have. During one of my midnight jaunts I'd found a secret bathroom hidden away on a top floor of the hospital that was restricted, and that none of the other patients knew about. I'd have known if someone had followed me up the long, steep staircase and she couldn't have heard from outside the toilet stall itself as it was set back through a set of double doors. Katie had said that Adaline had told everyone that she had heard me vomiting in the main bathroom several times. And in the mood I was in that morning, it was not a good time for her to try and pin anything on me. As she repeated her propaganda to the room full of people I interrupted, the snarl in my voice coming out in one long hiss as my eyes, like two black caverns, burned into her face.

'Why don't you come and ask me directly instead of running around making up lies like a snake because you can't deal with your own bullshit problems? And why are you listening to me in the toilet anyway, Adaline? Do you have a fetish for that sort of thing that we're not aware of?'

I heard a couple of people scoff as her face flushed red with something like embarrassment. She spat back, 'I never see you to ask you. *No one* ever sees you. You're *never* around. No one knows what's going on with you!'

My eyes still fixed on her, I replied, 'Oh I see, so because you don't know, you lie.' I did a mock laugh. 'Emma's not here so I'll just make up my own narrative!'

'I heard you throwing up!' she screamed across the room.

'You're lying, Adaline!' I shouted back.

Kane, sensing that Adaline was in danger of me launching across the room at her said, 'Well, she's here now, Adaline, isn't she, so you could ask.' Kane looked at me and smiled. 'Emma, can you say what's going on for you?'

I felt the anger turn into total devastation at the thought of him actually caring about me. I had liked him from that very first day he'd seen through my fear of having to eat with people in the dining room. I didn't want to lie to him, or be rude, and the thought of crying in front of all of them, especially Adaline, forced my lips shut. I wanted to answer Kane desperately; I wanted to tell him what Katie had done, that I'd read about Laura and that I was so angry and confused about Dan that I felt like slashing my wrists open, but the words would not leave my mouth, no matter how much I wanted them to, and so another long silence followed.

'Em?' Kane looked truly concerned and my respect for him meant that although the thought of talking mortified me, as I was sure I would start to cry, I had to say something. I looked at the floor again and clenching my teeth said, 'I'm sorry, I don't want to share today, Kane, so I'm not going to.'

To which Dr Finstard unexpectedly chimed in, 'At least Emma is being honest.' I dug my nails into my hands. The topic quickly moved to Prue and how much she was struggling. She openly told everyone that she hated herself, she wanted to be dead, she deserved to be dead and that she wanted to cut. They were my words, being spoken by someone else.

*

After firm I fled the building as though it were on fire, taking the little money I had with me to buy Christmas presents and to try to escape the thoughts of cutting. I was of course expected to go to the Christmas meal at two, but there wasn't a chance in hell I was going – especially after Adaline's bulimia comments. Added to that, a hundred odd people, patients and staff, all feeding at what might as well have been a mass trough, you couldn't have paid me to go. I had glanced at the seating plan the day before which saw me being sat next to Ellie and opposite a psycho social aid called Jennifer – who was not only four years younger than me, but had also gone to the same secondary school.

Added to that, slim, bleach-blonde Jennifer had a habit of watching me eat with unflinching scrutiny. She made me feel like I was a science experiment and I loathed her for it. I decided I wasn't going back to the hospital to accusations of eating disorders and running away from my problems, so I got up from the coffee I had been sipping on for an hour and went to my parents' house. My thoughts seemed too dangerous to spend any time with, so, popping a zopiclone into my mouth, I forced myself to bed and didn't wake up until 2pm the next day; if I was going to run away from my problems I was at least going to do it with prescription drugs.

*

I switched on the computer and clicked on MSN. Dan was there. To my surprise he said hello first. We chatted for a while and yes, it was really nice. After a few minutes he said, 'I'm really sorry, pet, but my brother needs the computer, call or text though.' My mind felt soothed for the first time in weeks. And an hour later we spoke more; he rang me and it was like nothing had changed. As I closed my eyes and listened to his voice it was like being back there with him in the garden of the hospital.

After we hung up, my phone beeped to a message from him. 'Emma, you're so funny. I miss you so much. I miss the fucked-up conversations and jokes, I can't talk to anyone else like that, or my family, they'd have me committed. I think about you all the time.'

I missed him desperately, but he was trying so hard to push me away, and it was becoming almost impossible finding the energy to stay.

*

After spending the day with one of my school friends, Sara, in a picture-perfect Camden under a blanket of snow, my mood began to drop. I had felt consistently happy for a whole day, which hadn't happened for a while, and the second it was over I felt the dread in me begin to stir again, the anxiety of being alone, trapped in my head with my thoughts.

I missed Nora. I needed her. I needed to be told that I was beginning to float off and wanted her guidance to tether me back to the ground. As night rolled around, the feelings got worse, and my mind began to wander into dark places. I was hoarding three 10mg Temazepam and swallowed them all at once lying on my bed listening to 'Daughter' by Pearl Jam on repeat. I hadn't cut myself for four days, which might as well have been four years. I felt so alone.

As the drugs began to seep into my system my thoughts slurred under their weight. Life. Ambition. Time. TIME. Slipping away. Lines. The lines around my eyes. I was dying. I was not alive. Fear wrapped its hands around my throat.

My fingers moved inside my bedroom drawer until they felt something sharp and familiar.

*

I woke up to the sound of my phone ringing as I peeled my arms away from my damp, stained sheets. It was Judy telling me I had a management meeting, so I dragged myself out of bed and began my journey back to the Caddick to be reprimanded.

By the time of the meeting at two forty I was ready to kick the shit out of someone, my mood had gone (as it had a habit of doing, the good old BPD way, the constant emotional rollercoaster) from depressed to violently aggressive. I'd waited in the alcove with Adaline staring at me for an hour, Katie's incessant rambling and Esther's quivering lip, feeling like my head was going to burst.

It was Dr Malone and a nurse called Sal in the room I was ordered into. I'd never even spoken to Dr Malone before, how was he supposed to help me? He didn't even know me, and Sal never seemed to know what to do in any situation, she always seemed so out of her depth.

I sat there, batting back any attempt at communication – mental tennis for the mental. Sal was as useless as ever and although I knew Dr Malone was trying to help, his words offered me no solace and every time he tried to get inside my head and figure out what was going on with me I'd say something precocious or damning and shut him down with my belligerence.

I left the meeting, and rushed back to my room; the anger and frustration once again began filling my stomach like shards of glass. Why couldn't I just open up? Why couldn't I just tell someone that I wasn't okay? I swallowed two zopiclone and was up until 6am crying and cutting in the secret bathroom far away from any prying ears or eyes. I got myself back into bed for 7am so when the staff did their checks I looked like I had been safe and sound in my bed the whole night. I got up early, showered, changed and went straight into my session with Nora, bursting into tears before the door even closed behind me.

Despite my histrionics and post-sleeping-pill state, we had a good session, talking a lot about my anger and the problem with not knowing exactly what it was I always seemed to be angry about. I picked another tissue out of the box next to me. 'It's like a washing machine effect. I have an idea of the various contributing factors of my mood, and then they just spin out of control, into each other and I don't know what's going on or what I'm so angry about.'

We talked about Dan and how it'd been in the hospital without him. Again, I cried. She waited for me to stop sobbing and said, 'It's really quite disturbing how much you get away with, Emma. The Caddick are vigorous with contact details and you've somehow managed to not give yours.' She sighed and continued. 'You have never so much as sat down to dinner here, no one questions your eating disorder, which is obviously rampant. You cut yourself and yet no one sees the damage you do. You seem to get away with everything. And honestly, that must feel awful. To actually be able to shut people down and for them to then stay like that.'

I nodded slowly. 'Yesterday, I desperately wanted to talk

to Dr Malone. But I couldn't help myself and tested him, and tested him, shutting him down over and over again until he just stopped trying. I do feel sometimes that I can get away with everything. No one notices, or bothers to step in, and on the rare occasion they do, if I tell them to fuck off, they go.' As I left the sanctuary of her office I rushed back to my bedroom and cried on my bed. I felt so hollow, and it just wouldn't go away.

*

My Christmas break from the hospital was not anything special. I was constantly depressed, obsessed with not eating, throwing up whenever I did eat and cutting myself every day.

I managed to go out on Christmas Eve, after being affectionately bullied into the celebrations by my friends, dressed in a cleavage-spectacular polka dot 1950s dress and six-inch patent high heels. A lot of my male friends hadn't seen me for a long time and I'd lost a considerable amount of weight in the interim. None of them had ever seen me in anything other than baggy jeans and a hoodie. Jaw after jaw dropped to the floor, and I spent the evening in a club in London with the majority of them hitting on me. I wasn't expecting it, and as much as I wanted to believe the compliments and offers of dates, their words translated inside me as: 'You've done well to get noticed, but you must stop eating completely now, remember; you're still ugly inside, nothing will change that.' I whored myself to each of them, letting them touch me, grab me, dance with me, try and kiss me before abandoning them all to spend the early hours of the morning with a ridiculously attractive Tom: leather jacket, tattoos, lip piercing, he looked like a cross between a young Elvis Presley and James Dean, with smoky dark eyes and a smile that would make you say yes to anything. I let him chase me for hours, with the lingering promise that he'd get me if he worked hard enough. I liked the attention. I liked the fact that every other girl in the club's eyes followed after him, even as his followed after me.

After a few hours I said I was going. He asked for my number.

'If it's meant to be you'll find it somehow.' I turned on my six-inch heels and left. I wanted to give it to him, sure I did, but what was the point? He was too good-looking for me anyway; I would have to stay as his Cinderella, only instead of searching the kingdom for the foot that fit the glass slipper, he'd be searching behind locked doors for the broken doll in the asylum. I should have told him then that he was never going to find her.

What I really wanted was to talk to Landon; he was still in hospital and I missed him a lot. If he had been there that night everything would have been different. I could have sat and talked to him, made us both feel normal, but the acute unit he was in wouldn't even let him have visitors, let alone calls.

34

SHORT-LEAVED

"It feels very much as if you are possessed, as if you have no will of your own but are in constant battle with your body, and you are losing. It wants to live. You want to die. You cannot both have your way."

— MARYA HORNBACHER,
Wasted: A Memoir of Anorexia and Bulimia

I was trying not to self-harm, for at least a couple of days. I wanted to prove to myself that I had control, that I could say no and not give in, but these cravings to feel pain will get you one way or another – no matter how much I tried to think about anything else, the urge kept finding me – I wanted to destroy myself, until there was nothing left to destroy. Without the distraction of Dan, the thought of suicide was very much back in my head. When the cutting and burning didn't soothe me, when the starving and binging and purging didn't work, all I could think was that perhaps I just wasn't supposed to be around at all.

I glanced at my clock: 10am. My mother pushed open my bedroom door. 'Get up, Emma, and go back to the hospital, or stay here and get a job, in which case you'll be up at seven every morning.' As the door slammed shut I lay there trying to think of my future: nothing. I was terrified.

I arrived back at the hospital in the early afternoon; not many people were around, still away after the Christmas break. Mena knocked on my door before I even had time to unpack my overnight bag.

'Hi, Emma, welcome back.'

'Hi.'

'I'm sorry to ask but Susie needs to go to A&E, would you come with us?'

I stood up and started putting on my coat, 'Sure. What happened?'

'She's used her hair straighteners on her arm... but she won't let us call an ambulance.'

Susie had been referred to the Caddick shortly after returning home from the Henshaw. Her funding had taken longer than mine to come through so she'd only been there for a couple of weeks now – which was about how long it had taken for both her black eyes and split lip to heal.

Susie was completely detached as we got in a cab and rode to the general hospital. 'You're both being absolutely ridiculous, you should just let me bandage it myself.' In that state, she was always fairly believable, why *didn't* they just dress her arm at the Caddick? It seemed a bit extreme going to the emergency room. It wasn't until I watched the grimacing doctor in A&E roll up her sleeve that I realised that, not only was she was lucky to be alive, but I was completely astounded at her ability to walk, talk and function normally when she'd burnt away a fairly large portion of her flesh. From her elbow to her wrist her skin was gone, a black and red hollowed out mess of charred flesh... it smelled and looked like a human barbecue.

'You'll need a skin graft and you'll need to be admitted into hospital right away, frankly I don't know how you're up and walking about.' The doctor looked confused and uncomfortable as he stared into Susie's vacant eyes.

'This is all very over the top,' she said again.

'She'll need to go to psych afterwards, either back to you on a one-to-one or I'll get her sectioned here, your call,' he said to Mena.

I didn't know what to do. I was so tired, so overflowing with my own crap that I really couldn't take anyone else's problems right at that moment. I was more than relieved when Mena turned to me and calmly said, 'You go back to the hospital, Emma. Talk to someone about this, share it with someone, don't hold it all yourself.' I nodded, kissed Susie's cheek and closed the door behind me to the sound of her still saying everyone was overreacting.

Of course, I didn't go back to the hospital. I went into town, got a coffee and cried. I felt like I had the weight of the world on me, like I had no boundaries around me to protect me from anything. I couldn't explain it, it was like suddenly there was no filter and everyone else's pain was mine. As I walked back to the hospital on my own, I realised quickly that I wasn't alone, the voice had woken. I saw a couple of homeless guys in sleeping bags and listened as it rasped in my ears. *You don't even know what suffering is, Emma. Look at those poor fucking men. You whining little bitch. You're pathetic. Cut yourself. Kill yourself, just do something, it would be so easy to make all this stop.* And so on and so forth, I couldn't make it quieten down, I felt totally powerless. *There's no point in going on, is there? You know that. You are worth nothing. Dan doesn't want you, no one wants you, your life is meaningless. Listen to me, Emma, I will help you.*

I cried for the entire forty-five minute walk back, but as my hand pushed on the bell for Len to buzz me in, the crying stopped, just like that. The mask was back on.

Up in the bedroom Ellie was listening to music, lying on her bed. 'Hi,' she said as I walked in.

'Hey.'

I glanced over to Sandra's side of the room and realised the lump that was her body under the duvet was gone. Ellie saw me looking. 'She's been short-leaved,' she turned down the music, 'left earlier.' Ellie shrugged. 'She got in trouble for not going to firm again, or anything else. It's a shame but then, how can she expect it to help her if she stays in bed all day, you know?' She turned the music back up and rolled over on to her side playing with her phone. It was true, Sandra never seemed to want to get better, she didn't make an effort or ever ask for help. I sat down and began taking off my boots, all the while berating Sandra's 'bad behaviour' in my head. I suddenly couldn't help but wonder if I was any different?

As if in confirmation of my fears, I too was short-leaved less than a week later. Being 'short-leaved' meant that you weren't cooperating in therapy and were sent away to think about how you were going to fix the situation. For the last few days I had been a mess, my mood had dipped horribly and I was cutting every time I could get away with it. I didn't want to be near anyone and refused to go to firm or community, and kept vanishing from the hospital without telling anyone where I was going. Derron continuously tried to engage with me, but I just couldn't talk to him. I felt like he didn't have the slightest idea of who I was, and what was worse, he seemed scared of me half the time. I would see other people sitting with their nurses, talking and laughing and in comparison Derron and I could barely say two words to each other. His attempts to connect with me were met with my unwavering shut downs and it was like a continual game of cat and mouse.

On Saturday night, as I sat in one of my friend's flats with a group of people doing drugs and drinking, I got a call from Derron.

'Emma, you're being short-leaved!' Derron trying to play the role of disciplinarian down the phone to me was amusing in itself. He sounded like someone who had been told to sound angry, but who was not sure why. I was pretty positive I could hear Judy in the background instructing him on what to say. 'You are not allowed to come back until Tuesday, okay?'

'Why not, Derron?'

He paused. 'Because you are not engaging in treatment and will need to have a management meeting.'

Being told I couldn't go back should have felt like someone granting me freedom, but instead it felt like a punishment, and a rejection. The idea that I wasn't even welcome in the hospital made me feel alienated and even more alone; if they didn't want me, who would?

I waltzed back into the Caddick on Tuesday afternoon and was collected in reception by Derron, who led me to my management meeting with Dr Bardo, one of the adult psychiatrists.

As I sat down opposite Bardo with Derron at my side I felt instantly defensive. The way she was staring at me, legs crossed, hands clasped on her lap, not speaking, it was making me anxious. I felt like she wanted me to throw myself down on her altar and beg for forgiveness, only to no doubt be told that I was getting kicked out of the hospital anyway.

'So, Emma, do you know why we're having this meeting?' she began, still staring at me.

I shrugged my shoulders.

'Well, we're having it because we feel you haven't been engaging with structures consistently, and you keep leaving treatment without telling anyone where you're going.' A pause. 'Would you be able to speak about that?'

I didn't want to *speak* about anything with her, I didn't know her, and I certainly didn't trust her. I stayed quiet, bouncing my knee up and down and looking out of the window. She let this go on for a minute or so before talking again. 'You seem quite angry, Emma?'

I looked at her, feeling the irritation start up in me. 'Because of this!' I blurted out. 'Because of this whole thing! Being kicked out over the weekend, then dragged back into a meeting and forced to talk or... you'll what? Throw me out? It pisses me off, it's like you're playing power games.'

She uncrossed her legs. 'That must feel quite frightening, Emma, to think we would just cast you out?' Bardo looked like she was attempting a smile but not quite managing it, the edges of her mouth creasing slightly at the sides.

'Obviously! Obviously it's frightening! I don't feel good at the moment, and this really isn't helping.'

She made an 'Mmm' noise. 'Could you say more about that?'

It was like trying to have a conversation with the fucking Riddler. I took in a long, deliberate breath. 'The self-harm isn't working like it usually does... I still feel bad afterwards. It feels like *nothing* is working, everything feels hopeless. All I think about is maybe I shouldn't be here, at all...'

Bardo cleared her throat. 'So you're feeling suicidal?'

I nodded.

'That must be very difficult, Emma, to feel so low and not be able to let yourself reach out for help. This meeting is not to tell you off as you seem to think it is, we're not here to bully you.' She looked at Derron, who nodded emphatically (he was awake after all then). She carried on. 'We want to help you, Emma, and make sure you're safe.'

I felt myself soften a little. 'I know. But I don't know how to change my behaviour. I feel like I can't talk to anyone about how I feel, so I just leave.'

Bardo smiled, properly this time. 'It appears to me that you do want to engage, but you seem to have this extreme claustrophobic anxiety that propels you out of the hospital and away from any help you might receive. Would that be a fair observation?' I looked at the floor and, perhaps sensing that the meeting was starting to get too much for me, Bardo said, 'I think you should return to treatment, with immediate effect. I'd like you to really try and challenge the urge to leave the hospital this week, Emma, and talk to the people around you.'

As I walked back to my room it surprised me how relieved I felt. I had to try and start opening up... somehow.

35

DO YOU LIKE LITTLE GIRLS?

"The hours wear on, while the surreal atmosphere of the
asylum does not wear off."

— M.D. ELSTER, *Four Kings*

My session with Nora felt long overdue.

'There's a part of you, Emma, for instance when you're
having a panic attack and you are desperately in need of help,
that will not let you get help. When you most need it, that voice
inside you says, "Absolutely no, you will not get what you need,
you will not get help." I think it ties in with what Dr Bardo was
saying about your claustrophobic anxiety.'

I told her I was terrified of life. That I was destined for failure
and so what was the point? That I'd already failed. I had failed
at the Henshaw; I was failing to engage at the Caddick; I was
failing to accomplish anything. I would fleetingly see a glimpse
of hope but then just as quickly it would fall to pieces in the most
tremendous way, resulting in thoughts of self-harm and suicide.
I had awoken the ranting, raving lunatic inside me and couldn't
stop my mouth moving.

'Kill yourself and put an end to all of this! Kill yourself so you won't fail! Kill yourself so you can no longer disappoint! Kill yourself, to save yourself. Kill yourself, to make the voices stop. Kill yourself to end the feelings. Kill yourself. Kill yourself. Kill yourself!' I shouted.

'You're angry, Emma. You're furious. You're angry because no one can see through your "I'm fines" and see that you're far from fine.'

I carried on shouting, 'How can I be angry at them if I don't tell them? IF YOU DON'T TELL SOMEONE YOU'RE GOING TO SELF-HARM OR KILL YOURSELF HOW DO THEY FUCKING KNOW?'

Her voice remained even. 'Sometimes people don't need to be told. You need to feel held. You need some maternal thing to make you feel held.' Another pause. 'There is a you that feels.' Her words spun around me like specks of dirt that rise up in the wind and get stuck in your eye.

There is a you that feels. There is a you that feels. There is a you that feels.

What I wanted to say to her was, 'Yes Nora, I do feel. I feel completely fucking empty and alone.'

*

As the morning rolled in I actually woke feeling better, lighter. Then came a crippling migraine. No matter how many painkillers I took it wouldn't shift. I'd only had a hundred calories by seven o'clock and although my head was pounding and I felt thoroughly sick, I couldn't stop smiling at my achievement. Dan was back on my mind again and I needed a distraction. I had been so sure we were meant for each other, but the reality that he couldn't be worse for me was starting to set in. After our chat a few weeks earlier he had vanished again, completely ignoring me once more, killing me off in his mind and leaving me for dead. I had noticed his status on Facebook had changed to 'Dan has got a job' – this little nugget, which might at first glance seem quite innocent, had spun me into a whirlwind of, *Well, if he doesn't care about me enough to tell me something as important as he's got a job then he really doesn't care about me much at all.*

And just like that, Stone was back in the bad books. Welcome to the borderline personality perspective prospectus – black and white, no grey, no medium – go fuck yourself Goldilocks, there is no 'just right'.

I couldn't help but worry that Dan had actually seen me, he had an understanding of me, and what if no one ever reached that again? It was hard enough to meet someone who could get their head around the hospitalisations, depression, self-harm, borderline, eating disorder, suicide attempts. Perhaps I would never find another Dan? Maybe I was destined to spin around a world of Toms, forever chasing my tail like a bored dog trapped inside on a sunny day.

'Your distress is a stranger to you' – Nora's explanation for why I found it easier to cry in random places like Starbucks, or the street, or on a bus surrounded by people who didn't know me. My own distress was a stranger. 'You don't want to push it into anyone else so you just shut down. You don't know what to do with it, or how to deal with it. You are constantly terrified of contaminating people with what's inside you.'

My therapy and her office had become a safe haven. Silence. Only interrupted by her thoughts, or my own voice. Nothing being pushed in, nothing being ripped out. Peace and control. The last three sessions had been subdued. Quiet. I sat, making small noises with words. She would say to me, 'We can sit. We can be in silence. It's *okay*. It's your space.' My space. Thank God for this.

*

As I closed the door to Nora's room and made my way back to my own bedroom I heard shrieking and a commotion. The bathroom door slammed with such force I wondered how it had not come off its hinges. I could tell it was Prue, I'd come to recognise the sounds of her screams. After what felt like an hour of begging her to let me in she eventually did but she was gone, totally dissociated. In the moments when she seemed to come back to herself she would smash her head onto the tiled wall; the crack of her skull was so loud that I kept having to check for blood.

'Please stop doing that,' I pleaded. CRACK. 'Please Prue stop, please!' CRACK. When she got into this sort of state she could be trapped there for hours, and all I could do was sit with her and try to tell her she was safe.

'I want to CARVE MYSELF INTO PIECES!' she shouted repeatedly, over and over again, louder each time.

Prue had become a friend. Dan leaving was the catalyst to us becoming closer; without the constant distraction of him I had started to rely on her as a confidante. We grew fonder of one another every day and I knew this sort of behaviour would lead to an ambulance being called and her being taken to a secure unit for days if not weeks.

A few months earlier Prue had tried to kill herself; quietly and without anyone noticing she had slipped off to her room one afternoon and attempted to hang herself. Some divine intervention had caused Poppy to go and check on her, and finding her unconscious she screamed for help and the entire staff came running. After spending the night in a general hospital Prue was taken to a high security unit and left there for what felt like weeks, completely traumatising Poppy in the process.

'Emma, you've been here for two hours, that's enough now. Let someone else take over.' Judy had appeared outside the bathroom door and was staring at me. I shook my head, resolved, but secretly wished she would drag me away. It wasn't that I didn't want to stay, but I was exhausted, and Prue was no better, she still wanted to hurt herself and other than half pinning her down, there wasn't much else I could do. Time passed slowly. I listened as Prue ricocheted in and out of her lucid state, one moment making sense, the next shouting and screaming. Another hour had passed and Judy reappeared in the doorway. 'Emma, get up now. I will sit with her.' She grabbed my arm, ushering me out. I felt useless but I was too exhausted to do any more and the demons in my own head had become loud enough to be heard even over Prue's shouts.

Katie appeared in front of us. 'Come on, wee one, I'll go out with you, we can go and get a coffee, would you like that?' I glanced at Judy who nodded approvingly.

'Go on, Emma, it's a nice gesture – go out and enjoy yourself.' Judy patted me on the back as Katie linked her arm through mine and began steering me away. Halfway into town Katie turned to me. 'Sorry Em, I've actually got a date, I just told Judy I was going out with you to get out without an inquisition. See ya later.' I didn't even have an answer for her, and bit down hard on my tongue as I watched her disappear into the crowd.

*

By 10pm I was finally settled in the empty TV room watching *Supersize vs Superskinny*, an hour of pure peace and body obsession. As the programme ended I picked up the remote to find something else to watch, but the door creaked open. Esther appeared in the doorway, crying, her lip wobbling in that way that had a tendency to annoy me.

'What's up Esther?' I said not bothering to hide the disdain in my voice.

'Susie's in the firm room… talking to monsters. I can't cope. I can't cope, Emma. Please, please can you do something?' I told her to go to bed and leave Susie to me as I walked into the firm room. Susie, who had only been back from the acute unit for a few days after the arm roasting incident, was on her hands and knees with her face on the floor screaming into the carpet. Christ. I gingerly approached her.

'Susie, what are you doing?' She didn't raise her head.

'They're here. They're everywhere. In the walls and in my head!'

'Who are?' I asked, looking naively around the room.

'The monsters! The monsters! They're going to kill me!' She shoved her face further into the carpet. The next half an hour consisted of me telling her she was in control, that she was a strong woman and a good mother, that she could beat this. I ordered her to tell the monsters to fuck off – 'Say it, Susie, tell them to fuck off.'

She nodded and shouted, '*Fuck off!*'

'And again, Susie, tell them to fuck off.'

'*Fuck off!*'

Although I knew she was in real distress, there was something darkly amusing about the monster exorcism. I felt like one of those over-elaborate American preachers claiming that Jesus was working through me.

'Make them leave, Susie, you can do it! Get away from here, monsters! You are not welcome!' My sermon was almost award-winning. 'Say it, Susie, order them!'

'*Fuck off! Leave me alone, monsters!*' As ridiculous as I felt, we managed, or rather she managed, to banish her demons, and after a while I got her up, got her to her meds and then to bed safely.

*

Still feeling positive about having helped Susie the next morning, I went to group with Ellie and Aaron. Sandra, although back from her short leave, had once again refused to get out of bed although Ellie, Poppy and I had all tried to rouse her. Ellie and I were steadily growing closer; as soon as Dan had left the rivalry between us had quickly diminished and rather strangely she had been very supportive, telling me she understood that I missed him and often suggesting we watch a film together or go shopping for baby paraphernalia to distract me from my perceived loss. She treated me like a big sister and I was happy to fulfil that role – it made me feel needed.

Two days prior to this session, I had been alone in group with Ellie when she launched into an unprovoked and aggressive verbal attack on Mr Newman. He had asked some seemingly innocent question about her childhood and she had lost it, her northern accent loudly filling the room as she slowly leaned forward and said, 'Why are you staring at my tits Mr Newman? Do you want to fuck me?'

Johanna sat there looking as taken aback as I was.

'You're a dirty old pervert, aren't you? Do you like little girls? I bet you'd love to fuck one.'

I pushed my hands over my face and heard myself saying 'Oh God' over and over again.

'You probably want me to suck your dick. Is that what you want? Why don't you ask me? You know I'm a prozzie, go on, ask.'

To his complete credit (and no doubt years of experience) he sat looking back at her completely reserved and controlled, simply saying, 'Ellie, I know you are behaving like this because you don't want to talk about the feelings you had as a young child.'

'I bet *you* want to talk about my feelings, you dirty old fucker! You're probably the bareback type, that's extra you know?' I felt sick. I felt awful for him. He was such a gentle, perceptive man. But she just wouldn't stop. He did his very best to sit there looking unaffected but the things that were spilling out of her mouth would make anyone recoil. I kept telling her to shut up, but it just spurred her on. I couldn't bear it any longer and got up. As my hand touched the door handle she laughed sadistically and said, 'Why are *you* leaving?'

I didn't look at her, 'Because I can't take listening to this for another second!' I slammed the door behind me.

So, back to real time and the morning after Susie's exorcism I was dreading going to the group because of what Ellie had done in the last session, even though Aaron would also be there to hopefully act as some kind of bolster. I sat quietly, wrapped in anxiety awaiting what was to come, but to my complete surprise Ellie came in, demure as can be, sat down and apologised to Mr Newman. With complete sincerity she said, 'The things I said were disgusting, I know that and I didn't mean it. You upset me, talking about my childhood and I got angry and I didn't know what to do with those feelings so I just turned on you. I'm sorry.'

This was something I liked about Ellie: yes, she could say the most abhorrent things, but she would reflect on her behaviour and deliver a real apology when it was needed. She would always own up to her feelings of vulnerability and exposure, and although I hated that poisonous side of her when she turned, I admired the fact that even as a teenager she understood accountability. She talked for some time about how thinking of her childhood had triggered her, that growing up with an alcoholic mother and moving with her brother from foster carer to foster carer had left her with hundreds of scars both emotional and physical.

Unexpectedly, Mr Newman turned to me. 'Emma, I'm aware that when this was going on in our last session it seemed excruciatingly difficult for you, to watch me being called those things. What was being stirred up in that moment for you?'

323

Spurred on by Ellie's unflinching honesty, I started talking. 'I just have this thing inside me that can't sit back and watch someone be victimised. Like Laura and the family unit, or when I see a parent being abusive in public to their child, or people being heavy-handed with animals, or kids bullying other kids. The rage rises inside me like a tidal wave, and I act before I know I'm acting, and more often than not it gets me into trouble.'

'Why do you think that happens, Emma?' Johanna asked, a look of amazement on her face at my opening up.

'As a child, as an adolescent, no one stuck up for me, no one ever got in the middle, so as I got older I became that person. When I see a random man in the street threatening to beat his unruly child, I become the child, with the power of an adult... I can't explain it really...' My voice faded off as Ellie started crying. I wasn't sure why and was suddenly worried I had triggered some terrible memory for her. Eventually, through her sobs, she whispered, 'I'm sorry, Emma. I'm so sorry I put you in that position. I didn't mean to do that to you. I was put in that position too when I was younger. I'm sorry, I promise I'll learn from this.'

36

I TEXT HIM BY ACCIDENT.
ON PURPOSE.

"I thieve love. I beg for it. People want what they cannot have."

— MERRI LISA JOHNSON,
Girl in Need of a Tourniquet: Memoir of a Borderline Personality

It was almost a week later on a Tuesday and London had not seen so much snow in a long time. Ellie had been trapped in Yorkshire because she couldn't get a train back to the Caddick after going home for the weekend, and Sandra was once again on short leave. After three months of not getting out of bed, not going to therapy, intermittently going to group, and only once going to firm since I had been there, the staff were pretty exasperated with her and didn't feel that they could offer her much more in the way of therapy. Sandra had almost died from anorexia a few years earlier, but was now very overweight to the point where she seemed out of breath a lot of the time without really moving. She had a phobia of bathrooms (a bathroom had been a setting for some horrendous abuse for her as a child), so she hadn't showered or bathed... for four years. Four whole years, just try and wrap your head around that one for a second. Occasionally, when her legs would stick out from under the covers, I would glance over at the thick rings of black dirt that looped around her ankles occupying the space between her socks and pyjama bottoms. Of course, I couldn't blame her for not wanting to go in the bathroom, who knows what awful trauma she endured, though as you can imagine, the smell that was created in our room was bad at the best of times; but luckily Sandra didn't usually emerge from under her duvet so Ellie and I would spray room freshener around her bed and open the windows when she was asleep – it was a fine line between not wanting to offend her and not wanting to lay in bed gagging every night. The nurses would bring her wet wipes and encourage her to at least try and use them, but it always fell on deaf ears.

So, needless to say, with both of them not being there, having the room to myself was a welcome break: I didn't have to huddle in the bathroom to change and could play whatever music I wanted, as loudly as I wanted.

I woke on that Tuesday and looked out onto the white canopy of snow that had completely enveloped the grounds of the hospital, thinking of the night before: another episode of feeling totally overwhelmed by everything around me, which had resulted in my cutting and having to get bandaged up by one of the nurses. I held my arm close to me and winced in pain as I slowly got ready and ambled up the five flights of stairs to the group therapy room. As neither Sandra nor Ellie were there it was just me and Aaron with Mr Newman. Exasperated, I tried to explain that I felt that no one could help me, that I felt addicted to the self-harm and often found myself clucking like a junkie or an alcoholic for a fix. I told them that I knew I needed to stop cutting but I just didn't know how. This confession somehow translated as me feeling 'triumphant' that no one could help me.

'Triumphant?! Yes! Oh I'm *so* happy that I'm totally alone with this, whoop-de-fucking-do.' I think Mr Newman may have regretted his choice of words as I then stormed out of the room after only half an hour.

Fleeing through the back door, which I knew was alarmed but a better alternative than having to face whoever may have been on the front desk ready to grill me about where I was going and when I would be back, I got the bus into town where I met my friend Sally. She hadn't been to see me in either hospital but was part of the group of school friends I still had and would go out on the weekends to see, or rather, do drugs with, although it hadn't escaped my notice that over the last couple of months the invitations had been dwindling. I sat fairly spaced out trying to make her understand the level of my distress, telling her that my friends did not understand how alone I was, that I wasn't using the word 'suicidal' for fun, that I felt it, all the fucking time.

'I am walking along the ledge of my life. No one has come to visit me here. Nobody invites me out on weekends any more. Do you all not understand how horrible it is being in hospital?'

Sally looked at me. 'Yeah, I totally get it, Em, I've felt like killing myself before,' she said resolutely, before clearing her throat and continuing. 'When I was younger I didn't have any money to go and see the Foo Fighters play and I was like, that's it, this is so unfair. I was going to take an overdose but I went out clubbing and got really drunk instead and it was so fun. I think you just need to try and find ways to be happy and think about other things.'

It was at that moment I decided to go and get another coffee. There was no point in continuing the conversation; it was glaringly obvious that Sally had never *truly* contemplated killing herself – I don't think she could comprehend suicide, the desire of actually wanting an end. Finished. Done. Sometimes we go along with friendships that do not sustain us for much longer than we should because we fear loneliness, though oftentimes staying in the friendship can be the very thing to make you feel lonely. I knew that she was trying to help, trying relate to me, and maybe I was just expecting too much, but seeing her that day did nothing but further my feelings of isolation. She changed the subject as I got back to the table with a slice of cake that I intended on throwing up long before it digested inside me.

I walked back to the hospital and cut. A lot, and deeply. After an hour of the blood not stopping I went and sought out a nurse named Kirk. Kirk had never been on night duty as long as I'd been there and when I knocked on the staff door a little after 9pm he asked me to show him my arm and almost recoiling in horror and disgust said, 'Your arm is a bloody mess, Emma.'

He gave me bandages and Steri-Strips (rather than bandaging my arm himself) and was completely unhelpful, just stared at me wide-eyed like a father would stare at his twelve-year-old daughter after she'd announced to him that she had started her period. There was a part of me (albeit a small part) that just wanted his attention. Just wanted someone to care, even for fifteen minutes – the only bonus of the self-harm being that he would 'have' to talk to me, 'have' to make sure I was okay. Naturally, it didn't happen like that, it never did, and I never learned. He sent me to bed and told me to speak about the incident in firm come the morning.

*

In my session with Nora the next day I started talking about Katie, as after Kirk had sent me to my room she had come in to check on me and so began the *mother* of all rants about how I leave myself open to people who are, have, and will continue to take advantage of me.

'People sense that they can get something from you because *you are* so vulnerable. Dan took advantage; that Curtis you messed around with did too.' She spoke incessantly for almost two hours without stopping for breath. 'You must be in a real state at the moment because you're self-harming constantly, Emma, and not telling anyone.' She said it almost boastfully as if she were imparting some new information I wasn't already aware of.

So I figuratively dragged Katie to my session with me and told Nora what she'd been saying. Then I told her about Curtis, who I had texted the night before. Upon not having received any attention from Kirk, I looked elsewhere. I'm not going into this, not here, not now. I'll give you the short version: Curtis was older than me, much older. I'd felt a connection with him from the first day I met him – he was brooding, tall, dark and handsome, a poet, a writer and I was drawn in like a lamb to the slaughter. Only, I was very willing and the slaughter wasn't quite slaughter. I may have had a small hand in the death of his relationship, okay, marriage, some years earlier... The wound in the heart of his union was already necrotic when I got involved with him, and in my (meek) defence he told me he was '*basically*' separated from his wife, so I carried on under that impression. He gave me what I needed, I gave him what he was missing; he was the Ted Hughes to my Sylvia Plath.

After he did actually leave his wife, I panicked like a little girl (spurred on by a call from him, telling me that she knew where I lived and 'was crazy and might do anything'), so booked a flight to Canada that day and left the country for several weeks. There were no hard feelings after I came back. And if I had been less fucked up and a few years older I would have been with him in an instant given the choice. I will always have feelings for him, and, although not totally sexual, they were not totally platonic either: somewhere in between. Curtis eventually moved away to America to begin a new life, but we would still often message each other. He had told me he'd met someone. I paused. 'So I thought it was safe to ask him if he'd write to me here, because he's involved with someone else now, he's in love with her and it can't get messed up between us again.'

Apparently this was very fucked-up behaviour and Nora did not approve that I was contacting him.

'There's a very jealous little girl part of you, Emma, that needs to be right there, in the middle of them. You *do want* Curtis to be involved with you and what's more, you want him to have control over you.'

I hated the thought that that might be in any way true. 'I messaged *him* Nora. If anything, I'm the one in control.'

She raised her voice in a mocking fashion. 'You don't have control over yourself, Emma! Let alone him! It's tantalising, and dangerous, and that's what appeals to you. He's a grown man in a relationship and you're a twenty-three-year-old in a psychiatric hospital. He shouldn't be signing texts with 'I love you' and nor should you! What would his girlfriend think? The same as his wife did I should imagine.'

Oh, snap. That shut me up. I sat quietly, wondering if all my relationships and friendships had this fucked-up element to them. 'So I do this with everyone? Every relationship I have is a fucked-up mess?' I eventually asked, no longer knowing my own mind.

Nora leaned forward in her chair. 'Emma.' She exhaled deeply. 'Not all your relationships follow this pattern, but the ones that resonate with you, the ones that really stick, are clearly not right, and you know it. You know the difference.'

I didn't know the difference, consciously at least, which is why her next comment threw me.

'Like Prue.'

I looked at her, confused. 'What about Prue?'

'The friendship is tantalising. Its danger attracts you. It has an almost erotic quality about it.'

Great, was she trying to tell me she thinks I want to fuck Prue?

'I also think there is something quite erotic about cutting for you, Emma.'

Oh God, is she telling me I want to fuck myself now?

'You and Prue are dragging each other into some underworld and feeding one another. I don't agree with it and I think it needs to be looked at.' She glanced at the clock. 'We'll have to continue next session.'

I stood up thinking, *No we bloody won't.* I probably should have opted to sit down and think long and hard about Nora's (incredibly accurate) observations; instead I decided to go to meet Jess and get stoned.

*

The next evening I went to celebrate Natalie's mum's birthday at a little pub not too far from my parents' house. A few of my friends were there with a lot of Natalie's family, including her cousin Ashley, a very beautiful twenty-five-year-old girl who had struggled badly with her weight and binge eating. I'd known Ashley for over a decade, and so she had no issue with sitting and talking to me about how low she was feeling about her body.

'You look so good, Emma, I can't believe how much you've lost.' I quietly thanked her, 'How have you done it?'

I swallowed hard. 'Just, changing my diet and mostly...' but before I could say anything else a very drunk Natalie appeared next to me and announced, 'I've told Ashley that you don't eat anything, Emma, *that's* how you lost weight. You just don't eat, or you throw it up.'

You could have heard my jaw hit the floor. Obviously, Natalie was right, but my problem with this was not only that it was done to humiliate me, but also that Natalie herself had a very difficult history with food and I didn't think her suddenly opting to address my eating disorder through a proclamation of concern for Ashley was genuine, as in the years she had been privy to my problem she had never mentioned it before. She laid her hand protectively on Ashley's shoulder and, slurring, continued, 'You shouldn't lie to her Emma, it's not fair, it's filling her head with shit. Just be honest, you lost weight through cheating, not hard work.' Ashley smiled apologetically at me as I said I needed to go to the bathroom. I walked straight past it, and out of the door.

*

I awoke in my bed in my parents' house on Sunday morning, anxiety-ridden and frightened, of myself, my feelings, my growing rage at Natalie's words the night before. Of having to go back to the hospital. I longed for ecstasy, Valium, coke, zopiclone, anything to get me away from me. I dragged myself out of bed and checking no one was at home I got on the scales. I'd somehow gained three pounds in eight days. Fan-FUCKING-tastic. No food for me this week then. I was apparently a size ten to twelve now according to the label of the dress I had bought the day before. What a joke. 'You're a size twenty-two and don't forget it,' I said aloud to myself, and I genuinely believed it. There was something wrong with the dress, it had been labelled wrong, made wrong, it must have been. For a fleeting second, I wondered if I wasn't perhaps as big as I thought I was, but sensing my break in self-hatred the voice swooped in. *Then why are you single? Why does nobody want you if you aren't a fat heap of lard? At nineteen stone, looking bad, feeling terrible, no one wanted you. At ten stone you're still disgusting and unwanted.*

Eating vs not eating vs thinking thin means happy vs secretly knowing that I was no happier now than I had been two years ago. I still felt huge and I was still totally consumed by food. I collapsed down on the kitchen floor and drew my knees towards my face, hoping the voice wouldn't start again, but of course it did.

Your friends aren't interested, you're fucking insane, you're not making any progress. You're scared of living, scared of dying. You're fat, nope, scrap that, you're obese, you're painfully ugly, you're stupid, you're boring, you're a liar and a fraud. Oh and don't forget you killed the only thing that ever loved you, murdered your own dog, I mean that's really something. And what about Dan, guess he must have seen you for what you really were?

I shoved my fingers in my ears and screamed, and screamed, 'Shut up, shut up, shut up,' until all I could hear was a ringing in my head, a violent drumming of bells that threatened to never stop.

By the time my parents got back home, I was showered, dressed, smiling and ready to visit my grandmother in Surrey. The moment they left me alone I went to the nearest pharmacy and bought blades. I used them in a public toilet and felt nothing as I bloodied the floor of the cubical. Prue had texted me asking how my weekend was going and I'd told her it had been bad, that I'd cut and was feeling like hell; she didn't reply.

*

On Monday I was woken by Derron who told me I had a management meeting in an hour. I'd slept through firm and found out that Prue had announced to them all that I'd cut whilst down at my grandmother's. In the rendition I heard from Katie,

Prue had made it as dramatic as possible and told them she had been in 'terrible turmoil' at having to carry the information all by herself over the weekend. Derron dragged me into a room with Dr Bardo. I was angrier than I had been in a long time with what I thought of as Prue's betrayal, which led to my lips slamming shut and refusing to open throughout the meeting. They eventually told me to leave the room halfway through as their exasperation was becoming obvious. I sat in the lobby for fifteen minutes until I was called back in.

'Emma, if you don't start talking this week, you'll have to be short-leaved,' said Dr Bardo. I rolled my eyes at her and again saying nothing walked out of the room. I was angering myself. I felt immature and stupid, but I just couldn't talk to them even though I wanted to. I couldn't allow myself to feel vulnerable; I didn't want to be exposed. Natalie had exposed me, Prue had exposed me, I wasn't going to let anyone else.

As I walked back to my room I bumped into Judy. 'Emma, Prue told us that you have self-harmed and I need to see your cuts.' I refused. I didn't want to show her. Again, the feeling of forced exposure took me back to the negative aspects of my mind that I was doing everything to block out. I should have told her that, I should have explained why I didn't want to show her, why I couldn't bear to lift even an inch of my sleeve up, that I felt all my boundaries and walls had been ripped away and I couldn't take anyone else jeopardising what was left of my safety – but I didn't. I maintained my cold expression and said, 'They're superficial, Judy. I'm not showing you anything.'

She pursed her lips, looking like she was doing her best to remain professional. 'Right, Emma. This is refusing to work with us, not engaging in treatment, and it's just not acceptable.' She turned around and shut the staffroom door in my face. Now I'd done it. I walked away, bumped into Katie in the hallway and started crying.

'What's wrong, Em?' she pleaded as I began to hit the wall and scream. Her sympathy quickly turned to annoyance at my refusal to open up to her and she shouted, 'How can I help you if you do this?'

I began hollering back at her. *I try to talk to Prue and she tells everyone – I try to talk to you and you get annoyed. I can't talk to anyone! I don't trust any of you!* I saw Prue out of the corner of my eye – but I didn't care, I was glad she'd heard me. It hadn't occurred to me that she really was worried about me; in my mind she had told everyone to get attention for herself.

The next morning, with Johanna's help, I did manage to speak in firm, ever so slightly. But thankfully it was enough to get Judy off my back and ensure I wasn't sent home on short leave. Prue apologised to me, and me to her, and we spent a lot of the following week together along with Ben, Laura and Ellie. Ellie was now five months pregnant and I'd gone out with her a few times to buy baby clothes and a sky-blue bassinet, which sat empty opposite my bed in our room, she would fuss around it, holding up pastel babygros, asking me what baby names I liked and pondering for hours on whether she would prefer a boy or girl.

*

Over the next week we had some new arrivals and departures at the hospital. Katie had finished her treatment and left for a new life not too far away in a one-bedroom flat in East London; Sandra had finally been discharged as they felt they couldn't help her any more; and Angela also left. I had started to form a friendship with her and it was a shame that she was going but her funding had run out, as had her year in the Caddick, so she had no other option but to leave, back out to the real world and whatever awaited her there.

37

THE BABY'S COMING

"Actually I don't remember being born,
it must have happened during one of my black outs."

— JIM MORRISON

One of the new faces and Sandra's replacement in the room I shared with Ellie was Leah. At first glance sixteen-year-old Leah looked like any other teenage girl and she quickly set about decorating her side of the room with drawings of unicorns, cards with embroidered flowers on them, and dozens of photos of herself with various people, kids that looked about the same age all hanging out and having fun together. She was pretty, with an almost cherubic face, light eyes and strawberry blond hair that rested perfectly on her shoulders. But Leah had a life that most sixteen year olds couldn't conjure up in their worst nightmares, she was a prostitute and had been heavily addicted to heroin before being admitted. She had been due to start at the Caddick several months earlier but had had to go in to hospital for a termination that had been the result of a night of work that had 'gone wrong' – whether that meant she had been raped or was just too high to know what was going on was anyone's guess. Leah was a fan of spaghetti-strap vest tops and short skirts, which ordinarily wouldn't have bothered me but her milky skin sat underneath hundreds of cherry red gashes. The fresh cuts and scars covered her body like ivy covers a garden wall and every time I looked at her I felt triggered, but of course, I couldn't stop looking. A part of me wanted to ask her to cover up, but what right did I have? And did I really not want to see?

Leah had only been in our room a couple of nights when one afternoon I was sitting in a coffee shop in town and got a call from Prue. Her voice sounded frantic.

'Emma? It's Ellie, she went to the hospital with a stomach ache, none of the staff went with her, but she keeps ringing me asking me to go, will you come?'

I thought about the fact that earlier that day Prue had been told by the staff not to get so involved with Ellie's pregnancy and to try and get some space from her – they had, however, failed to tell Ellie not to call Prue. 'We just think, given everything you've been through, that you need to create some distance from Ellie,' Judy had said, pushing her glasses back onto her nose. Ellie of course wasn't in firm, she was still in bed snoring when I had left the bedroom to go downstairs.

'Why?' asked Prue sitting back in her chair with a blanket pulled around her.

'It must be very triggering for you, Prue,' began Nurse Max, 'considering your past, to be around someone who is pregnant, and who relies so heavily on you?'

Prue picked at a small pink stain on her jeans. 'Well, it is… it can be. But she needs me. She needs support.'

Max nodded empathetically. 'I agree, she does, but you need to take a step back. I doubt the staff are alone in feeling this way?' He looked around the room beckoning others to speak up. A few people nodded.

'I think they're right,' said Kane raising his gaze from the floor to look at Prue. 'You can't get too involved with this. It's going to trigger you, badly...' Kane shrugged, 'But, maybe that's what you want?'

'What do you mean?' Prue stopped picking at the stain and stared at him.

'Hey, don't give me that look,' he said smiling gently at her, 'I'm not trying to piss you off... I think that sometimes we need a reason to do damage, to hurt ourselves... so we chase things that could harm us, just so that when they do, we can pretend it was *that thing* that caused it, and not just the demons inside.'

'Emma?' Prue said again. 'Will you please meet me at the maternity wing, we need to make sure Ellie's okay?'

'Of course I will.' If Prue was going to be there for Ellie, I was going to be there for Prue.

Within an hour we were standing by her bedside in the maternity ward, not too far from the Caddick. She was hooked up to a monitor to hear the baby's heartbeat and was propped up in her bed looking scared and out of her depth. A couple of doctors came and went mentioning the possibility of a urine infection or appendicitis. I went to the vending machine to get us all some chocolate and Ellie a drink. When I came back in the room Johanna had arrived.

'I'm sure it's just a urine infection,' she said. Prue and I gladly accepted her words and all sat talking, waiting for Ellie's tests to come back. It was 7pm and technically Johanna was off duty. We stepped outside the room with her.

'Guys, I'm actually supposed to be meeting someone for a drink, do you mind if I go? You can call the Caddick and ask them to ring me if anything happens.'

Prue looked worried but I chimed in, 'Yeah, go. We'll be okay. It's just an infection.' So off Johanna went.

It was almost two hours later as Prue and I were getting up

to leave, when suddenly Ellie sat bolt upright in the bed. 'Oh no. I've just weed myself.' She covered her mouth, embarrassed and began to laugh. Prue turned and looked at me, the colour draining from her face. I knew what she was thinking but it couldn't be right. Ellie was only six months pregnant. She shrieked again, not laughing this time. 'Seriously guys, I can't stop weeing! I haven't wet myself for years!' Prue ran out to get a doctor as I sat with an increasingly panicking Ellie. 'My waters can't have broken can they, Emma?' I felt my eyes widen as I searched for a reassuring smile that didn't come. Prue walked in with a doctor who felt Ellie's stomach.

'Okay, we're going to have to do an internal examination.' Another male doctor came in behind her. Ellie shook her head. 'You're not doing an internal examination.' As the male doctor stepped towards her saying they had to, she shouted, 'Get away from me. You're not touching me. Get out! Get out!' Amid the escalating shouts, Prue and I convinced her that she had to have it done, for the baby's sake. 'Will you stay with me?' she said grabbing onto my arm, her eyes filling up.

I knew this whole thing must have been killing Prue, and quickly said, 'You go call the Caddick, hon, I'll stay.' She looked at me as if I had a halo above my head and scurried out. I could hear her from outside the door trying to be quiet as she hissed, 'Get Johanna back here *now!*' I moved to the top of the bed and looked down at Ellie.

'Please Emma, don't let them do this to me?' I gripped her hand. 'El, we need to know the baby is all right, I know it's horrible, but I'm here, I won't leave.' She was crying hysterically as they began the exam. A couple of times I had to push her down as she tried to get up – I was mortified for her, and myself and even the doctors.

'Stop! *Stop* it! It hurts! Emma, please make them stop!' I squeezed her hand and kept telling her it was almost over, silently wishing myself dead for being the person who was holding her down and letting these people hurt her... I knew they were doctors, I knew this was normal, but I couldn't help it.

As Ellie cried the doctors covered her back up and Prue came in. 'Johanna will be here soon,' she said sitting next to me on the edge of Ellie's bed. Ellie looked at me. 'It's not my baby is it? He's not ready yet, it can't be, can it?'

I smiled a neurotic smile and said, 'No, it can't be.' Half an hour trickled by like a year, and like the second coming a bleary-eyed Johanna appeared in the doorway. As she sat down I could smell the alcohol on her breath but was so glad to see her I could have thrown my arms around her.

Prue told her what had happened and what was now a clearly tipsy Johanna sat stoically back in her chair and said, 'Definitely a UTI.' Prue flashed her a look that made me glad I wasn't Johanna and we all stood up as the doctors came back in.

The female doctor had an expression on her face which meant one thing – one thing Prue and I saw coming before she opened her mouth. The words we were dreading toppled out like a car crash in slow motion.

'Well Ellie, it seems your waters have broken and the baby's coming.'

Ellie began to shriek. 'No! No! He's not ready, he's not ready yet, he'll die. Don't let my baby die!' Her sobs filled the entire room like a deafening siren. I looked at Prue, her hazel eyes were black. I was obviously petrified for Ellie and the baby, but I was equally scared for Prue at this point. I knew she must be somewhere around the seventh circle of hell by now and I didn't know how I could help her. My own head was floating so far away that the only thing that was keeping me grounded was knowing that if my face changed from a neutral expression in the slightest way we would lose Ellie completely to her panic.

The baby wasn't in immediate danger and although her waters had broken the doctors said labour had not properly began, but yes, her twenty-four-week-old baby was on his way and it would be nothing short of a miracle if he survived. As Ellie continued to speak with the doctor, Johanna, Prue and I huddled outside the room. Johanna opened her mouth, and I saw Prue's expression change as she waited for the words of hope to come out, the words that were about to save us all.

'She's...'

Yes, come on, Johanna, I quietly pleaded, *give us the magical cure, fix this.* I smiled reassuringly at Prue as if to say, 'Don't worry, she's about to make everything okay.' Johanna started again. 'She's... just... a kid... fuck.' Oh dear. Hello Dante, I know I'm late but can I come in? It suddenly dawned on me that we were no longer two psychiatric patients standing with our therapist. We were three sailors clinging on to the same life raft as our ship sank and the sharks encircled, each as terrified as the next, each hoping the other would save us.

After putting our Stepford smiles back on, Prue and I happily agreed to go and pick up some of Ellie's things. Once in the car, we were silent. The only sound was Prue's Nissan's screeching brakes every time she realised she was going too fast. In what seemed like a second we were parked outside the Caddick. She turned off the engine but neither of us moved an inch. Several minutes passed and, eventually, Prue spoke.

'I can't go in.'

I let her words fall into the dust all around us and unable to blink said, 'Me neither.'

'I can't face them, Em. I can't speak to any of them.'

'I know, I don't want to either.' We sat there in a thick, heavy silence for what seemed like forever. And eventually devised the best route to get in and out of the Caddick without being noticed.

Somehow, we managed it. Up through the staff's staircase, past the closed dispensary, into my bedroom and back to the car without a soul spotting us.

We hugged Ellie tight and promised to be back in the morning, Johanna had agreed to stay with her and we were finally, and thankfully, told to go back to the ESPD unit and get some rest.

As I tiptoed past a sleeping Leah and slipped into my bed in the darkness, I prayed for sleep to find me and miraculously, it did.

38

DYSMORPHIC

"How blessed are some people, whose lives have no fears, no dreads; to whom sleep is a blessing that comes nightly, and brings nothing but sweet dreams."

— BRAM STOKER, *Dracula*

The following morning's firm saw Prue and me team up to tell the staff how useless they all were (bar Johanna) for allowing Ellie to go to the hospital alone the day before and then we jointly batted away any attempt to find out how being at the hospital had been – it was not something that could be discussed with anyone that hadn't been there; it was too horrific to try and make them understand and attempting to explain it would have somehow cheapened the whole ordeal. It was better kept in the darkness where we had left it. Prue and I walked out of firm together, got in her car and left.

It was Friday and after a stop-off at the store to buy Ellie a few things, we dropped them into her as she lay in her hospital bed and said we would be back the next day. But as it happened, her baby came that afternoon so neither of us got to see her until the following week when she came back to the Caddick. Her son,

Jack, was born weighing just three pounds. He was put straight in an incubator and all anyone could do was to hold their breath and hope that he would survive. I took two days leave to visit my grandmother who had been taken to hospital, and after forty-eight hours away from the Caddick, I was actually pleased to be returning.

*

It was early afternoon when I buzzed the door to be let into the reception area. I knew group had begun, so made my way up to the room where I was naively expecting Ellie to be sitting with Mr Newman and Johanna. As I opened the door I was met with Aaron, and Leah, who had just started in the group. There was also a new face there, Harriet.

Harriet was the same age as me and at around thirty stone and six foot she was hard to miss. She had only been at the hospital for a few days before I left for my forty-eight-hour leave and I hadn't really spoken to her, she would stare at me in firm and community and there was something about her I just found incredibly disconcerting. Although it hadn't been brought up in any of the meetings she obviously had problems with her hygiene and, like Sandra, refused to wash or bathe herself. This obviously caused Harriet to smell really bad. Added to that she was also in the habit of wearing teeny tiny outfits – little crop tops, very short skirts – which meant that the scent that came off her could never really be masked by layers of clothes or a coat or anything like that. And it was rancid, suffocating, but she hadn't been there long enough for anyone to bring it up with her yet.

The three of them were sitting in the group room quietly with Mr Newman; no Ellie, no Johanna. I sat down.

'Where's Ellie?'

Mr Newman looked back. 'She's at the hospital with the baby, Emma.'

'Oh.'

The room fell silent again. I knew that I should be the one to coax them all to talk, but I just couldn't, I was too consumed by my own problems. I needed someone to ask me how I was; they all knew what had happened over the last few days, first the hospital with Ellie, and then my grandmother being unwell. Predictably, I started to feel the gnawings of annoyance start up. The fact that I was so upset about not being asked how I was only goaded the internal voices to tell me how selfish and unreasonable I was being. It's a strange thing, to be in a silent room and have a ferocious screaming argument going on inside your head. After what felt like a lifetime Mr Newman spoke.

'There has been some concern for you, Emma, about your safety. The staff have heard from Johanna that you had a very difficult experience last week with Ellie.'

'My safety? You mean self-harm? Yes, I'm close to it.'

The admission came more easily than it ever had. I continued, 'What happened last week was horrendous. I'm sure Johanna told you about it?'

He nodded his head once as if to say yes. 'Not only did you have to support Ellie, but I should imagine you had to support Prue as well.'

I swallowed hard, worried about betraying Prue's secrets to Leah, Aaron and Harriet; none of them knew about Prue's history and I wasn't about to tell them. 'Prue kept it together. We both did. But yes, I will never forget that night as long as I live. And yes, I don't feel good at the moment, I feel pissed off. And overlooked.'

Mr Newman paused, I'm sure silently urging one of them to speak, but of course they didn't – and why would they? Leah and Aaron were sixteen years old, and Harriet was brand new. After half an hour of silence I couldn't take any more and walked out. As I got down the five flights of stairs the rage, the voices, the urge to destroy something, *anything*, was deafening. It was the frustration of being in a room with a therapist, and a good one at that, but not allowing myself to interact with him, or utilise the space. The idea of opening my mouth and saying how I was feeling seemed mortifying to me – the potential judgement that could come with it felt unbearable. So instead I would sit in my self-inflicted silence, simmering like a pot of boiling water, all the while watching myself from the edge of the room thinking 'Talk Emma! Just talk'. I kicked open the dining room door with full force – how it didn't slam back in my face as it ricocheted off the wall I don't know. Judy, Prue, Esther, Adaline, Marie and Sal all jumped about two feet in the air. Esther (of course) started crying – which only stoked the embers of my anger even more. *Oh good*, I thought, *someone else to take the emphasis off me.* I sarcastically smiled, sadistically quipped 'Sorry' and continued marching upstairs like a drill sergeant.

It was there, on those stairs, that the memory blocks begin, where it all must have begun to get too much for my conscious brain to digest. As I pushed open the bedroom door the room was dark, my curtains were drawn and as I heavy-handedly tried to open them they fell down. When the curtain rail snapped, so did whatever it was that was keeping my sanity in place. Hot salty tears began to stream from my eyes, and I began to shout. And shout, and scream. About what, I don't know, I just remember the sound of my roaring voice echoing around the large space. I threw my lamp across the room and in one movement swept everything off my dresser. Susie came in, I think she hugged me, I don't remember. I also don't remember how I got on the other side of the room but suddenly there was a glass in my hand, and just as suddenly it was hitting the sink in the corner of our bedroom with full force. The shards shattered into a thousand pieces – an almighty crash followed by the glass curling and rising back out of the sink, coming towards me like a wave. At that point I was on my knees on the floor screaming like I was being murdered; Susie's voice was occasionally audible through the noise. And eventually her shouting snapped me back into reality.

'Emma! Stop it! Stop it!'

Her words began to sober me up, I looked ahead of me at the sink. Half of it was in bits on the floor – it was a big industrial porcelain sink, how an earth had it broken? I was confused.

'What's that?' I said aloud.

Susie looked angry as she squealed, 'You did that!' To this day I have no memory of it breaking.

As I looked around the war zone of my shared bedroom I pinged back into reality, and desperately knew what I needed. I scrambled up from the floor, grabbed my bag, went to the toilet and cut. At this point Susie must have rushed off to get the staff. I came out a few moments later, completely calm, tissues wedged down my sleeve to stem the blood from dripping onto the carpet. I walked back to my bedroom, gracefully knelt on the floor and began to pick up the shards of glass, neatly and gently placing them into an open newspaper. The door flung open and I looked around to see Sal, Susie, Prue and Judy standing over me; to say they looked panicked would have been an understatement. I turned back away from them and finished picking up the glass. Smiling, I got up and slightly too chirpily said, 'I'm off to get a hoover.'

Prue followed me, grabbing my arm. 'You need to stop, honey.' She made me sit down on a little sofa outside the bathroom.

Judy approached us and nervously sat down opposite me. Her voice was soft as she said, 'What on earth's going on, Emma?'

Once I began to speak, all my pretence fell away. 'I just don't want to do this any more. I can't. There is no point. No future. No past. No one needs me right now; it's the perfect time to die. It's the perfect time to do *it*.'

Judy, for the first time since I had been there, looked at me like she understood. 'I'm so glad you have been honest with us. Well done for speaking and letting us in, Emma.'

I was crying again as I said, 'I'm so sorry about the room, I didn't mean to do that to the sink, I really didn't. I would never do that on purpose.'

Putting her hand on my knee, Judy answered, 'I would rather you smash the sink than hurt yourself.'

I promised Judy I would go and get her if I felt unsafe and went back to my room. I walked in expecting to have to clean up, but every trace of glass and porcelain was gone, my curtain rail was in it's place and my things had been put back on my dresser. I sat down on my bed for a few moments thinking about how grateful I was that even in that state people had not judged me, and had instead come to my aid, cleaning up the mess I had made and talking me back around. And although I had said it to Judy, it wasn't that I actually wanted to kill myself, far from it – I just couldn't see a way out of my own mind. Every time I felt a glimmer of hope it seemed to be destroyed just as quickly. The despair within my brain was so powerful, so all consuming, that with little effort it could shut out any trace of hope and every attempt at moving forward. Once you've thought about suicide (and I mean *seriously* thought about it), the idea itself becomes a worm in your ear, like a song that gets stuck in your head for days or weeks on end. You find yourself singing along to the words without even realising it; it becomes the screen saver of your mind, the default key, and no matter how you try to shake it off, or out run it, it's always there, silent and undeterred loitering in the shadows of your every thought.

Realising it was my day to cook I went down to the kitchen to make dinner with Prue. After cooking for everyone (with no intention of eating the calorie-filled cheese and tuna bake that had taken two hours to construct), I sat with Prue as she ate, feeling like the day was catching up with me; the urge to escape and be by myself seemed tempting. I glanced over at Judy who was busy eating and chatting to the other patients and quietly said 'I think I'm going to go out and get a coffee.'

Prue swallowed the food in her mouth. 'But you haven't had any dinner?'

'I just want to get out and, if I don't go while everyone's distracted, you know they'll stop me-.'

Prue, no doubt sensing that if left alone my mind would begin to once again turn on me, said 'I know you want to be on your own but I don't think it's a good idea.' She spooned another mouthful in, talking around it, 'Why don't we go and see Ellie in the hospital instead? We can take her food? If you still want to be alone after that, I won't stop you.'

Perhaps she was right. I nodded, 'Alright'.

Ellie had been staying at the hospital with Jack and was clearly deprived of human contact; she didn't stop talking from the time we arrived to the time we left. She told us about the birth, despite my several attempts at pulling a face that suggested she not talk about it in front of Prue. It was of course good to see Ellie, I had missed her, but it left us both drained of all life and when we got back in Prue's car I said I wanted to go for a walk. She reluctantly nodded her head. 'Okay.'

I got the bus to the nearest cafe and tried to regain some semblance of myself. Of course, sitting in a coffee shop surrounded by over-indulged teenagers loudly talking about their 'problems' (not having the right outfit to go skiing in France – perish the thought) and trying to write in my journal about the last few days only dragged up all the feelings of upset and anger within me and, by the time I was walking back to the Caddick, the only thing I could think about was self-harming.

Slipping into the hospital completely unnoticed was becoming a skill I was good at, the only person who ever witnessed my comings and goings was Len as he peered at me from behind the reception desk, always pointedly staring up at the clock as he buzzed the doors open. As usual, I bypassed him, silently climbed the staircase no one used and went straight upstairs into the bathroom, locked the door and cut. Although I thought I had been stealthy someone else must have spotted me as a little while later Prue knocked on the door.

'Emma? Can I come in?' I quickly used toilet paper to clean up the blood around me, and shoved the razor blade into my bag. I opened the door and she sat next to me on the floor. We spoke for a long time. She told me that whilst I had been out she had lost herself completely and kept hearing the voice of one of her abusers shouting at her. 'It was like he was here, I kept thinking he was in the room.' She stopped abruptly and looked at me. 'You've cut haven't you?' I nodded. There was a long silence as I waited for her response 'Well. If you don't need stitches, and if you aren't going to keep going, I understand. I understand you need to do it. I wish you wouldn't, but I know you have to.' A mutual understanding between cutters. She got up and held the door open for me to follow.

'I think I might have a bath actually, hon, seeing as I'm in here.'

She didn't look convinced as she closed the door behind her and left.

I sat still staring at the wall of the tiny bathroom for what felt like the longest time and thought about what she had said about her abuser. It didn't take long for me to start cutting again, though this time, more deeply.

Lost somewhere inside myself I suddenly heard, '*Emma? What are you doing?*' It was Kirk ('Your arm's a bloody mess' Kirk). Shit.

I called out, 'I'm fine,' but his blunt reply was simply, 'Come and see me in the office, I want you there in five minutes or I'm calling the police.' Fuck.

Blood dripping through my sleeve despite my best efforts to stem it, I went to the office. I knocked on the door as quietly as I could hoping he wouldn't hear, but he opened it quickly and said, 'Well, you've cut haven't you? Let's see.' I obediently rolled up my sleeve, he cringed but gently said, 'Come on, I'll get some bandages.' I sat down in the dispensary and as a stark contrast from the last time, Kirk couldn't have been more empathetic and caring. As he unsuccessfully tried to stop the bleeding he said, 'You know, a lot of people here find you very intimidating to confront. Even the staff! You're scarily good at deflecting.' I sighed and looked down, but he continued, 'But I don't find you at all intimidating.' He smiled warmly and I felt relieved.

'Kirk, I know I can be acidic and I'm really difficult most of the time, but I don't mean to be. The people who know me can break through that barrier in seconds.'

He smiled again, 'I know. It takes time, Emma, that's all. You'll get there.' After he bandaged my arm he led me out of the room. 'Come and find me if you need support. I'll be up all night!' he said laughing to himself. I thanked him and went back to my room.

The place was mental that night, my little episode didn't hold a candle to the other things that were going on inside its walls. I was dreading the morning's firm in which I would have to confess my sins to the world, smashing the sink, self-harming not once but twice, or was it three times? I'd lost count. I had also been told a few days before in firm that I would have to move rooms to share with Harriet. This came as blow to me as there was just something about her I didn't like, I couldn't have said what it was exactly, but every fibre of my being told me to avoid her; something that would be increasingly difficult once sharing a bedroom with her – it was hard enough being in group with her.

For some reason I was not challenged in firm, even by Judy. I told them I'd broken the sink, told them I'd cut, then cut again and it was pretty much left at that. After moving all my things down the hall into my new bedroom I sat on the bed trying my best to feel in control and not upset at having to leave Ellie who I'd been sharing with for so many months. The door swung open and Harriet came in and lay on her bed facing the wall.

It bothered me hugely that I felt as uncomfortable as I did when she was around but I didn't have any legitimate reason for feeling that way. A feeling was not a good enough answer for anyone, the staff or me included, to dislike her as much as I seemed to.

I was starting to feel very excluded from the group. Ellie was rarely there now, and Leah and Aaron were so young that I just couldn't relate to them. Plus, the way Harriet looked at me made it impossible for me to talk. I didn't want someone I didn't trust listening to anything private I had to say, so I stopped saying anything, and then stopped going to the group. I would walk in, stay for five minutes and walk out despite Johanna's attempts to stop me.

I did, however, go to my sessions with Nora, which were becoming increasingly strained. Something about Harriet was triggering my feelings about my body to grow much worse. I often sat opposite her in groups wondering if there was in fact much difference between us physically. My image of myself was so distorted that I actually believed that at ten stone I looked the same as someone who was nearer thirty stone.

'There was something wrong with Dan. There must have been for me not to have disgusted him.'

Nora sat forward in her chair. 'Dan felt that way about you because you allowed him to have an opinion, without contaminating it with your delusions about yourself.' I shook my head as if it would stop her words getting in, but she ignored my attempts to rebuff her and went on, 'Emma, your feelings about your body are in your head. Your feelings about your personality are in your head.' She paused. 'Why are you surprised you do not receive love if you put out a message that says "I am disgusting"?'

I had nothing to say. I just stared at her. I wanted to believe her but I just couldn't.

*

'Oh, that was a poor effort!' Prue fingered a scar on her arm. Watching her paw at her skin was as enticing to me as looking at skinny girls on the Internet. Only this wasn't on the Internet – it was next to me on a bed, letting me get a first-hand view. I was completely drawn in by her arms. To the point of obsession. I didn't want to see because I knew it would trigger my urges to cut, but I couldn't look away. Her skin was a car crash that I knew I shouldn't look at, but I just couldn't help myself. She was provocative sometimes in the way she spoke, knowing full well that her 'poor effort' scars were gashes that had required thirty-plus stitches and could have quite easily killed her. It wasn't so much like looking at the scars on her skin, more like looking for the skin around her scars. I was jealous. It was a strange, lustful jealousy that I couldn't understand but when I looked at her arms I saw clear, defined pain, justified, obvious, terrible, heartbreaking, and that's what I thirsted for, for people to look at my body and feel the things I felt. Lying there next to her I remembered Nora's words about Prue and me 'dragging each other into an underworld'. Perhaps that idea wasn't so absurd after all.

39

HARRIET

'I dare anybody to look at me and say I'm anorexic.
I'm so totally not.'

– Fiona Apple

I was at my lowest weight, surpassing my ten-stone goal and still determined to lose as much as possible. Every comment that was made about me 'not looking well' just spurred me on further. I had started off at the hospital trying to hide my eating disorder, but as no one was challenging me I'd stopped bothering. If ever there was the question of me having dinner there I would literally laugh in the face of whoever was asking me. As long as I turned up to lunch, with my plate full of iceberg lettuce and a spoonful of couscous, I felt like no one had a right to say anything. I wasn't skinny, I wasn't in danger of fading away, and I was prepared to restrict and purge until I got to what I deemed was 'perfect' and no one, *no one*, was going to get in my way.

Living in a room with Harriet was accelerating my weight loss dramatically. I had begun to despise her. I continually had the windows open in the bedroom because I could not get the smell she created out of my nostrils. And when it wasn't her unwashed body I was smelling, it was the food leftovers under her bed that wafted out and over to my side of the room. Plates of moulding sandwiches, chocolate bars, glasses of fizzy drinks that were fermenting they had been there so long. The dirty underwear left in the middle of the floor, the smell of her feet, her unwashed hair. I couldn't bear it, and I couldn't bear her. I had walked in to the room one afternoon and found her standing over my bed with my diary laying open in front of her. 'What are you doing?' I said as I snatched it up and closed the book. 'It was already out,' she grunted, not a flicker of remorse on her face. I glanced at the bedside table where I kept it, the drawer open and everything looking as though it had been rifled through. I stood there staring at her, fury coursing through my body. 'You went through my things? You read my diary?' She ignored me and began to walk out of the room 'You can't just go through my stuff, Harriet!' I shouted after her. She turned to face me and with an odd, callous smirk snickered, 'I can do what I want.' Who knows what she read? What private thoughts of mine had been violated? From then on I carried everything with me, my journal never left my side again.

As well as going through my things, and the hygiene problem, she lied, constantly. She made up stories, about herself, and about everyone else. She tried to turn people on the ESPD against each other and had successfully nestled in with one of the new ringleaders on the family unit, Kiera. Kiera had just got out of prison and she was angry. Angry about everything. This anger manifested into a cold, bloody rage that cocked, aimed and fired its way at Laura on a daily basis, and obviously, as I was friends with Laura, I too was in the firing line.

*

355

'Your delusions about yourself are just not real, they border on psychotic.' Nora did a mock laugh. 'I mean, they're mad, Emma!'

I paused as I tried to absorb her words. She continued, 'You're like a geisha, your make-up is your mask. You need to wear less make-up to test out whether people find you as vile as you think they will.'

It was my turn to laugh. 'Nora, if you think for one second I am going to start parading myself around without make-up on you've got another thing coming.'

'I didn't say *no* make-up, I said less. You do not test these things out about yourself, you keep them locked up secretly so they just fester inside you. You need to let someone in.'

*

The following night I refused to sleep in the same room with Harriet. When the evening came, my facade crumbled and I simply couldn't take any more; the idea of even one more hour in the room with her was too overwhelming. I locked myself in the bathroom, swaddled inside a deafening anxiety and paranoia, and cut.

But the cutting wouldn't stop the fact that I still had to go in to the bedroom, so what was I going to do? Admitting defeat I went to the staffroom where I found Poppy, and bursting into tears said I couldn't take any more, that I felt ill and depressed and if I was made to stay in the hole of a room again I would snap. She gently put her arm around my shoulder and said, 'That's fine, Emma, I understand. We'll make up a bed for you in the spare room. Let's dress those wounds.'

Poppy Steri-Stripped my cuts closed, bandaged my arms and took me to the spare bedroom where she'd had the bed made up for me with fresh white sheets. As I got in and nestled under the covers I noticed a chair at the foot of the bed. 'It's for

Petrice, Emma,' Poppy said, catching the look of concern on my face. 'I'm putting you on a one-to-one for the night.' A one-to-one meant that a nurse had to watch you all night in case you did anything to harm yourself. 'But, Poppy I don't want...'

'Shh, shh,' she said gently as Petrice walked in. 'It's just Petrice. We want to make sure you're safe, you've had a rough night. Any more cutting and you'll need stitches, and no one wants that. So, your options are here with Petrice, who you know...' Petrice smiled sweetly at me, '... or on a ward that you don't. It's your choice?' I didn't answer, and lay down. 'Good call!' said Poppy over her shoulder as she left the room. I listened to the wooden chair creak as Petrice sat down. She sighed heavily, resigning herself to a night of boredom.

The next morning in firm, without Harriet there and back on my own without Petrice at my side, I spilled my guts about how being in the room with Harriet was damaging my health, physically and mentally. I was careful with wording, and knew that I had to be open with them to get what I wanted – the goal of which was to get back in my old room. I needn't have bothered constructing what I thought was going to be a convincing argument, Poppy had taken Judy and a couple other nurses into the bedroom to show them the squalor and, disgusted, they all agreed it was not appropriate for Harriet to be sharing a room with anyone. I was relieved when Poppy smiled across the firm room at me and said, 'It's fine, Emma. We all agree, the room is, well, vile, to be honest. Although we aren't in agreement with your cutting, we understand why it happened. You can move back into the room with Ellie and Leah.' Sweet, sweet justice.

*

THIN. THIN. THIN. I was obsessed. A four-letter word that controlled every breath I took. Every thought would connect to a calorie and a way to lose it. I had gone past my goal weight and I was determined to get lower.

I didn't care that I had bags around my eyes, I didn't care that I spent most of my days glugging water and eating watermelon in a desperate attempt to not pass out. My BMI and counting calories were the most important things to me. Dan had been gone almost three months and, without him around to distract me, my weight was the most pressing thing on my mind. He had stopped contacting me altogether at this point, and I should have been feeling the pain from that, but instead I doused the upset in a balsamic dressing, swallowed it, threw it up and flushed it down the toilet. When I was thin enough, he would come crawling. None of the staff at the hospital seemed to notice – or if they did they didn't challenge me. I would watch Kane eat dinner every night and then leave afterwards to go for 'a walk'. He'd wink at me as he sloped past with his backpack on and his coat done up. I was one of only a handful of people who knew he had about 40kg of weights in his bag, probably about the same amount tied to his wrists and ankles, and as if that wasn't enough, several hundred layers of clothing for the maximum 'how much will it take to sweat this weight off?' effect.

*

My dislike of Harriet grew with an unbridled passion every moment of every day; the mere sight of her made my head start thudding as if it were going to explode. She reminded me of everything I didn't want to be, and in my warped mind I couldn't help but compare our sizes, constantly worrying that I was as big as, if not bigger than, her. It was consuming me like a black smoke, filling up my lungs and choking me from the inside out.

*

'Smile all you want, Emma. You're jealous of Harriet. Think about it, what do you actually despise so much about her?'

The smirk lifted off my face as, annoyed now, I stared back at Nora. 'Hmm, let's see, her stench, the rotting food she left in the room when I was in there, the lies she tells about everyone. The complete meltdown I had as a result of having to share a room with her? That she read my diary? The fact that I think she's in this hospital because she's a compulsive liar who is absolutely desperate for attention and nothing more?'

Nora ignored me. 'I think it's because she's so big and doesn't care. She wears tiny clothes and flaunts her body and doesn't give a rats what anyone thinks of her. She certainly doesn't care what you think, of her body or her behaviour. She couldn't care less what she looks like. I think you're jealous of that.' I glared at Nora, clicking my tongue against my teeth, knowing that as usual she'd got it completely right.

'But of course this just leads back to your delusions about yourself. Harriet is a mirror for you that tells you that you need to drop the mask. The baggy clothes, the make-up, not letting anyone close to you.'

'I've told you before, Nora, I'm not going to walk around here looking like a fucking tramp, spilling my secrets to everyone who wants to hear!' I uncrossed my legs and leaned forwards slowly. 'And by the way, in case you forgot, I let someone in, didn't I? And where the fuck is he now? I'm not letting anyone else in to fuck me up even more.'

She sat in her chair, not at all fazed by me, almost smug in her resolve. 'Well then, how will you ever know if you really are what you think you are, Emma?'

*

I got to group a little late after my session but just in time to hear the most heavenly news in the world which was that Harriet had gone home for unscheduled leave. Aaron and Leah sat there with Johanna and Mr Newman looking a little sheepish; I wondered if there was more to the story about why Harriet had left.

'So, she just went?' I asked, looking at Mr Newman.

He in turn looked at my fellow patients wanting them to answer. Leah cleared her throat and began slowly, 'She... she didn't want to see you.'

'Me?' I said incredulous, as if I hadn't just spent my entire session with Nora bitching about her. 'What have I done?' Another long pause.

'No, it's not what you've done to her... It's what she's done to *you*,' said Aaron peeping up at me from behind his clump of black hair.

What? Now I was really confused. I was seven years older than both of them and wanted to shout, 'Just spit it out!' but didn't want to scare either of them; after all they were trying their best to fill me in. Leah was a bit bolder than Aaron and no doubt due to her 'profession' was much more streetwise. Oftentimes she had a twenty-year-old's head on her little sixteen-year-old shoulders, whereas Aaron seemed incredibly breakable. The staff had insinuated that he was showing signs of schizophrenia (we'd heard abstract tales here and there of sexual abuse at the hands of an older sibling, the trauma of which was obviously causing some sort of splitting inside him, I'd often see him chattering to himself – not the regular talking to yourself that most people tend to do, more of a full on back and forth conversation) but besides that he was the sweetest boy, so fragile – I really didn't want to upset him, so I tried to relax and took a deep breath trying to summon some patience and waiting for one of them to tell me what was going on.

Johanna, sensing my growing irritation and anxiety, tried to prompt them, 'I think it would be helpful for Emma if you could tell her what has happened, so that we can have a discussion about it.'

Leah started picking at one of the scabs on her pale arm. 'Me and Aaron were hanging around, sitting in the dining room this morning. Harriet was there with Kiera and a few others from the family unit but they couldn't see us from where we were... Harriet starting talking about you... started talking about things you had said in group...'

'What things?'

Leah glanced up at me then back down at her arm. 'About when you went to the hospital with Ellie.'

'Okay?' I replied keeping my voice light, trying to sound encouraging.

'She was telling Kiera everything you said about how hard it was, she basically repeated everything you'd said in our group, and also in firm. All about you wanting to self-harm, and when you were talking about Prue, it being hard for her because of her past... But she kept making stuff up, stuff you never said, making you look bad.'

'Yeah,' Aaron murmured looking up at me. 'It pissed us off cos we knew it was lies, just so she could get attention or whatever from the family unit people... So we got up and confronted her.' Aaron bit his lip as Leah continued on.

'I told her she was breaking confidence and that I was going to tell you when I saw you, and tell the staff. She knew if you found out you'd...' she trailed off trying to find the right word.

I smiled. 'Go fucking mad?'

Leah did a little smile back at me. 'Well, yeah. I mean, I would too, Emma. It was out of order.'

Aaron pushed his hair out of his eyes and began to speak again. 'So she left, she made up some crap about needing to go home but it was just to avoid having to admit to what she's done.'

Johanna and Mr Newman were looking at me, probably both trying to pre-empt how I was going to deal with this. I think my cool demeanour took them both by surprise. 'Thank you. Thank you for standing up for me, and for protecting my confidentiality, I really appreciate it. What she did was wrong, and believe me she won't get away with it.'

Johanna nodded. 'Breaching confidentiality like that is a serious issue, and you have every right to be angry, Emma. It will be dealt with when Harriet gets back.'

*

I came out of group smug and over-inflated, knowing I was the reason Harriet wasn't there and thrilled about it. Don't get me wrong, I was irate about hearing what she had done, but I was so glad she was gone that the confidentiality issue seemed secondary to me.

I walked into the alcove where everyone was occupying themselves in various ways, Kane on his guitar, Adaline sewing, Annie and Esther wrapped up in some religious conversation I was glad I wasn't part of.

'Where's Prue?'

Adaline didn't look away from her sewing as she answered, 'She's in the garden sitting behind a tree.' She paused and then somewhat triumphantly added, 'She's been there for three hours.'

I glared back at her, 'And you just left her there?'

Her accent twanged, 'Go out and find her if you're that bothered.'

I found Prue sitting behind the largest oak tree in the grounds and quietly sat down next to her not saying anything. As usual it was beautiful out there, the bright green leaves and flowers trying their best to cover the darkness that emanated around the building. A few minutes passed and Prue looked up into the distance. 'Dr Bardo made me go through the rules.'

I felt my stomach drop. 'Oh.'

I'd heard about them briefly before, the rules that she had been taught as a child by those monsters. They made her learn them like a kid would learn the alphabet. 'Rule number one, don't open your eyes. Two, don't answer back. Three, don't speak. Four, don't scream out. Five, don't fight back. Six, don't cry.' She listed the lot of them, I cringed into the bark of the tree knowing better than to interrupt her and yet wanting to somehow make this stop. But as I had learned by now so many times, sometimes you have just sit and let someone speak without trying to fix it – though of course you'll find it's like sitting under a waterfall, being hit full force by the weight of the water and having to let it hit you; you mustn't move, mustn't falter, or you might get washed away.

'Come on, we're going to get coffee.' I grabbed her hand and led her out of the hospital.

*

We got back a few hours later and I went straight into the night meeting. Much like the Henshaw, the Caddick choose a few people to chair meetings. They would gather together every night and discuss the 'top issues' of the day – I didn't enjoy it, but the only bonus was that as a member of the chairing group your own issues were slightly skirted over, which, much like it had been in the Henshaw, came in handy for me.

Laura was being hunted by the family unit's self-enforced paedo police again. The bloodlust would occasionally die down for a couple of weeks and then rear up once more with full force; this was one of those times. The other families were all holding secret meetings, talking behind her back and threatening her.

That girl was going to pay for what she'd done for the rest of her life, and who knew, maybe that was apt. I certainly couldn't call it any more. I just knew that I felt sorry for the Laura I *knew* today. The sixteen-year-old Laura was someone else. I was torn, knowing that the people who disliked her had a right to do so, their judgement was understandably coloured by their own awful experiences and here they were being forced to live, eat and breath the same air as a walking, talking daily reminder of that very thing they were trying to escape from. And, just like them all, I too had recoiled in horror when I had learned of what she had done. But she was being bullied, threatened – she was at risk, Sam was at risk, and I wasn't going to sit back and let it happen, even if it meant going against Kiera and the rest of the family unit.

I walked Laura to her room after the night meeting and then went back to the ESPD only to see Prue pacing around the garden. As I got out there she was bent over, hyperventilating. I ran over to her and pulled her towards me. 'Prue, come inside.'

'One keep your eyes closed… five d… don't fight b… back.' She began screaming and slumped down onto her knees on the damp grass. I wrapped my arms around her and held her like a child, rocking her back and forth as she cried. 'Shh, you're safe, you're okay now.' Kane must have heard her screams from his room and came rushing out; without saying anything he sat next to us on the grass. The sound of her sobs filled the air like glass shattering in a silent room.

Just as I felt I couldn't take any more Kane reached for my hand, squeezing it tight in the darkness, and we let Prue's waterfall cascade over us without moving.

40

THE EXORCISM OF ELLIE ROSE

"You don't blame us for being here, do you? After all, we have no place to go. No home... Incidentally, what an excellent day for an exorcism..."

— WILLIAM PETER BLATTY, *The Exorcist*

It was March. The spring was finally settling over the hospital like a welcome breath of fresh air. And with the new season, new patients had arrived: Grace, Brooke and Joe.

Grace was petite at only five foot, attractive but with an edge about her. She made no secret of the fact that she had a long history of drug addiction and had spent a lot of her younger years in juvenile detention centres and then doing various prison stints, or as she put it, 'learning lessons the hard way', as she got older. Grace spoke in a husky cockney accent and was always smiling, always friendly – I warmed to her quickly. Brooke was unconventional to look at: she was tall and broad but had such a pretty, feminine face with blindingly bright eyes. She wore an oversized red hoody everywhere she went, with a blue bandana around her neck, men's size baggy jeans and a baseball cap. Every part of her skin I could see was scarred. Her hands had cigarette burns all over them, her neck had long thin scars across it, even her cheeks had traces of silver tracks on them. Brooke was quiet, she twitched and ticked a lot, fiddled with her fingers constantly and barely spoke. Although I didn't dislike her, she made me slightly nervous – she felt like a bomb that could go off at any moment without so much as a warning.

And then, last of the trio, was Joe. Charismatic, confident, tall, slim, and tattooed. He made friends quickly in the hospital, often being the first to step in when help was needed and was always offering to support the other patients when they were in crisis. Joe could read a room instantly, he was an empath, but much more than all of that, he had the sort of deep sea green eyes that told me one thing – I was in big, big trouble.

*

In the TV room that night Petrice opened the door.

'Shouldn't you be going to bed, darling?' She gently tapped the gold watch around her wrist, her wise tone warm but firm.

'I will soon, Petrice, I promise! Ten minutes!'

She rolled her eyes disapprovingly and left. I sat there staring at the TV and sure enough ten minutes later the door creaked open again, 'Petrice, I was just going I swear...' but it wasn't Petrice, it was Joe. 'Oh!' I stopped, embarrassed. 'Sorry, I thought you were Petrice.'

He stood in front of me and gasped, holding out his hands and turning them over theatrically to examine them. 'Huh, and there was me thinking I didn't look like a voluptuous black woman any more?!'

I laughed and looked back to *Supersize vs Superskinny*.

'Can I sit in here?'

I looked back up at him. There's always that moment, isn't there? That second where you think, *This is the bit where fate is in the palm of my hand and I can choose which way to throw it.* It was nearly eleven, I was desperately tired and I needed to go to bed; I should just get up, say good night and make the right choice. I looked back at the wobbling joggers on the TV.

'Sure you can.'

Eleven o'clock saw midnight, midnight saw one and one turned to two, and with the only occasional interruption of Petrice's not-so-silent disapproval, we talked non-stop. He was twenty-eight, an Aries, his birthday had just passed – the same date as his dad's death. He had three sisters and loved to write. We quickly learned we were into the same music, taking it in turns to challenge the other on our knowledge of lyrics. Joe was well toned but very thin. I couldn't help but ask.

'I eat like a pig!' he chuckled.

'Oh God you're one of those,' I teased jokingly.

'One of what?' he said, suddenly defensive.

'Well, we're in a psychiatric hospital, Joe, and you're very slim. So you're either one of those ridiculously lucky people with a metabolism that runs at 500 miles per hour or you're like Kane.'

'Kane?' he tilted his head.

'Weights in your backpack and a pressing urge to go for "leisurely" walks after mealtimes.'

He grinned at me again but didn't respond. I had my answer; he didn't need to.

As I finally got into bed not long before the sun came up, I felt the gentle burn simmering in my stomach: something more, something good.

*

'That's what I think you're terrified of, Emma. Me getting pulled into the misery, and being stuck in there with you.'

I couldn't stop crying. I sat in Nora's office sobbing. I didn't know what was wrong with me; I had been fine just hours before as I sat with Joe but as soon as I'd woken up that good old well-trained black dog was nipping at my heels.

I was supposed to be going directly from my session to meet Ellie and get her a tattoo. She wanted 'Jack' written on her arm with his date of birth. I tried to pull myself together; this wasn't about me today and I needed to stop being so self-centred.

I sat in the bathroom, breathing slowly, reapplying make-up, putting in eye whitening drops and once my face was back to normal and I had my perfect little Stepford smile on, I went downstairs to meet Ellie and Prue.

*

Ellie got her tattoo then, as we'd already decided, we took her out to a pub with Laura for a pre-planned *two* drinks. Ellie had been under so much pressure for weeks now, constantly at the hospital watching over Jack, as well returning to the Caddick and going to all her sessions daily. It was like she had done a total one-eighty and was suddenly the all-empowering vision of self-reliance and responsibility, so we thought going out might be nice for her.

It was a quiet Tuesday evening and everything was going well. Prue, Laura and I sat chattering around the table of the little pub, not noticing as Ellie sneaked two double vodkas at the bar. She came back to the table and went onto beg us for *one more* drink.

'Oh, please guys, it's just one! I've been so responsible lately! I've done so well, I've proved everyone wrong!' She draped her arms around Prue's neck. 'Please? One! Then we'll go back! I have to be up early to go and see Jack anyway!' The pleading went on and on like a child who has set its sights on a doll it wants and, despite its parents' objections, everyone knows that doll is going home with them one way or another. We were only five minutes away from the Caddick, which foolishly lulled us into a false sense of security. How much trouble could she get into, really? We should have said no, we should have made her go back to the hospital with us then and there, but we didn't.

*

Hindsight is a beautiful thing. Ellie, right on cue, less than an hour later, vanished. She was spotted by Aaron walking from the off licence with six cans of beer and a bottle of vodka under her arm. The night staff chased her down the road and dragged her back.

She walked in with them, crying, hugging me and Prue and asking if we hated her.

'I'm sorry, I'm sorry, please don't hate me, I love you. I'm back now!' Her northern accent dragged and slurred over her every word. I said nothing as she clung to me, kissing my head. 'I love you, Emma, please forgive me?' I got her into bed with Laura's help, and waited until she fell asleep. It was so hard to be angry with her. She was only nineteen, her baby was in intensive care, she had no family and she was in a mental hospital. It's not as if she'd had much time to work on her own problems during the short pregnancy, and from the small glimpses I got in group, the last few years of her life had been fraught with pimps, violence, drugs and abuse. She desperately needed help and support, despite how tiring that would often get for everyone around her.

With Ellie fast asleep I decided it was safe to leave her and I desperately needed a time out; the evening had gone from calm and contained to a shit show, yet again. I walked downstairs and pushed open the back door. Joe was sitting on the steps leading to the garden. I hesitated as I saw him.

'Oh, sorry, I didn't realise you were here, I'll go.' I began to close the door but he stood up.

'No, wait! Stay. I could use the company.' He motioned for me to sit on the step. Reluctantly I did – suddenly thinking it had been hours since I'd touched up my make-up.

'I heard Ellie's gone off the deep end again,' he said, lowering his head to light the cigarette that hung from his mouth.

I couldn't help but scoff, 'You were still under the impression she has a shallow end, eh, Joe?' I shook my head wearily as he laughed.

There was a long silence and then he got up, took a few paces away and turned back around. 'So, I've been wondering about you since we spoke the other night.' Another pause. 'You're one of the quietest people here, but I get the feeling you're one of the ones with the most going on.'

I didn't know if it was a question or a statement. I chose the latter. 'Okay?' I knew I sounded stupid but for some reason I was incapable of talking normally to him; he made me nervous.

He half smiled. 'Is it *okay*?' His eyes burned into me and all of a sudden I felt horribly vulnerable in front of him. I opened my mouth to reply but Grace pushed open the door before I could answer.

'Fuck me, it's cold!'

I smiled at her, glad of the interruption. 'All right, Grace?' I asked.

She shook her head. 'Brooke's gone loopy. She's hiding under the table in our room. Talking about a tent or some bollocks, said she needs to sleep in the garden tonight... dunno. I sent Kirk in.'

I looked up at the swirling clouds above the hospital and groaned. Joe lit her cigarette for her as she wrapped her arms around herself and shivered.

I sat there in the cold with the two of them for a while, Grace talking about her most recent court case in which she pleaded guilty to 'accidentally' stabbing her ex three times – how you accidentally stab someone three times was a little beyond me but I chose to go with it. 'I mean, she was fucking... she just, she got in my face, you know? Kept going on and on. And it just happened, the knife was in my hand and then she was bleeding and calling me a stupid cunt. I still love her, best lay of my life!' Grace stopped for breath as she sucked on her cigarette.

Joe glanced at me, flicking his eyes wide for a second, a little look of 'What the fuck?' on his face. I grinned back at him, stifling my smile before Grace noticed. As Grace began speaking again there was a long, awful scream. The sort of scream that reaches in, right down to your core. I jumped up quickly, followed by the others and ran towards the noise.

Joe flung open the doors leading to reception and there was Ellie, out of bed, fully dressed, being held down by three people. If you've ever seen *The Exorcism of Emily Rose*, that was what I was witnessing. Ellie's eyes were wide, she was writhing, arching up on her back and slamming her head back down on the floor with full force, the crack of her skull vibrating on the wooden panels under me with every blow. She was screaming about devils coming for her. Erica, a quiet, easily intimidated nurse held her legs while Kirk, red-cheeked and out of breath, held her shoulders, beads of sweat rolling down his face as he tried to keep her in place. Ellie would repeatedly struggle out of his grasp, stand up for a matter of seconds, before falling face down, seemingly unconscious, stay there for a few minutes, get up, and do it again. And again. The ambulance and police were on their way. Patients, as it seemed was the common theme, took over from the nursing staff within seconds.

Prue clung on to Ellie's left arm, at the same time as holding a pillow under her head; Marie held her other arm down; and

I sat on her legs putting all my weight on them. If I moved, she kicked us, a high-heeled boot to the face or stomach. Prue and I took it in turns to tell her where she was and that we weren't going to let anything hurt her. I held onto her like she was a rodeo horse, listening as Prue tried desperately to soothe her, but nothing was working.

'He's coming, he's coming!' The screams were piercing.

'No one is coming, El, you're safe,' Prue would coo down to her.

'*He's here!* He's standing here, you fucking idiots *can't you see him?*'

Marie actually looked around at one point. 'Who Ellie? Who's here?' she squealed in a shrill little voice.

'My stepdad, you dumb bitch! My stepdad! He's the devil! The devil is here!'

The police came, stood over us and did nothing. Then the paramedics. Equally ineffective.

Being in a psychiatric unit and watching this little show was of course shocking, but not surprising – it is extraordinary how quickly your brain adjusts to what is normal and what is 'the norm'. You expect in these moments for a medic to be able to impart some wisdom (usually in the form of a tranquilliser) to help alleviate the situation, to 'fix' it. But tonight, the paramedic in charge stood over her, arms folded and to all our utter horror, staff and patients alike, said, 'You're an attention-seeker love, you're making a real fool out of yourself. What a joke!'

Prue's face turned into some sort of snarling demon as she glared at him and shouted, 'If you had any idea of what her life was like you'd shut your fucking mouth! Her baby just almost died!'

Erica pulled Prue away. She'd risen to her feet inches from his face – a bold and strange move for Prue, I was quietly proud of her. I was left alone with the police, paramedics, and Ellie.

Marie had found it too overwhelming and fled down the hall in tears. I got Ellie to the ambulance where she was tied to a chair, kicking, screaming and banging her head against the insides of its walls. For some reason they untied her, probably worried she was going to give herself a concussion, and predictably, untethered, she started to run. I grabbed her, reeling her back in before she had a chance to get anywhere. The police said they weren't prepared to take her to A&E 'like this'. Prue came back and we ended up dragging Ellie up to bed. She had seemed a little more sedate, as if she was calming down slightly, but then the screaming started again; added to that she tried to smother herself with her pillow, and clawed at her own face with her long nails. I didn't know how much more I could take, or what we could do; this wasn't our job. It was at that point that Judy arrived, her stony face emulating some sort of Greek goddess as she stood in the doorway of our bedroom. I had never been so happy to see the woman in my life. She looked at Prue and me.

'You girls need to go, you need a break, you've done enough now.' There was genuine concern and empathy in her voice as she led us away. We stood in the hall as seven police came running up the stairs. Not speaking I pointed them in Ellie's direction. At 6am (when she was sober enough) they carried her out and sectioned her.

*

A mere five hours later I was sitting in an emergency community meeting, about fifty people filling the room. I walked in late, exhausted, defeated, and sat in my usual chair by the door. Crystal, a new young mother with a young daughter on the family unit, had stood over Ellie the night before saying things like, 'Aren't the attention-seekers done yet? You should let her kill herself. The baby will probably die, so just let her top herself,

373

who wants a deformed baby anyway!' Although I had heard her, I hadn't had time to respond; I was too taken up with trying to stop Ellie causing serious damage to herself, or someone else.

Dr Finstard was in the community meeting which was a rarity; obviously Ellie's episode had had a real impact. He spoke about her, and then mentioned myself, Prue and Marie.

'Emma, I was told you were very helpful to both Ellie and the police, and I'd like to commend you for that, I gather it was a very difficult situation...' He hesitated. 'But I must say, you look incredibly angry right now.' Everyone expected me to say nothing as was my usual MO, but anger had me over any sort of social fear and my words toppled out.

'Yeah. I am angry. I have no anger for Ellie's behaviour last night. She's my friend and I understand why, when her baby is still so sick, still in hospital fighting for his life, she did that last night.' I was now shouting. 'I care about her, and so I'll pin her down and stay there, and get the crap kicked out of me until she's safe. The thing that I'm angry about, is the bullshit that came out of your mouth, Crystal.' I then repeated her words, for everyone to hear, sparing no detail, airing her filthy laundry for the entire room. 'You told her she should kill herself! You stood over her and said her baby was going to die.' My eyes were fixed on her face, my soul taking no comfort in the little gasps from people around the room as they heard what I was saying. I asked her if she was at all remorseful.

She crossed her arms. 'No, I'm not.'

Aghast at her arrogance, I said, 'You're disgusting.'

She laughed, Harriet and Kiera sniggering along with her.

I lowered my voice, trying again. 'You aren't at all sorry for what you said?'

She shook her head, completely defiant.

'Well good for you, how clever,' I said, livid, my face feeling hot and flushed.

She smirked back at me. 'Yeah it is good for me!' Harriet and Kiera laughed out loud.

Sensing that I was about a minute from catapulting across the room, the staff interjected and ended the meeting. I sat shaking with anger as the room emptied. Some of the staff, Mena, Judy, Alison and Johanna, patted my shoulder and said various 'well dones' as they passed.

*

The next few days were remarkably quiet. Ellie returned from the acute unit forty-eight hours later with her tail between her legs, making her usual apologies and promises never to do it again. I wasn't angry with her, not at all, but silently simmering under the surface, my contempt for Crystal grew. Naturally, Harriet, revelling in my obvious dislike for Crystal, became inseparable from her.

Along with Kiera, the three of them became the new mean girls on the block, and they certainly didn't like me. I should have been worried, perhaps not about Harriet and Crystal, but Kiera was rough – she'd been in prison several times for GBH, ABH, theft and unsocial behaviour, but for some reason the three of them never scared me. I was too fuelled by my hatred for them, their ignorance, their prejudice, their bullying, and I made no secret of my distaste. What they might have had over me in brawn, I had over them in brains; they weren't going to get the better of me and they certainly weren't going to intimidate me.

41

GIRLS GONE WILD

"Deeply vulnerable and hurting within as you act tough outside. You do need people; you need them so much so that it scares you to death. You drive them away so they don't get too close; yet you regret it every time you do."

— RACHEL REILAND, *Get Me Out of Here: My Recovery from Borderline Personality Disorder*

The time had come for Prue and Kane to leave the hospital. I'd been dreading it for weeks. I liked Kane a lot and it was sad to see him go; I'd become used to watching him in the alcove every day strumming on his guitar or reading. And of course Prue was my lifeline, the one I turned to, the one who sensed when I'd been in the bathroom just that little bit too long – I knew I would feel completely lost in that place without her.

After the goodbye teas, cards and multitude of hugs, she and Kane were gone. And I was once again left alone in the hospital. Ellie and Laura were my main sources of comfort – we would sit together and talk about how much we missed her. I would call her most nights and chat, hearing about how her transition back into the land of normality was not an altogether smooth one. In what seemed like the blink of an eye Prue had gone from being surrounded by people who knew her, to finding herself alone in a one-bedroom flat far away from all the relationships and support she had built over the last year. It seemed almost cruel to me – like giving someone the world they'd always wanted, always needed, and just when they came to rely on it, snatching it away.

The days following Kane and in particular Prue leaving were hard for me. I was consumed by my role of chairing the meetings and by helping everyone else. I was beginning to crumble internally, I could feel it creeping in, but I felt like I was not the priority.

The days and nights rolled into each other in an intolerable mixture of everyone else's problems. I would leave in the afternoon once therapy was over, go for coffee and to write, get back to the hospital in the evening just in time for the night meeting, discuss everyone else's problems, and then go and sit with Marie and Susie in their room. The usual scenario was that Marie would give me a Migraleve to soothe the raging inferno in my temples and I'd relax on the spare bed. It was a Tuesday evening and I was following my usual pattern, lying in Susie and Marie's room, on what had been Prue's bed, Katie's before her, and Ashley's before that. It was peaceful and quiet and I was starting to drift off to sleep when there was a crashing and slamming against the wall by my head. It was Ellie, going to town on our bedroom. I could hear chairs being thrown against the walls, the banging and breaking of various different trinkets and belongings. I reluctantly got up and tried to push open the door, but she'd locked it from the inside. I hadn't even realised the lock worked. *Bit of a fail on the Caddick's side there*, I thought, as I rushed to get Brian, who was the duty nurse for the night.

It took forty-five minutes after he unlocked the door (then promptly disabled the lock) for us to talk her down as she screamed about one of her foster dads abusing her. As Brian consoled Ellie, I took the opportunity to go to the bathroom and have some quiet, just for a second, before I went back to try and help some more. I didn't want to self harm, I just needed a moment away from everyone. As I pushed open the bathroom door and stepped inside, my bare feet landed on something sharp. I switched on the light and looked down. I was standing on half a CD. It lay there under my foot snapped in half; someone must have used it to cut. I gingerly picked it up and put it in the bin. I couldn't help but roll my eyes at how little damage you could actually do with CD shards. I mean, you could get a bit of blood, sure, but it wouldn't do much, what was the point really? Why not just use a blade? As I washed my face and stared at myself in the mirror it occurred to me: where was the other half?

I was supposed to be watching a film with Leah as part of her evening crisis plan to stop her from doing anything destructive, but, because I also had Ellie to look out for, I had to recruit Aaron and Grace to be part of the 'keeping Leah safe' gang. I put on a film for them and took Ellie outside for a cigarette. Her bloodshot eyes, which I hadn't noticed up in the bedroom, suggested she'd been drinking. She must have a secret stash hidden away somewhere. Brian had managed to calm her down a little more and she was something resembling lucid by the time I had got back from the bathroom.

Joe was in his usual spot on the stairs, chain-smoking, as I held Ellie's hand and ushered her through the door.

'Have you seen Brooke?' he asked, stubbing out a cigarette before finding another and lighting it.

I let my eyes trail off Ellie. 'No, why?'

He inhaled sharply. 'She's not good. I just got that vibe, I think she needs some help.'

I put my head in my hands. I left Ellie with Joe and tried to locate Brooke. I searched the whole building but couldn't find her;

I even did a round of the grounds, but there was no sign of her. Dejected, I sloped into the empty kitchen. I poured myself a large bowl of cereal, and gulped it down. It wasn't enough. I poured another mound of cereal into the bowl and ate it. Not enough. A packet of crisps. I wasn't full. Two more packets of crisps. After half an hour I had managed a box of cornflakes and six bags of crisps.

Brian came into the kitchen, not noticing the box of empty Kellogg's I had rammed into the open bin.

'Emma, I have to go to A&E, Sal and Petrice are on duty and in charge until I get back.'

I didn't look at him as I washed my bowl in the sink. 'Why?'

He cleared his throat nervously. 'Brooke has self-harmed quite… badly. She needs a doctor.'

I turned around. 'What did she do Brian?'

He scratched his head looking uncomfortable. 'She has injured herself, internally.'

I didn't bother to ask what she'd done, instead I waited for him to leave and opened a second box of cornflakes, ramming another bowlful into my mouth. I felt overwhelmingly to blame for Brooke. Being firm chair meant that you had extra responsibility; it was your job to be the all-seeing eyes and the all-hearing ears of the unit and I was failing miserably. There were just too many people to look after and I couldn't do it on my own. If only Prue was here, she'd have known how to fix it, she'd have known how to fix me.

And then the answer to all my problems. *Throw up!* I didn't stop until I saw blood, and even then carried on.

I finally went to bed at 2am knowing I'd have to get up early to ensure I had enough time to ply myself with make-up – conscious my swollen face and burst-blood-vessel eyes were now a total giveaway as to what I'd been up to.

*

I walked through my day with no one knowing what I'd done, and I wasn't about to volunteer the information. We were told in firm that Brooke had 'inserted' half a CD inside her vagina and had managed to get it so far up that she needed a general anaesthetic for the surgeon to get it back out; they said she'd be gone for a few days. Guess I was wrong about the CD not being able to do much damage, Brooke had certainly found a way around that one. People tend to assume, and up until going to the Henshaw I was one of them, that self-harm consists generally of cuts or burns on your arms, legs, chest. Sorry to burst the bubble but it's just not accurate. People find ways that you couldn't imagine to hurt themselves when they need to. I met people in there who ate glass, made ligatures, swallowed razor blades, set themselves on fire, and yes, cut internally – you name it, and I can almost guarantee someone's out there doing it.

*

By the time 8pm rolled around the next evening I was sitting in the TV room with Ellie, enjoying the first bit peace I'd had all day – away from everyone and their endless issues, myself included.

'Em, I want a drink.' She was doing her baby voice, which she thought worked on me like it did on everyone else.

'No, Ellie.' I picked up the remote and began to channel-surf.

'But why not? Just one, and I'll stay with you.'

'El, I'm not doing this tonight, please. Everyone seems to be okay, so let's just relax, yeah?'

She settled back into the sofa. 'Okay, Em.'

After a quiet night meeting I headed up the stairs to my room, only to see Ellie walking down the hallway, teetering on her high-heeled boots. When you've lived with a prostitute for long enough, you know those boots mean business, literally. She'd tucked her stripy pink pyjama bottoms into them, coated her face with a thick layer of foundation and thrown on some pink lipstick to finish off the look.

'Ellie where…?'

She didn't let me finish. 'Fags. See ya.'

Before I could go after her, Leah came flying down the stairs, thigh-high PVC boots, a full face of make-up, her short hair straightened to within an inch of its life. She looked ferociously angry.

'Leah, stop. Where are you going?' She ran past me, vanishing through the doors and calling behind her, 'Shop!' And so it began.

Sal suggested that after twenty minutes of neither of them returning I take another patient and go and have a look for them.

Susie and I walked around the corner a stone's throw from the hospital, just in time to see a man stride out of the local Indian restaurant and hand Ellie and Leah a bottle of wine; there was already an empty bottle alongside them on the bench they were slumped on.

Susie sat down and began her motherly emotional blackmail act on Leah, a perfectly honed symphony of 'Please sweetheart, everyone is so worried. Come back with me. You're the same age as my daughter and I'd be so upset if she was doing this.' It seemed like it was starting to work; Leah's angry expression was softening. This process of talking her down, however, came at the cost of Ellie feeling ignored.

'Oh yeah, don't worry about me, I'm fine! I'm A-okay,' she said snatching the bottle of wine out of Leah's hand and taking a long, deliberate swig. She put it down on the floor looking as infuriated as I'd ever seen her look. I should have said something to her then, tried harder to intervene, but as awful as it might sound, I was losing all interest. Perhaps Leah could still be swayed to do the right thing, but I knew that look in Ellie's eyes all too well – I'd seen it so many times by now. It was a look which said to me that whatever happened, whatever I said or did, we had already lost. Ellie was checking out, drunk and dissociating, already committed to abandoning us, and herself. Before the thought even had time to leave me, Ellie got up. She began to cross the road but quickly lost her balance, falling hard on to the concrete and scrabbling to get up as cars honked and swerved around her. I rushed over to help, but was stopped dead in my tracks by the almighty shattering of Leah smashing the bottle of wine. I turned around holding up my hand to shield my face from the glass that flew towards me, watching in dismay as Leah grabbed the largest shard she could, and clutching it, started to run as if her life depended on it. 'Go after Leah, I'll get Ellie!' I shouted to Susie, and we split up.

I looked around and saw Ellie clambering towards a bus stop on the other side of the road. She was sitting down staring vacantly into space by the time I got to her, blood starting to soak through the knees of her cotton pyjamas. 'I didn't give Leah any drink...' she said, sounding almost upset, '... she just followed me, so I let her stay.' I glanced behind her to Susie, who was running down the road after Leah, who had now rolled up her sleeve and was angling the shard of glass toward her wrist. I watched as Susie changed course and ran to a nearby payphone. I assumed she was calling the staff or, worse yet, the police – I knew if she got the police involved all it would do was pour gasoline onto this whole situation.

'El, stay here for a second, don't move, all right?' She nodded and I rushed back over to Susie. I reached her just as she had her finger on the number nine. 'Susie, don't call anyone, let's swap! Ellie's calmed down, get her back to the hospital. I'll go after

Leah!' She agreed, wearily putting down the phone receiver as I left her, running as fast as I could in the direction Leah had disappeared off to. Clutching my sides and out of breath I turned a corner and saw Leah sitting at another bus stop, cutting. I approached her the way you would approach a hungry lion, if you were stupid enough to do so. My adrenalin spiked, fear oozing out of every pore – as I walked towards her I hoped she wouldn't smell it on me.

I perched a few feet away, and for what seemed like forever watched her cut herself. Over and over, deep enough for me to wince every time she slashed the glass across her forearm. Blood, like scarlet rivers running from her skin, rushing away from her and onto the pavement. I tried to speak to her, gently, softly, but she ignored me.

'Leah, honey, please.' Slash. 'Leah, please stop.' Slash. 'Leah, stop.' Slash. It was like I wasn't even there. And suddenly, my cool demeanour abandoned me and I was filled with a blinding white rage. *Why* wasn't she listening? *Why* wasn't I able to stop this? And, more disturbingly, why did I have an urge to go and grab the glass out of her hand and use it on myself? She stood up and began to walk away. I rose to my feet and before I knew it I was shouting at her, 'Thank you, Leah! Thanks very fucking much! You know what I'm going to do now? Go back to the hospital and probably cut myself because I feel like an absolute fucking failure that couldn't keep you safe!' My voice broke before I finished the sentence and tears began cascading down my face.

She stopped dead in her tracks, and looked at me, staring into my eyes for a few seconds and then throwing the glass into the road, collapsing as she did in to a heap on the floor. I quickly moved forward, kneeling next to her. After a few minutes she looked down at her arm, the blood pooling on the concrete. 'Did it at least help?' I asked.

Tears fell one by one from her face like rain and in a very small voice she whispered, 'No.' I put my arm around her and pulled her in her against me.

Susie appeared a little way down the road and as she walked towards us, angrily shouted, 'I've called the police, they're coming!' *Fuck! No Susie! Why?* As I knew she would, Leah, panic-stricken, jumped up and started to run again. I didn't go after her this time.

Susie was furious, stammering as she spoke. 'Ellie hailed down a car with some man driving and got in!'

'What? What man?'

'I don't know, Em. She flagged him down, got in, grinned at me like a Cheshire cat, waved a bottle of vodka at me and he drove away.'

We walked to the petrol station and used their phone to call the Caddick; a few minutes after hanging up Ben and Aaron jogged past asking where Leah had run to, assuring us they'd find her.

I sat in reception at the hospital with my head in my hands crying quietly into my palms. Eventually the door buzzed and I looked up to see Ben and Aaron return, with a reluctant Leah following behind, her clothes covered in blood, gaping wounds on both her wrists, the night staff quickly leading her away and up to the meds room.

Ben sat down and put his arm around me.

'Is she okay?' I asked, not taking my eyes off the floor.

He gave my shoulder a little squeeze. 'To be honest I'm more worried about you, Emma.' At that second my phone beeped. I glanced down and saw a text from Ellie: 'I'll be back in a little while, *if* he lets me.'

I didn't have time to reply to her before five police marched through the door, I didn't know what had been said to them but they looked as though they were prepped for battle, fired up and ready to take down some armed gang, not deal with a sixteen-year-old, seven-stone little girl. I was asked to speak to them to fill them in about why they'd been called as Sal floundered helplessly at their questions. I walked into the kitchen and stood by the window watching an ambulance arrive for Leah. I caught my reflection in the glass and looking down realised I was covered in her blood. I looked back to the window and watched as a red car pulled up to the gates. The passenger door opened and Ellie flopped out onto the gravel. The guy driving pulled away before she'd even had time to scramble to her feet, the passenger door still open as the car screeched away from the hospital. I watched her stagger in, smiling, not wanting to lose face. As she pushed open the door Leah bolted past her on the run for the third time. Ellie turned and watched her for a moment and then started screaming, those high-pitched, blood-curdling screams of hers. In a flash she was held down on the floor and restrained by the police, thrashing and spitting in their faces as the paramedics tried to inject her.

It was at that point I realised how much my bloodstained hands were shaking, and how much I wanted to be anywhere else.

I pulled Susie aside. 'I'm so sorry, but I have to get out of here for a while.' I told Sal I was going, her blank expression did little to dissuade me, and I left – out into the blackened sky and endless rain. The sound of Ellie's screaming, along with the flashing blue lights of the ambulance, grew more faint with the lingering echo of my every footstep. I walked until I couldn't walk any more and finding a bench on a secluded road, sat down and rolled myself a spliff. Drugs had never seemed like such a wonderful idea and as I took the first pull on the joint the cold water of relief spilled over my head like God answering my prayers. I sat there stoned and unfeeling for a couple of hours, until the gentle rain turned into a raging storm. So, giving up, I reluctantly headed back to the hospital a little after midnight.

My room was empty, the lights off, both Ellie and Leah were nowhere to be seen, I didn't know if that was a good or a bad thing, or if I cared either way. I got into bed and fell asleep.

*

I went out first thing the next morning, skipping firm and the meetings. I wasn't doing it. I was still so tired and I needed time by myself. As I sat in Starbucks writing I got a text from Leah.

'I'm so sorry I upset you. Please reply. All my love x'.

She must have been back. Within the hour another text from Ellie. 'I'm sorry. I love you. Forgive me?' I didn't reply to either of them.

Perhaps it was Kate Bush blaring out from the speakers, or the reality of having to really think about the effect the previous evening had had on me, but the clouds within began to descend, and soon I found myself in a familiar place: queuing in a pharmacy, with razor blades in my right hand and money in my left.

*

I sat in a perfectly picturesque scene, slightly set back from the river, green leafy trees, yellow daffodils and a busker just out of sight. People – couples mainly – walking past, all spring smiles, laughing and holding hands. Joggers. Cyclists. Little dogs wagging their tails as they chased squirrels, and then me, in the most harmonious place I could have found with those deafening drums banging in my head, the same old tune, the steady rhythmic beat: *Cut, cut, cut.*

Rip. Ping. Open. Rustle. Out. I sat there with the blade in my hand for some time, trying perhaps to feign some sort of control. It didn't last. With my arm in my bag so no one could see, I began to cut. But it was too busy, too many people, I needed privacy.

An hour or so later I walked through the Caddick's doors, a quiet anxiety churning inside of me. Up, up, up to the bathroom, 'Emma's bathroom' as Ellie referred to it. Hello misery. Cut. Hello punishment. Cut. Hello failure. Cut. The last made me yelp out loud as the new blade sank into the fat of my arm, sliding through me like butter, six, five, four, three, two, one, then the blood. Gushing.

42

THE PICNIC

"If you could have anything in the world, what would it be?" he asks. "Love," I say without a seconds hesitation. "But that's the biggest setup of all."

— KIERA VAN GELDER, *The Buddha and the Borderline*

'Let people celebrate it, do something differently.' Nora was talking about my upcoming birthday. I'd never really been a fan of birthday celebrations; all eyes on me wasn't an appealing thought. On my second birthday my parents bought me a life-size talking doll called Cricket – apparently I went into hysterics and hid under the sofa refusing to come out until Cricket had been appropriately disposed of. My fourth birthday: I remember quite vividly pouring myself a large cup of bleach and downing it in one. Fast forward to my sixth birthday and I spent my pool party hiding in the public toilets sobbing into my swimming costume, hating everyone, convinced that my father liked the other children better than me. The year of my eighteenth, when all eyes were finally on me, coked up to the gills and dancing on tables with my friends, I was so uncomfortable that I ran off and spent the early hours cutting myself in some godforsaken alleyway in Vauxhall. Trust me, the grass is never greener. And in a borderline's mind, you're pushed to find the grass *at all*; on the other side of the fence is more often than not a steaming pile of cow shit. I didn't tell her about Cricket, the bleach, the pool party, the alleyway. Just nodded.

*

Nine o'clock at the Caddick and I was agitated. I walked out into the warm night air and sat on the swings next to the family unit's playground. I swung for forty minutes, singing and looking up at the night sky, feeling the tension release a little. As the cool calm of spring settled inside me I felt the weight begin to lift – all of a sudden there was a torch shining in my face. As I tried to see past the bright light I saw Ellie and nurse Claire.

'Get that fucking light out of my face!' came Regan's voice snarling out of me. Perhaps not so calm after all.

'Well! Good evening to you too!' came Claire's reply. Claire was one of the few nurses I had time for, but she could be fierce and tonight she was out for blood, my blood. 'Emma, *what* are you doing? It's ten o'clock at night and you're swinging around like a lunatic!'

'I'm just trying to get a bit of peace, Claire, that's all.' My voice rose up as my swing sailed above their heads.

'You need to come inside!' Claire's words lingered there for a second before Ellie piped in, 'Em, come in, I'm worried.'

'Oh for God's sake. I'm not self-harming, I'm not hurting anyone; in fact I'm getting some good old-fashioned mood-elevating exercise. I'd have thought you'd be praising me, Claire!' I swung above their heads again.

'Emma, you only sing when you're angry or if you're struggling.' I knew exactly where Claire had got that from but I didn't have time to say it before she went on, 'The music, singing, isolating, Esther told us this is a pattern for you.'

Fucking Esther. 'Claire. I'm on some swings, singing. That's all. You know I like you, you know I respect you, but I'm staying right here. And as for Esther and her gossiping, she can go and fuck herself.'

Something like a laugh from Ellie as the torch flicked off and they both disappeared inside.

I stayed out there for another hour. When I came in I'd relaxed almost completely and spent the evening righting my wrongs with Claire, apologising where needed and standing firm in my resolve that Esther was an idiot.

'Have you calmed down yet?' I turned around and saw Joe's head peering out of his room, Dan's old bedroom. I stepped away from the meds window as Claire slammed it shut behind me and swallowed my little green and yellow pills.

'Oh, from my crazy, crazy swinging?' I rolled my eyes.

Joe nodded, doing a mock scowl. 'Yeah, for a second I was gonna suggest we called the police, I mean if there was ever a need to section someone...'

I grinned at him. Thank God, someone normal.

'But seriously, are you okay, babe?' He'd moved out of his doorway and was standing in the hall with me now.

'Yeah, just missing Prue. Feeling like I've got to constantly look out for Ellie, and Leah. And everyone else. Gets tiring, you know?' I looked down, feeling embarrassed.

Joe ran his hand through his hair. 'My session was shit today... I feel like running away,' he said.

I smiled again at him. 'Perfect, where are we going?' Derron opened the office door a few meters away and gave me a disapproving look.

'Shouldn't you be going to bed?'

I couldn't resist, 'To bed with Joe, Derron? Oh my God, can't a male and female be friends without having to jump into bed? I'm honestly disappointed – I thought better of you.'

A deep sigh. 'Emma, you know what I mean.'

'Seriously, Derron, I think you're being highly inappropriate.'

He shook his head tiresomly and shut the door.

Joe burst out laughing 'You're evil!'

'You try having Derron as your nurse!'

He laughed again, then leaning against the wall asked, 'So, if you could be anywhere in the world, where would you want to be?' His dark emerald eyes were pulling me in but I wasn't sure where to. I thought for a moment.

'I think... I would be in a park by a lake, on a picnic.'

He moved his head back, perplexed. 'A picnic? But I thought... food and you... you never eat here?'

'It would be a fruit picnic, Joe, obviously! All varieties of fruit!'

He stifled a laugh, 'Mmm, delicious!'

'Okay then, if a fruit picnic is so lame, where would you be?'

He thought about that for a second, leaning back against the wall. 'Hmm, road trip? America maybe. Driving, rolling mountain views, something like that.'

The staffroom door opened again, it was Claire.

'Why are you still here, Emma?' She looked at Joe then back to me.

'I'm just going...' I said as she crossed her arms watching, waiting for me to leave. 'I guess it's my bedtime.' I smiled at him as I started to walk away.

'Night, Em,' he called down the hallway after me. He was good-looking, any idiot could see that, but it was something about the way he spoke to me that lured me in, calling out to me like a siren's song... He wasn't scared of me and I liked that.

*

The next morning in firm I was challenged on my behaviour from the night before by Judy and a couple of others; all the while Esther hid behind a cushion on the sofa not daring to make eye contact with me. I defended myself and was let off without much of a fight, but still the whole thing got under my skin; they were acting as if I had committed some awful, unspeakable act, not sat on a fucking swing for two hours.

*

'You wanted a release, and you chose singing and exercise instead of self-harming. I don't see a problem,' said Nora as I sat with her in my session. I threw my hands up in the air.

'Thank you! Jesus!' Finally someone with some sense.

'Having said that, Emma, clearly there was something bothering you; normal people don't hang around in playgrounds in the middle of the night. So you could have chosen to talk to someone instead of isolating yourself.' Ugh, so close.

Nora went on, 'It must be excruciatingly difficult to have a constant fear of infecting everyone around you with what's inside you – it must be exhausting?'

I shrugged ' I just prefer to be alone when I feel like that.'

Nora crossed her legs. 'I don't buy that.' She leaned back in to her chair 'You don't want to be alone at all, and that's the problem. But that voice inside won't allow you to seek help, it won't allow you to seek out any kindness or comfort.' She paused as if waiting for an answer.

I looked down at the dreary brown carpet in her office and sighed. 'I don't feel like anyone can help me.'

'How would you possibly know that?' she scoffed. 'If you never reach out? If you keep everything bottled up inside you? It only causes those anxieties which usually start off as manageable, to spiral out of control in their absurdity. You divert attention away with your behaviour from the real problems; you create a storm in a teacup and hide behind it, when in actuality the issue is not sitting on the swings late at night, or continually leaving the hospital, the issue is your need for love, your need for understanding and your need for connection. It's screaming out, desperate to be heard, but you just won't let it.'

I walked back down the stairs from my session feeling fed up and tired. Nora's observations of me were always so apt, but having a torch shone on my behaviour didn't then mean it was automatically easy to change it.

Joe was sitting in reception and jumped up when he saw me.

'Go and get something to read!'

I pulled a disgruntled face and kept walking past him.

He tapped me on the shoulder. 'Ahem. Something to read!' He held up a big bag and said, 'We're going on a picnic!'

I didn't know what to say; I covered my face with my hands for a second before looking up. 'Really?' I was suddenly aware of someone behind me. I looked around to see Nora slowly coming down the stairs, eavesdropping. She smirked at me ever so slightly as she passed us.

He took me to the pond opposite the hospital, laid out towels for me to sit on then began unpacking the bags, putting out fresh grapes, raspberries, blueberries, strawberries, mango, plums, you name it. I was at a bit of a loss for words, I couldn't get over the gesture.

'Are you serious with this?'

He looked at me. 'With what?'

'All, this.' I held out my hands and motioned to the banquet that now lay in front of us. He looked confused, slightly hurt, so I quickly sat down and continued, 'I mean, it's so nice. Why would you do this for me?'

He picked up the punnet of strawberries and took off the lid, then did the same with the blueberries. 'Because, you deserve it.' He shrugged before carrying on, 'Because, I like you. I know you're feeling shit, I wanted to make you smile.'

'This is possibly the nicest thing anyone has ever done for me. Really... I can't believe you went to so much trouble. Thank you.'

'Don't mention it,' he smiled, passing me a strawberry.

We sat and talked for hours, about his life, mine, the hospital. I played music out of my tinny phone speaker and we watched the ducks lazily swim across the water as the sunlight bounced off their feathers. Two brawny men in gym gear walked past us, and I could have sworn that I didn't change my expression, but when they had passed by he looked at me and said, 'Why did those guys make you feel so uncomfortable?'

A bit shocked, I squeaked, 'What?'

'You just looked like you were really worried?'

How was he so perceptive? He seemed to notice every little thing. After a moment, and mentally selecting my words as best I could, I said, 'Well, look at me.'

'What do you mean?' He seemed genuinely confused as he popped a blueberry into his mouth.

'Well, I'm fat, pink hair, piercings, tattoos and you look... different. You're good-looking... I don't know... We probably look weird together.' I sighed. 'They probably wondered what someone like *you* is doing with someone like *me*.'

His eyes looked like they were going to bulge out of his head. 'You're kidding?' I shook my head, trying to change the song that had come on. 'Emma, you're crazy! You're beautiful.'

I rolled my eyes. 'Said the man from the asylum.' We both laughed.

It was a gorgeous afternoon. The sun kissed everything a shimmering gold as we sat there surrounded by the smell of fresh cut grass. I found myself laughing and relaxing into his company as though I didn't have a care in the world.

Four hours later, as the temperature began to dip and the weary sun began to set, we walked side by side back to the Caddick.

That night we ended up together in the alcove until the early hours. The sort of conversation that starts off quite innocently and soon moves onto the darker things people try so hard to hide, the deepest secrets lurking in places that most would never dare to venture.

'I was seven. There was a festival every year where we used to live. Music, drink and dancing.' He stopped to smile, lost in the memories of some good time he must have forgotten about, and then carried on, the smile fast fading away. 'It attracted a lot of people who were just passing through the village: tourists, travellers. I was little, stupid. Some guy lured me away, round the back of some old building...' his voice trailed off for a second. 'He raped me.'

I tried to think of something to say but when I opened my mouth the words caught in my throat.

'I want to know why he singled *me* out.' He continued. 'What was it about *me*?' He shook his head.

I bit my lip, what do I say? They are degenerates, hunters, they single out the vulnerable, they're opportunists and more often than not they get lucky. 'Joe... he was a predator. If it hadn't been you it would have been the next little kid that had looked lost or alone.'

The anger began to flow out of him then. 'I should have known better. What a stupid idiot I was, to wander off like that.' I was in danger of losing him to his memories and I desperately wanted him to stay with me a bit longer.

'You weren't stupid, you were a child, Joe! Kids wander off all the time; this wasn't your fault!'

'Mmm.' He began to pick at a scab on his hand. 'Anyway, I need a smoke.' He stood up without looking at me and walked outside. I stayed sitting for awhile. I wasn't sure if I was supposed to follow, or just leave him alone. I waited a moment longer then got up.

The evening air was warm as I walked out into it. He had his back to me sitting on the steps leading down to the garden.

'You know,' I started, as I sat down next to him, 'I think you might be almost as crazy as me!' I playfully elbowed him.

'I doubt that very much,' he said, a smile spreading across his face.

I elbowed him a second time. 'Hey! Fuck you!'

He laughed as he flicked his fag butt into the sand bin then said, 'It's actually really nice out here, isn't it? Peaceful.' I looked out onto the moonlit garden as he spoke, 'I can see why you spend so much time out here.'

We were quiet for a long while after that. Finding someone you can share silence with is a rare and wonderful thing, being alone but not alone was exactly what I needed in that moment, perhaps what he needed too. The wind rustled the leaves in the trees around us and a light went on in one of the bedrooms above. He asked if I wanted to go for a coffee at the weekend.

'Yes.'

43

BAG OF NEEDLES

"Stop my heart, and my brain will start to beat.
And if you consume my brain with fire,
I'll feel you burn in every drop of my blood."

— *RAINER MARIA RILKE*, *The Book of Hours*, *II*

On Saturday I met Joe for coffee. I had spent Friday night at my parents' house and lost most of the morning curling my hair and applying layer upon layer of make-up. I felt like an open book when I was with him; it was so easy to talk, so natural. I had been called 'censored' or 'closed' by so many people in my life, but I was nothing like this to him, and there was a part of me that liked that he could see into me, through the bullshit and past the pretence.

Joe took a sip of his coffee, black, extra shot, no milk. 'So last night, Ellie got quite drunk.' My stomach sank and I worried about what was about to follow. 'She kept asking for hugs!' He laughed and opened a sachet of sugar. I tried to smile but felt my eye twitch with annoyance as I watched the white grains fall into his cup. 'There was something else too...' He looked at me for a few seconds until the reddening of my cheeks prompted him to speak. 'Crystal texted me, asking me to meet her.'

Oh my god. He fucked her. It ran through my head like a sleigh with bells on, the image of them, hands over each other, a writhing mess of flesh and groans. Jesus Christ, is this why I was here? To be told he had fallen in love with Crystal? One of my worst enemies in that place? Unaware of my impending mental breakdown he went on, 'She kept asking for me to go to her room, for sex.'

I felt my coffee threaten to come through my nose as I cleared my throat and began fiddling with my hair. 'Oh?'

Whatever look was on my face made his answer come quickly. 'Obviously, I didn't respond. After the third text I went and showed the staff. Apparently it'll be discussed on Monday.'

That fucking whore.

'How weird.' I tried to nonchalantly examine the braid I had just done.

'I know… She's *really* not my type either.' Oh, hello. Why did he say that? Was he prompting me? Wasn't this the bit where I coyly ask what his type was? Then he looks at me and says 'You' and we kiss? I refused to play along, namely because I felt my face was already resembling a beetroot and I wasn't sure I wanted to know the answer anyway. There was a part of me – a big part – that understood Ellie's behaviour. I'd seen it before with Dan, and even with Kane to some degree. But I couldn't wrap my head around Crystal's – I wondered if she really liked him or if Harriet had put her up to it, part of some stupid little game just to get a rise out of me? They'd seen us coming back from the picnic together, maybe it was in retaliation to that?

Afternoon turned to evening and we moved to a nearby pub. Saturday night in the rowdy town centre and I began to flinch as pretty, thin girls swarmed around us like unwanted gnats in summer.

'What's going on, what are you thinking about, Em?' I debated saying nothing, making something up, but what was the point? It felt like he could see right through me anyway.

'I feel... intimidated. Surrounded by all these girls, in their nice dresses, with their nice bodies. And here I am, looking like something out of a horror film.' Right on cue some stunning blonde in a dress the size of my socks banged into our table, laughing hysterically as her Prosecco splattered all over the floor. Her friend dragged her away as I continued, 'It puts pressure on whoever I'm with to not have to look at them.' The truth made me shudder to myself.

He stared, all eyes on me and said, 'But am I looking around?' *Oh God.* 'Well no...'

'No. I'm looking at you. Just you. I don't need to look at anyone else.' There was something like an edge of aggression in his sincerity. I felt my cheeks flush again. He swallowed what was left in his glass in one go and stood up taking my hand. 'Come on, you're not comfortable here and I want you to be, let's go for a walk.'

We walked slowly back towards the Caddick. Len's disapproving eyes peeped at us from over his glasses as he buzzed us in and watched as we disappeared through reception. I thanked Joe for a good day.

'It was my pleasure,' he said, smiling back at me.

'Em! Where have you been? It doesn't matter! Come on I got some new Babygros I want to show you!' Ellie grabbed my hand and began leading me away.

I looked back at him over my shoulder. 'Goodnight.'

He winked at me. 'Goodnight.'

After the baby-clothes fashion show I got ready for bed and, as I lay there wide awake and unable to sleep, I texted him saying, 'Time seems to go so fast when we're together! Hope you sleep well.'

He replied, 'Know what you mean about the time together going fast. Not sure I should be saying anything, but I fear that a combination of your stunning good looks, wicked personality, obscure but intelligent and very funny humour, plus a spooky kind of connection, or similarity, or something, is making me enjoy your company more and more. It makes me want to learn more about you, and maybe let you learn more about me, which is unusual for me. Message me if you need to talk or anything.'

Of course his reply only threw more slabs of raw meat to the hungry lion who had awoken in me. It gave me the nudge I wanted... needed.

*

Monday afternoon I fled to the pond a few yards from the hospital and was lying on the grass looking up at the sky. I had to escape – my head was doing overtime in a world of make-believe.

Joe. I liked him, more and more with every hour. The ache. The ache for him twinged inside me, like a knife twisting. But the potential rejection, the loss that could happen again, just like Dan. Just like all of them. Lust. Loss. Love. Pain and ugliness entangled with a need, my need for so much love, just as Nora had said. How was it possible to feel so empty and so full at the same time? He had said in passing that the inside of my head was like a sadistic *Alice in Wonderland* – Curtis used to say I was like a dark *Alice in Wonderland*, he would call me 'his Alice', but back then I was in Curtis's wonderland, not my own. Despite how I felt, I couldn't help but think that this, after all, was exactly what had happened with Dan. I became obsessed, and not only with Dan, but with so many more before him. Joe, however, felt different. It wasn't like obsession, it wasn't a clawing, desperate creature screaming inside me, hungry to get out; it felt safe and serene. Joe, to me, felt like an elixir, like ice to a burn, soothing, sweet relief.

I thought about the night before our little jaunt. I had been leaning against the smoking door as the moon lit up the sky around me. Joe stubbed out his cigarette and then lingered a few inches from my face, staring down at me. I thought he was going to kiss me, instead he put his arm around my shoulder and hugged me goodnight, pulling me in towards him and stroking my back as he did.

I wanted to get away from him. I couldn't deal with it. I wanted him. And I wanted him to want me. I had no one to tell, nowhere to vent my feelings out to. Prue and Joe's paths had crossed briefly in the run-up to her leaving and I knew she was attracted to him. I'd encouraged it, actually. I thought he perhaps liked her and that this would be her fairy-tale ending; maybe if she had stayed it could have been, I don't know. It meant that not only was liking Joe against the rules of the hospital (and after Dan they would no doubt come down on me like a ton of bricks: the wretched whore of the Caddick, the terrible temptress, Bertha up in her tower), but it also felt like a betrayal to someone who had (and still did) mean so much to me. I was too worried to tell her, and prayed she wouldn't find out until I could find a way to say it. If Prue had still been at the hospital and she had shown an interest in him, I would have put my own feelings on the back burner, I'd have killed them off… But she was gone… and I was alone.

*

'Emma, are you awake?' It was two nights after my date with Joe, and I was lying in bed half asleep. 'Emma!' Leah was stage-whispering my name from her bed next to me. I rolled over to face her,

'Yeah?'

She got out of bed and crept over – I could barely make her out in the shadows. 'Can you take these?' She began handing me something. I sat up in bed and switched on my lamp, careful not to make any noise and wake Ellie. It was a carrier bag, filled with something.

STORM IN A TEA CUP

'What is it?' I said quietly, sleepily peering down into my hands; she didn't answer so I looked at her and realised as I did that her face was wet with tears. I clenched my jaw and opened the bag. 'Oh, shit.' Inside were hundreds of used needles.

'I'm sorry,' she said, kneeling on the floor.

'It's okay, Leah.' I blinked at the needles, there were so many of the things. 'It's fine. I'm really proud of you for giving them to me. Are they for heroin?'

'Some, yeah. Some, I… bloodlet. I know it's fucked up… but it helps.' She looked away nervously.

'I knew a girl that used to do that.' Chrissie from the Henshaw flashed through my mind. I looked down at Leah, her pale face lit up by the lamp light. 'You've never told me you do that.'

She pushed her face into my duvet and mumbled, 'I've never told anyone.'

I laid my hand on her head and said, 'It's all right, I'm not judging, we all do fucked-up things.' I took my hand away and put it on her arm. 'But, sweetie, I can't keep them here – it's really not safe… if someone else got hold of them. I'll have to hand them in.'

'I know,' came the whisper.

*

I walked down the hallway and knocked on the office door. A grumpy-faced Kirk opened it, looking straight at the bag in my hands. 'They're Leah's. She handed them in.'

He peered into the bag without taking it from me. 'Jesus Christ, Emma! Fuck! Did you touch any?'

I felt mildly annoyed on Leah's behalf. 'Kirk she's bled all over me and my open cuts before. I think if I was going to catch anything I'd have already caught it.'

'Okay, fair enough – there's just *so* many.' He gingerly took it from me, holding his hand outstretched like he was worried one of the needles might jump out and stick him in the eye.

'Tell them not to give her a hard time in firm, at least she handed them in.' With that I started walking back to the bedroom leaving Kirk standing stiffly in the doorway not quite knowing what to do with his bag of needles.

*

I didn't want to go back to the bedroom just yet. Memories began washing over me like a tsunami: Chrissie, the Henshaw, events leading up to the Henshaw. I felt uncomfortably full of emotion. I was thinking about Joe, and Crystal and how inopportune meeting him was. Why in a hospital? Why not somewhere where we could just be, just let things happen organically? I thought of Leah cutting in front of me the week before. I missed my dog, I missed my friends, I missed not being in a psychiatric hospital. I wanted Prue. I wanted Natalie. I wanted a joint. And then... I wanted to cut. I crept into the bedroom where both girls were once again asleep, got my bag and crept back out. With razor blade in hand, I locked the bathroom door. Peace. Quiet. Obliteration.

*

I got a bollocking in firm from Judy and Finstard in the morning with Slime sticking her twopence in for good measure. I had told Kirk about the cutting. I'd returned to him a couple of hours after originally giving him the needles and he'd dressed my arm. Kirk had been nice enough but told me he would have to tell someone and it would need to be talked about in the morning. Unluckily for me, Dr Finstard was in firm, and from what I could tell, he didn't like me. I couldn't put my finger on it; it just seemed to emanate from him, this distaste for me. He was able to get answers out of everyone, dredging their souls for scraps of information with his psychobabble, but when it came to me, I think he had met his match – I didn't trust him, and he knew it. He may have only been trying to help, but I took him as invasive and cold and I kicked against his attempts to get through my walls at every opportunity. I knew he would try his best to undermine me in firm, because this seemed to be the dynamic between us: we'd butt heads, egos would be hurt and then one would try and outdo the other.

'Do you even want to be here, Emma?' Adaline snarled at me curled up from a large armchair in the corner of the room; she was wearing that stupid shell suit again.

'Yes, Adaline, I do. But I am a self-harmer and I self-harmed; is it really that surprising?'

Adaline flicked her hair over her shoulder. 'I could have self-harmed last night, but I didn't!' She glanced proudly at Judy. 'I fought it!' She was so triumphant, as if she were talking about some great historical achievement. I wanted to punch her.

Instead I rolled my eyes and spitefully chimed back, 'Well done you. You didn't fight it last week though, did you? When you sliced through that artery in your arm? And when everyone was having a go at you, I stood up for you.'

She slipped back down in her chair, quickly covering the stitches on her forearm with her hand.

'I don't think that's the point, Emma,' said Judy, coming to Adaline's rescue as usual. 'You could have got help. You could have talked to Kirk.'

'I could have, but I didn't. I can't get it right the whole time. I cut! I'm okay now. I want to stop talking about it. I'll talk to Nora.'

'No, you should be made to talk here!' Adaline ducked her head back down as quickly as she had raised it, going red as she did. I couldn't tell if her reddening was anger or embarrassment, I hoped the latter.

Judy spoke again, angrier this time. 'So your life is *just fine*, Emma? There's nothing wrong with you?'

That upward inflection was so irritating. I'd had enough, I looked her square in the face and said, 'I'm not going to talk to you if you're going to be facetious, Judy.' She shut up looking humiliated.

Dr Finstard crossed his legs and cleared his throat. 'You have an amazingly skilful way of shutting people down, don't you, Emma?' He probably hadn't intended for me to take his words as a compliment. I didn't have time to think of a clever response for Finstard as the agenda quickly moved on to Esther.

'It has been brought to us that you are deliberately overdosing on your medication in order to cause your seizures,' said Judy, smoothing down her brown, floral skirt as she spoke.

Esther's face flashed burgundy. Ah, this again. The staff had said this in the Henshaw, too, but it was only in passing and never proven. Esther's eyes flicked over to me, probably wondering if I was going to say just that, but I stayed quiet.

'Perhaps you feel you need the attention and have no other way to get it?' asked Finstard staring at her.

'That is far from accurate,' Esther spat back at him. She was fuming. 'I am so sick of it here, there is no support! All you do is accuse me of things I haven't done!'

'We are simply opening a line of communication,' said Finstard in his even, monotonous tone, his grey blazer matching his grey complexion.

'No you're not, you're trying to get me to admit to something that isn't true!'

Judy chimed in again, 'Esther, this is very serious, to potentially be overdosing on your medication to make yourself ill? It's dangerous and it's going to warrant looking into.'

Esther stormed out of the room shouting as she did, 'This is bullshit!' Mike's face flashed through my mind, he'd have so enjoyed that.

44

A BIG WHAT?

"O, beware, my lord, of jealousy;
It is the green-ey'd monster, which doth mock
The meat it feeds on."

— WILLIAM SHAKESPEARE, *Othello*

Waking up in the hospital on Monday morning I instantly felt the depression inside start bubbling up, although I wasn't sure why. I had gone home for some of the weekend, managed to see Natalie and spent a good day with her, hanging out and watching films. I'd avoided doing any drugs or cutting and I should have felt okay. But as the sunlight glared through the bedroom window at me, all I felt was hollow. I was greeted, as I crawled out of the bathroom looking like roadkill, by Madison, a very pretty twenty-two-year-old who was at the hospital on a day visit. Blindingly bright blue eyes; flowing locks of Pantene advert hair; thin, chavvy perfection.

She had a strange, self-satisfied expression on her face as she sat in firm smiling at Joe, then eyeballing me and Ellie in turn.

It was a look weighted with enough behind it to send me into an episode. She wants Joe. Joe fancies her. She'll get him.

I'll leave and he'll fuck her. I'm so ugly, I'm so stupid, I'm so fat. The usual.

Judy cleared her throat forcing me to break my gaze away from Madison for a second. 'I have to inform you all that, at present, Esther has left the hospital.' I hadn't even realised she wasn't in the room.

'On leave?' asked Grace as she picked at her nails.

'No Grace, she has left permanently. Of course we will leave the door open for her for a certain amount of time to change her mind, but as it stands she has discharged herself.'

'Why has she left Judy?' Susie squeaked, looking worried and upset, like she might start crying. Judy sighed. I loved Judy's sighs, they were always preceded by some bit of information that Judy obviously didn't agree with, but felt she had to parrot back to us verbatim so as to not sully the pot and ruin the truth broth.

'Esther felt she wasn't getting the right treatment or support, from the staff.'

'That's convenient,' Grace muttered quietly.

Judy looked at her. 'Could you say more, Grace?'

She stopped playing with her nails, dropping her hands onto her lap and looked up. 'It just seems convenient, doesn't it? You tell her you think she's causing her own seizures and that you're all going to investigate it or whatever, and she leaves... Pretty big coincidence.'

'I don't know why she was allowed to get away with it for so long,' said Leah, yanking down the sleeves of her jumper.

'What do you mean, Leah?' asked Mena.

'Well, if you all thought I was back on heroin I'd be pulled up on it straight away, but for some reason Esther was just allowed to get away with it? It doesn't seem fair.'

'It's because she's a goody two shoes Catholic girl, and you're a dirty druggie prostitute!' announced Ellie, laughing from her chair next to me.

'Uh, so are you!' shouted Leah back at her.

'Girls, please!' Judy shuffled around in her chair looking like an exasperated headmistress.

'*I've* got a baby,' Ellie said, smug as could be, her lips curling up at the edges, 'and *I* haven't done drugs or owt else in ages!'

As the two of them kept bickering, I thought about Esther. What was she going to do out there in the real world? I didn't even know where she lived, or with whom. The Henshaw had suited her so well, she probably would have stayed there forever if she could have. Madison's birdsong voice cut through my thoughts of Esther as she began to tell us about why she needed help. I wasn't listening to the words, I just gazed at her like you'd stare at a beautiful painting, wishing that you'd created it – the jealousy soaring through my veins like a thick venom. As she spoke she looked only as Joe, casting her sparkling blue eyes down to the floor then back up at him several times – those eyes of hers didn't say 'mental patient in trouble' they said 'come get me'. I dug my nails into the back of my hand as I tried not to run out of the room. She was so pretty, so perfect, there was no way he couldn't want her. Ellie leaned over to me, whispering into my ear, 'What a fucking skank.' She quickly sat back in her chair, grinning at Judy as she eyeballed us.

I flew into town after firm, my head filled with visions of Madison, locked myself in the public toilets of the big mall where I figured no one would notice me, rolled up my sleeve and began cutting. I felt the blood flick up onto my cheek and onto the toilet stall door as my flesh gave way to the steel blade, but it wasn't enough. I pulled a lighter out of my bag and burnt the surface of my hand thirteen times. The release was otherworldly. The intense pain of my body under fire, as the rush of endorphins kicked in, soothing the scalds. However, the second my rush was over, I realised how hideous it looked. My skin instantly puffed up in huge blisters, my hand bright red and throbbing. Shit. I should have done it on my arm… Why did I do it on my hand? There would be no hiding it this time.

I went back to the Caddick, looking like I'd been dragged through a hedge backwards and stopped off to audition for *The Crow* en route. Laura, Grace and Joe were outside smoking. Joe clocked instantly that there was something wrong, though it wasn't hard judging by the state of me. He got up off the wall and rushed over. 'What's wrong, hon?'

'Nothing.' I kept my hand in my pocket and walked past him towards the door. As I waited to be buzzed in, Harriet and Crystal came up behind me. I kept my eyes fixed ahead, not bothering to look back at them. As I waited for Len to let me in they sniggered and giggled, keeping their voices deliberately low, only letting me hear certain words: 'pathetic', 'emo', 'bitch' and so on. As the lock clicked open I rushed away from them and into my session with Nora.

I sat down staring blankly ahead in her room; two minutes slowly ticked by like two years. Eventually she broke the silence. 'You look like you've got something on your mind, Emma?' Pause. It was an effort to open my mouth at all.

'That day visit this morning… Madison.' My words felt heavy, too heavy for me.

Nora inquisitively cocked her head to the side. 'What about her?'

But I couldn't do it, expose myself, I didn't want to. I looked off into the window behind her. 'I've just self-harmed pretty badly.'

Her relaxed expression changed. 'What? Where? What did you do?'

I didn't look at her. 'Hand, arms. Burnt, cut.'

She stood up walking to her desk and picked up the phone. I wondered who she was calling as she pressed just one button. 'Hi. It's Nora. I've got Emma David in my office, she's just self-harmed and I need someone to look at it please.' She sat back down. 'You need to get it sorted, Emma, then we'll continue.' There was a knock on the door and a few seconds later Johanna poked her head in. 'Come on then, let's get you seen to.' She smiled warmly at me and gestured for me to follow. I was surprised to see her, usually she wouldn't be called on to dress wounds. 'Well, it was you, so I thought I'd come and check out how you were doing?' I held out my hand and attempted a smile. 'Ah! Not very well I see! Jeez, you've really done a number there haven't you, Emma?'

I adored Johanna. She was the most straight-talking, honest, best-intentioned person in the whole hospital. Completely trustworthy and one of the few people the medical room didn't seem sterile with.

I was in post-destruction ecstasy, delirium, and began to ramble, my censors down. 'I hate myself. I hate my body. That fucking new girl this morning. I don't want her coming here. I can't stand to look in the mirror, Johanna, I can't even tell the difference between me and Harriet any more. I really can't. I know she's bigger but by a fraction, if that. And it doesn't even matter because if someone is ugly, their personality can make them beautiful over time, ugliness can be replaced by inner beauty, you know? But when it comes to me, you firstly have to get past the way I look, fight your fucking way through it, then, after all that, you get confronted with a shit personality as well. Double fucking whammy.'

'Emma, you must stop this. You are not the same size as her. You are nothing like her, full stop. Okay? Are you hearing me?'

I nodded, 'I'm listening.'

'But not hearing, eh?' She nudged me gently.

'Listening and trying to hear, Johanna.'

'Well I suppose that's good enough for now.' She bandaged my wounds and sent me back to continue my session.

*

'So what was it about seeing the day visit this morning that triggered everything off for you?' Nora was back to herself, her calm demeanour beckoning me towards her like a light in the dark that I needed to follow.

'That girl.' I made an 'ugh' noise. 'That girl was so pretty. I felt... disgusting next to her. Disgusting. She made me feel like every other pretty girl who comes into my field of vision... I literally feel like a disease compared to them.'

'There you go again, Emma, berating yourself, making up your own version of things.'

'Nora, I'm not making anything up, she *was* pretty.'

'So what if she was? What does that mean? That you're not?'

I didn't want to hear this... I didn't want my feelings being challenged. It felt mocking, I knew what I was, she knew what I was, why wouldn't she just admit it?

'Emma, is this perhaps in part to do with a new relationship which is forming?'

I stared at her without blinking. 'You mean, Joe?'

She nodded.

'No.'

Raising her eyebrow ever so slightly, she said, 'I think it is.' She could be so smug sometimes. Nora had this habit of dropping psychoanalytical bombshells on me without much warning and I sensed this was about to be one of those moments, turns out I was right. 'I see now what happens to you. You get into a blind panic. You freeze.'

'What, in here?' I asked, confused.

'No Emma. With Joe. With Dan. With men. You need to anticipate every second to the next. His every move, what you should do, what you feel you have to do, what you think you're expected to do. You scrutinise yourself to the nth degree, and I think that girl this morning played into all that for you. I think she played into those fears you have about control, who you're in control of, and who's trying to control you.' Nora had turned into an AK47, and I was the intended target. Not pausing for breath she went on, 'I think you feel completely invaded by people, as though you have no boundaries against anyone and can be so easily violated, emotionally, physically and sexually. Even here in this room, I think you feel I am trying to invade you, your mind, your space, your body. At times I believe you see me as a big penis that's trying to get into you.' Before I had time to even attempt to answer her she quipped, 'Anyway, something to think about for next time. Session's up.'

I walked down the stairs like a zombie, did she just say she was a big penis trying to get into me? Did she actually just say those words?

*

'Where d'you think you're going?' I turned around as I walked past the kitchen to see Joe standing in the doorway.

'I'm going to go to bed for a bit.'

He looked down at my bandaged hand. 'What happened?'

I shrugged and leaned against the wall 'I... got upset over something.' Just then the hallway door creaked open; it was Kirk.

'You two better not be planning to skip dinner this evening. I want to see you both there.' He turned and walked into the kitchen opening the fridge and staring inside.

'Do you want to get out of here?' Joe whispered as he smiled at me. I glanced back at Kirk, who was now examining a box full of leftovers, 'Yeah, I do.'

He took me to a little pub along the river not too far from the Caddick, ordering himself a lager as I sipped a Diet Coke. 'So, you know one day you'll have to start opening up to me?'

I put my glass down. 'And why's that?'

He leaned forward. 'Because I care about you. And I'm persistent! And more to the point I don't like seeing you unhappy.'

'I'm not unhappy, Joe...' I didn't even finish my sentence before he cleared his throat and pointed at my hand. I quickly shoved it under the table and looked at him mockingly. 'Fair point.'

'Was it something to do with that girl who visited today?' I felt the heat rise up my throat and spread to my cheeks. Do I tell him? He's said it now so I should just be honest, right? I shrugged. 'I'm going to take that as a yes then.' He put his glass down. 'You really don't see what's in the mirror do you?' I stood up half jokingly, but half seriously, and said, 'I'm leaving if you do this!' He reached out for my non-bandaged hand and pulled me back down. 'Okay, okay... I won't,' he winked, 'for now.'

Being away from the Caddick with him had made me feel so much better – all the upset from the day just washed away and I fell into a tranquil, contented place – but as we walked back into the hospital I felt the noise in my head start up again. I had really burnt my hand quite badly; I knew instantly after I'd done it I'd have those scars for decades to come, if not forever. But even though a mere six hours before I had sworn off burning myself to that extent ever again, it was all I could think about.

I sat in the alcove with Joe, Laura, Ben, Brooke, Aaron, Leah and a few others and tried hard to follow their conversation. I laughed when they laughed and smiled every time Joe caught my eye but it was a lie, I wanted to feel pain – the need in me was a wanton screaming that threatened only to stop when I gave in. I kept thinking of that girl. Of Harriet. Of my horrible fat thighs. Of Crystal. Of Joe. Of how much I liked him but how he couldn't seriously ever be attracted to someone like me. I sat on my hands in a feeble attempt to stop them trembling, the frenetic energy pulsing through me like an over-shaken bottle of Coke. After a few moments I couldn't take it any more, I stood up but as I did Joe was quickly on his feet facing me.

'Where are you going?' he asked. I didn't say anything, just sat back down.

'Ugh I feel sick I can't eat any more!' Laura said as she put a half-eaten slice of cake back onto her plate and set it down on the coffee table in the middle of us all.

'Then stop eating, you pig! That's your third slice!' Leah was laughing as she pushed the plate away from Laura who in turn playfully kicked her over the table.

'I'll get rid of it.' I grabbed the plate but again before I could even stand up Joe took it out of my hands. 'I'll do it, you relax.' I huffed at him as he winked at me and disappeared off into the kitchen. That was my chance. I quickly said goodnight to the others and left the room. Instead of going up to my bedroom I crept out of the smoking door and into the garden, gripping my lighter tight in my hand.

I was halfway across the grounds when I heard a noise behind me – I turned around to see Joe jogging over. He caught up and grabbed my shoulder. 'What have you got?' I swallowed hard as I stared back at him. 'Pass it over.' I raised my hand above his and dropped the lighter into it.

I began walking away from him, angrily saying over my shoulder, 'Happy now?'

'Yeah, actually I am. You can't burn yourself. So that makes me happy.' I stopped and turned back around apologetically. He moved a little closer and said, 'I know you got annoyed earlier but I don't care, I'm saying it now. You're beautiful. Why do you think you're not?' We went and sat down on the bench and I tried to talk to him about how I felt about myself.

'It's just this voice inside me, it won't stop. It tells me I'm disgusting and fat and monstrous all the time... it never shuts up.'

'But where does it come from? You need to stop believing it, Em. You're none of those things... and you're certainly not fat... In fact I'm worried about the food stuff with you... You can't exist on iceberg lettuce and coffee.' I felt the need to quickly take the attention off me and my food habits.

'You can't really talk, Joe.'

'What do you mean?'

'You don't eat. I've watched you, I've seen you eat maybe twice since you've been here.'

He took a cigarette out of his pocket and lit it with my lighter. 'I need to get the food thing under control, I know that. It's just I have to feel starving or so full that I feel ill... I can't stand that middle feeling of just being "okay". I've always been that way. I don't throw up, and I don't not eat at all... I don't think what I do is that bad to be honest.'

I considered that for a second, then said, 'So, if I didn't eat anything for four days then ate five loaves of bread would you think that was fine?' He went quiet as he flicked his cigarette.

'No.' I put my hand on his knee, which was as usual bouncing up and down. 'So why's it any different for you?' Before he could answer me, Kirk stuck his head out of the back door. I quickly pulled my hand away.

'It's late, you two need to go to bed. Come on please.' We walked inside, but Kirk had already gone back up to the staffroom and I didn't feel tired, so we went and sat in the alcove. It was empty now, everyone else having gone to bed.

'I'm so cold! This place is freezing,' I said huddling on the sofa. He took his coat off and wrapped it around my shoulders, rubbing them as he did.

'Better?' I nodded. 'So you realise you still haven't actually told me what happened today, why you hurt yourself?' He smiled reassuringly but I didn't feel reassured, I just felt consumed with him, wholly. He was becoming like heroin to me and every hit I took just made me long for the next.

I opened my mouth to finally tell him the truth and, just as I did, Crystal and Harriet strode in and, through a barrage of bitchy sniggers, sat opposite on the other sofa, nudging each other, snorting and laughing as they reclined there in silence staring at us, mostly me.

Joe got up. 'Really mature, ladies.' He took my hand and guided me into the TV room; I followed like a willing child against the backdrop of their jibes. But as we stepped into the room I stopped him.

'Let's go back outside.' He rubbed my arms again.

'But you're cold.'

I picked a blanket off the armchair. 'I'll be fine.'

So back out we went. We walked right to the edge of the grounds, far away from them all, partially hidden from the hospital on a small bench. 'I never even knew this was here,' I sat down facing away from him.

'I found it a little while ago,' he said. 'I come out here to think, for some peace.' I looked around at the trees kissed in moonlight and found my breathing ease in the silence all around us.

'I can see why.'

'So c'mon, Em. What happened today? You can talk to me… More than that – I *want* you to talk to me.' I took a deep breath, as my hands began to shake ever so slightly, anticipating the impending confession.

'That day visit. That's what happened today. That's all.'

He looked confused. 'What do you mean?'

'I felt threatened, I suppose. She was, she is, really pretty. And…' I put my hands over my face. 'Oh Joe, this is so embarrassing!'

'I'm not judging you, I wouldn't.' He moved my hands away. 'Tell me?'

I pulled the blanket tight around myself and sighed. 'I… I wondered if you were attracted to her, I thought about when I leave and she comes here and, I lost it a bit.'

'Oh.' He stopped for a second, not long but long enough for me to feel like I'd blown it, like I'd said too much. He got up then knelt down on the grass in front of me; I froze like a deer in the headlights. 'Do you know how perfect you are?'

I looked away. 'Joe, please, don't.'

'No, I'm going to. I like you, I like you more than I should, probably. And I can't bear you hurting yourself. That girl is nothing compared to you. Nothing.' He pulled me in and hugged me to his chest. It felt so right, but terrifying at the same time.

'Why are you interested? Seriously? I don't understand. I'm damaged, I know that much, but I'm not interesting in the slightest!' All the things you should never say? I wrote that book. Perhaps if you say, 'I am not interesting' enough, you will paradoxically become more interesting? Despite how I felt about myself I had a small ember of hope glowing in my chest, so I changed chord. 'You make me feel safe, but I'm scared of getting closer to you. I don't want to fuck with your mind, or therapy.'

He shook his head, 'You aren't, Emma. You're making this place bearable. I don't care that I met you here, I just care that I met you.' He stood up. 'Come on, you're freezing, let's go in.'

Ellie was snoring when I eventually got into bed, and Leah was in her pyjamas with her headphones on and eyes closed. I moved down inside the covers and switched off my bedside table lamp as my phone beeped. It was Joe.

'Good night darlin', really is good to see you again after the weekend, I've missed you. I know you already have the one irritating voice saying nasty things about you and I know you'll probably find mine just as annoying but I'm afraid you're going to have to just put up with it telling you the truth, which is that you are beautiful and sexy, inside and out. See you tomorrow, sweet dreams.'

I lay there thinking about him for what felt like hours. For the first time in a long time I didn't feel lost. When I was with him the world seemed to go quiet and those voices in my head became all but distant whispers.

45

BLESS ME, FATHER

"Sometimes someone will be standing in front of me, and already I feel him walking away. It's only a matter of time, so what's the point?"

— ELIZABETH WURTZEL,
More, Now, Again: A Memoir of Addiction

'Your perception of your body is distorted Emma, very distorted.'

'No it's not.'

'Yes, it is. And what's more there is an envious, controlling voice inside you that ruins every chance of you feeling any tiny bit at ease with yourself. This voice, Emma, prevents any progression. It is quite literally trapping you.'

'I don't want to be trapped with it, Nora.'

'I know, but that's how big and terrifying it is. I know you don't want to be tied to it. But it won't let you change. It won't even let you put less make-up on or coloured clothes. And even now, it is so quick get in and ruin anything remotely positive that I say to you.'

Nora was right of course, but I couldn't let her words in. It was hard enough trying to let Joe's words in. All I saw when I looked in the mirror, any mirror, was obesity, rolls and rolls of fat that threatened to smother me at any second. Every fibre of my being stung with self-loathing.

I hate myself.

I hate myself.

I hate myself.

I want to cut.

And cut.

And cut.

The drum beat over and over again.

I am fat.

I am disgusting.

I must ruin myself.

I left my room at the hospital, my head swirling, and walked out into the darkness. It was feeding time, everyone would be focused on dinner and not me. I slipped through reception, my heart thudding. BANG, BANG, BANG. I sat on a bench just outside the gates of the hospital and tried to self-soothe, tried to calm the thoughts, tried to behave. The urge to run began whirring through my already spinning brain, the need to feel something, anything, other than the thoughts. So I did, I picked myself up and ran to the duck pond. Sprinting all the way there, barely breathing but finally alive, I only stopped when I thought I might fall down. I stumbled over to a nearby bench and lay on my back watching the indigo sky drifting above me like a lullaby. 'Cut,' came the whisper. I needed to do it. I had to. I knew I should go back, talk to the staff, talk to Joe, Leah, Ellie, any of them. But what was the point? So what if they convinced me not to? If I didn't do it right then it didn't matter, the urge would be back tomorrow, or the day after… This is how it had been for as long as I could remember – if I distracted myself, if I forced the thoughts to the very back of my mind or just ignored them until they went away, they would only lie in wait for a short time, then come bubbling right back up to the surface. It felt like fighting a war I seemed predestined to lose. I didn't want to do it, but in not doing it I was only putting off the inevitable, and most of the time it just felt easier to get it over and done with so that my mind could return to some sort of equilibrium, whether that be for two hours or two days.

I got back an hour later and sat next to Joe and the others in the alcove, blood seeping through my sleeves. After a few moments I felt it drip onto my shoe, I made my excuses and went to find the night nurse, Max. Sweet, lovely, Max. He shook his head as he bandaged my arms.

'You're angry with me, aren't you, Max?' He stopped what he was doing and sighed. 'No, not angry. I'm upset, Emma, I won't lie, I feel disappointed. I wish you had come to me first.' It is one of the few times in my life someone has ever told me they were disappointed in me for cutting, and one of the few times that it stung.

*

The next morning in firm, fuck did I get it. Poor Joe was chairing as they all grilled me. 'WHY did you self-harm? WHY didn't you find support?' followed by the inevitable and awful 'We don't know how to help you.'

Slime, in the nastiest voice her bones could muster, rasped, 'Do you even want to stop self-harming?' I looked at her, and more genuinely than I usually would, said, 'Yeah, I do Adaline. But I don't see how I can. I can't see the exit sign.'

My honesty did nothing to help me and her venomous response flew back. 'Why are you bothering to be here? I keep saying it!' she was almost exultant, staring at the staff in the room. 'There's no point! She doesn't want help!'

I sighed heavily. 'It's not that I don't want help, it's that I know that stopping will have to come from me, no one else can solve this.' I was actually trying to be open for once, I was trying to let them in.

'That's a cop out. You shouldn't be allowed to stay here.' She looked yet again, for approval from the staff who even though they didn't show it, I'm sure were starting to feel the same way. I switched off at that point feeling empty and downcast. What was the point? They didn't even want me here.

As firm came to a close they filtered out, Susie patted me affectionately on my shoulder as she walked past, followed by Joe who came and sat next to me. He rubbed the back of his neck, a look of anguish on his face, 'I found that really hard. I didn't want to put you on the agenda.'

I tried to open my mouth to talk to him, but I was already on the train to insanity town and eventually just said, 'Can you go. Sorry, I need to think. If I move, I'll smash this room to pieces.' He wouldn't leave. So I went upstairs, and true to my word, smashed my section of the bedroom up. Grabbed my blades, grabbed my bag, and fled through the back door. But he saw me, and followed.

'Joe, *please* leave me alone!' I sat down at the bus stop. '*Please* just go!'

'No Emma!'

The emotional pressure cooker inside me was threatening to blow and as the tears started, I began to shout, 'Look, you're going to get sick of me eventually so go! Just fucking go! Don't drag it out!'

He shouted back, 'I'm not going to get sick of you! I'm not ever going to give up either.' His voice softened, 'I can handle your anger, Em. Please, just come back with me, let me be there for you. Please baby?'

I wiped the mascara from under my eyes. 'No!' He wasn't going to move. I began to beg, 'Please, Joe. I need to get this out. I can't do that here.' I put my head in my hands. 'I don't want you to hate me, I'll be okay. I just need to be alone.' He pleaded with me to go back with him as I started to yell again, the people around us subtly stepping away. The bus came. 'Look. I'm going to get on this now. Are you pissed off?'

He looked at me, those green eyes bigger than ever. 'Yes. But that doesn't mean I care about you any less.' I got on the bus without looking back. There was a moment, a fleeting four seconds of relief before that old familiar voice hissed into my ear. 'My, my, my, you are *pathetic*. He won't want you now. You'd better rip yourself to shreds.'

Sitting on a long black bench in a deserted churchyard in the centre of town, I began to cut, and cut, and cut until the floor beneath me became a ruby sea about eight inches across and I felt dizzy. I let my arm hang limp as if it weren't a part of me, the blood making a drip, drip, sound every time it splashed against the concrete, hot relief pouring from me, the world quiet and my mind finally at rest.

I crept back into the hospital at 10pm knowing I would be in for another grilling in the morning. I hoped that that if I threw myself on their altar the punishment would be less. Bless me, Father, for I have sinned, it's been fifteen minutes since my last confession. As I walked through the alcove to my room, Joe was sitting alone playing on his phone.

'Come and sit here, you.' He patted the sofa. Obedient, I did as I was told. He put his phone down. 'You have no idea how worried about you I've been.' He looked deep into my eyes, that feeling of exposure again.

'I'm sorry,' I said quietly.

He looked away. 'I know you are.' He put his arm around me and I let him. I disappeared into his body and felt safe for the first time all day. And just as quickly as I had found my solace again, he was kissing me, and I was kissing him back. Explosions. Forbidden emotions, bright red and blinding. Finally. Finally I was where I needed to be. His arms around me, his lips against mine.

*

Wednesday was slow. I was still walking on air from our kiss the night before and strangely in firm I had got off lightly. I told them what I did, told them I wanted to stop, told them that I would make the effort to find help and support if I needed it during the day. Head nods and smiles spread across the appropriate parties' faces; without knowing how I had somehow avoided going to slaughter. With my urge to feel hurt still lingering around me, I decided to go and see Jim. Going to the tattoo studio was a break for me. It was pain being inflicted by someone else, the rush of which I could still benefit from. He had started his half sleeve on me, and I thought he could add to it today if he was free.

I walked in as usual, straight past reception and up to Jim's station where he was happy to see me, but as we hugged hello he suddenly grabbed my hand.

'What the fuck is that?' I looked at the floor.

'A burn.'

A strange look spread across his face that I wasn't used to; it prompted me to ask, 'Are you angry with me?'

He somewhat coldly said, 'It's not my body.'

I left quickly, feeling like the disgust located in me had been validated and that the man who had never once judged my body, had just done so. Bring on the voices. I am disgusting. I am hideous. I am ugly. I am unlovable.

I had never felt rejected by Jim like that and I couldn't stand it. I rushed back to Joe who was waiting for me in town. 'That was quick!' he said stubbing out his cigarette. 'He was overbooked.'

We walked back to the Caddick holding hands and it felt so natural, normal, safe.

'Emma?' I turned around to see Ellie behind us. I let go of Joe's hand and whispered, 'Fuck.' But surprisingly, she didn't seem fazed as she caught up and walked in the middle of us. Her voice was light, inquisitive.

'Why did you stop holding hands when I came over?'

I fumbled over my words as Joe said, 'Cos you're standing in the middle of us!'

She laughed. 'Okay, fair enough.'

My heart was thudding in my chest. 'El, you won't tell anyone will you?'

She linked her hand through my arm and laughed as she said, 'Don't be stupid.'

*

That night at ten, when everyone else was occupied either handing out medication or taking it, Joe and I met in the garden. We sat at the back of the grounds in his spot again, far away from prying eyes. Our legs and arms tangled up in each other, his mouth on mine, the distant glow of the hospital lights glinting in the darkness, small silhouettes dancing across its windows. I tried so hard to stay in the moment, trying not to flinch as he put his hands on my body.

'What's wrong?' he asked, pulling away from me.

I quickly shook my head 'Nothing!'

Joe took me at my word and began to kiss me again, but I couldn't help myself, and every time his fingers swept over my skin I felt my body recoil. There were three fights going on inside me. The first was that I didn't want his hands accidentally stumbling upon a roll of fat, or some other self-perceived distasteful part of me, a scar, a stretch mark. The second fight was that I didn't want to make him angry by pushing him away like this, make him feel rejected to the point where he'd then reject me… And the last fight? Yes, I did want him. I wanted to submit, I wanted to touch and be touched and trust him, but it felt almost impossible – trying to relax, trying to be inside that moment with him. I was a coiled spring, ready to leap up at any moment, desperate to escape, desperate to stay. He was going to get pissed off, any second now, just like all the Toms – their redundant faces flashed through my mind like a film reel of bad decisions. He pulled away from me again; this is it I thought, he's going to huff and puff and ask me what my problem is? But instead, he put his arms behind his back.

I half laughed, confused, 'What are you doing?'

He smiled at me, 'I want you to know you're in control. I'm not going to touch you if you don't want me to. I'm not going to make you feel uncomfortable…' He paused. 'Do you feel nervous when I touch you because of the way you feel about your body, or is it other things as well?'

I looked down, suddenly feeling stripped and vulnerable. 'Yes to both.'

He pulled me into him and held me there for a moment, the silence enveloping us like a warm blanket. As I sat back again he gently moved my hair away from my face and said, 'Has something happened today? You seem down?' I told him about Jim and how that whole interaction had made me feel, and then I began to tell him about the voice in my head, the constant, hostile narration – determined to undermine and ruin everything I tried to do. Every track of every thought inside my mind it ran parallel to, always there, poised and ready to spoil it. Every idea, every good moment, every second of the fucking day. The relentless, never-ending attack. I sucked the night air into my lungs.

'… It just goes and goes until I break, until I am shaking and crying and unable to think or breathe, and then it swoops back in and says, "You're fine. You're okay, I've got you, as long as you do what I say" … so I listen to it, I do what it wants, and then when I feel human again, when I've calmed down, it repeats the pattern.'

His green eyes stared back at me, I felt my cheeks flush under their persistent gaze. 'I've said too much.'

I didn't look up but heard him quietly say, 'You're perfect.'

I rose to my feet, and refused to look at him as I said, 'Shall we go back.' It wasn't a question, I was already walking away, but turned and held out my shaking hand for him to take. He didn't get up but looking at me with an intensity that I'd never seen before he said, 'What do you need, darlin'?'

In a frightened, frantic voice that I didn't know, I heard myself shout, 'I need you to hold my hand!'

When we got in, Joe went to get his meds and I rushed away, up to the top of the building and into one of the secret rooms where no one could find me. I sat in the shadows, over-exposed and anxiety ridden. I didn't know what was wrong with me, why were my brain and body reacting like this? What was it? My chest was tight. It was like a huge influx of emotion, a monstrous surge of feelings that I couldn't untangle in my mind, like coming up on ecstasy, like that fourth, thick line of cocaine in the space of twenty minutes. My heart beat thunderously, as if the storm inside me were about to break at any second. I spent an hour in the dark, my body curled up beneath one of the huge windows, staring out onto the grounds, watching the night sky, as it watched me. But the longer I stayed there, the worse I felt. I wanted to be with Joe, in spite of feeling I'd told him too much, and despite feeling like I needed to run away from him. So admitting defeat, I got up and went back to him. Pull the strap, flick the needle, plunge it in.

I found him in the alcove and led him outside again where we sat on the smoking steps. 'When I don't touch you,' he said moving around to face me, 'I don't want you to think it's because

I don't want to, or that I don't like the feel of you, because I do. But I care about you, and I know me touching you makes you feel bad.' He put his hand on my knee, 'and I don't want to make you feel bad, Em. I'll only ever do what you're comfortable with.' My eyes filled up with something like relief, something like love. He kissed me hard as the world fell silent around us.

*

As we got up to come back inside Marie trotted past. 'Hi Marie,' called Joe behind her, but she ignored him. He glanced at me quizzically and we decided to follow her as she went into the kitchen. Marie lay down on the hard concrete floor. Not talking, not moving, eyes open, staring at the ceiling, her curly hair framing her round face. She had asked for diazepam earlier on in the evening and been refused it, and now this – what should we call it? Selective mute exhibition? – was the price we were all going to pay for that decision. I knelt down on the floor and tried to talk to her, but every word I uttered evaporated into the air like white noise; she was having none of it.

It was two in the morning. Joe went hunting for the night staff and came back with Brian. Eventually the two of them got her to stand up; she hunched over one of the tables rambling incessantly under her breath, 'I saw a beetle today. Beetles don't manipulate you. If I were a beetle I'd be much happier. Queen Marie they'd call me, queen of the beetles!'

Staring at Joe and Brian I began to get the giggles; Joe had to stop looking at me and shoved his hand over his mouth to stop from laughing. She went on. 'I like vegetables. Vegetables don't manipulate you either, I suppose I could be queen of vegetables too, but which vegetable would I choose, there are just so many.' She sighed heavily. I was shaking with laughter as I linked her arm and led her to her bedroom. Brian, fearing this escapade might go on all night, gave her that diazepam, and delighted at her win, the queen of the beetles fell into a deep sleep.

*

Back in the alcove once again and Joe and I were wrapped around each other. He pushed into me as I lay back in his arms. I kissed his neck, pulling him onto me as hard as he was begging to be pulled, barely coming up for breath. Eventually I stammered, 'Joe, I have to go to bed, it's 4am,' but he kept kissing me. I pleaded as I began to get up, 'No I really have to go to bed... it's... so... late!' He grabbed my hand and pulled me back down onto him before I could finish the sentence, making an 'mhmm' noise as our lips found each other once again. A few moments later I stood up, stumbling, sighing and exasperated; I could barely think straight. He stared at me smiling. 'I'm going to bed, Joe. See... Watch me go.' I looked back at him as I disappeared through the double doors that led to the staircase. Before I had even got up to my room my phone beeped. 'You blow me away.'

*

The next morning I sat opposite Nora, listening as she debunked Jim's behaviour from the day before. 'Usually, Emma, you and he collude and put something under your skin together, but you had done something without him, you burnt yourself badly, and he found himself not agreeing with that and not wanting to collude with it, so it separated you. He was on one side of the fence, while you were on the other. Isolated yet again, and on your own.'

I huffed, annoyed. 'I don't understand why everyone takes it so personally. It's me I'm burning!'

Nora scowled slightly, an unimpressed look spreading over her face. 'I think you do know why. People care about you. As much as you like to pretend you're this unreachable, unlovable "thing" that no one could possibly care about, people do.'

I sighed. 'So what shall I do? With Jim?'

'Talk to him! Let him have his feelings, and experience them with him.'

I left the hospital with Nora's words still fresh in my mind, and went to see Jim. I told him flat out that his comment the day before had really upset me. I repeated what Nora had said, word for word.

Jim smirked, 'I'm sorry to say it, Em, but the shrink is right.' I put my hand over his, he gripped it tight and then let go, grabbing for his tattoo gun. 'Seeing as you're here, how about we work on that tatt?' I nodded. The needle hit my skin, that familiar buzz. He was gentle, asking frequently if I was okay and when he reached a sensitive part of my arm and I winced, he pulled the gun away asking, 'Does that hurt?' When I said 'Yes' he said 'Good', a big smile on his face. I looked at him, confused, waiting for an answer. Putting the needle back onto my skin he said, 'This can be your pain for the day then, can't it? No cutting and no burning...' He paused, trailing his fingers softly over some of my scars. 'God, you've been doing this for a long time.'

46

THE TREETOP WALK

"When I see you, the World stops. It stops and all that exists for me is you and my eyes staring at you. There's nothing else. No noise, no other people, no thoughts or worries, no yesterday, no tomorrow. The World just stops, and it is a beautiful place, and there is only you."

— JAMES FREY, *A Million Little Pieces*

Trying to have a secret relationship in a psychiatric hospital is at best challenging, at worst a total nightmare. You never know who might have caught on (Ellie, Aaron, Leah), who's out to get you (Harriet, Crystal, Slime) and who couldn't care less (Brooke, Susie, Grace). The problem with a romance in a therapeutic environment is of course the potential effect it can have on your treatment. I saw no such problem, but of course that's not to say there wasn't one. Getting through my days quickly meant the sooner the night would roll in, and under cover of darkness I could get back to Joe's arms.

I still hadn't told Prue about him and me, and now with people figuring it out, I needed to tell her before someone else did.

I went down to meet her near where she lived and before I knew it I was crying into my hands as we sat in a café, begging her forgiveness. 'I'm so, so sorry. I can call it off if you want?' I think I did genuinely mean it as it left my lips, but in reality I couldn't have given him up if I wanted to. I'm not sure what I'd have done if she had said, 'Yes, call it off.' Thankfully, Prue took the news gracefully and said it was okay, that I was already proving my worth as a friend for telling her the truth, but despite her kind words, I did see a flash in her eyes that gave me a glimpse of something else. I could have pressed it, but I didn't want to; I didn't want to be told I had hurt her, or betrayed her, or that, yes, she did want me to end it.

I sat on the train back to Waterloo scribbling in my journal. It was after 9pm and no one else was in the carriage. I had my headphones in and jumped as I felt someone touch my shoulder. 'Yes?' I stared at the tall black-haired man in front of me; I hadn't noticed him get on. 'Can I sit here?' he gestured towards the seat opposite. I shrugged, wanting to say no but not finding the resolve. We sat opposite each other separated by the small table in between the seats. 'I wanted to talk to you, girly.' He was drunk, I could smell the whisky on his breath. I didn't say anything, just stared blankly back at him. 'You're pretty. What's your name?'

'Emma.' I probably should have lied.

'Well hello, Emma. What's a lovely thing like you doing sitting here by yourself?' I didn't feel particularly intimidated by him but I wished he'd just leave me alone.

'Writing. And I prefer being on my own so if you don't mind?' He cut me off, 'No, I don't mind. Can I have your number?'

'No, my boyfriend wouldn't like it.'

He theatrically threw his head back and laughed sinisterly. 'Oh, but Emma! Emma, Emma, Emma! We're here all alone, how will he know? How will anyone know?' He had stressed the 'all' in 'all alone.' I *was* alone with this man. On a train in the middle of nowhere, the apocalyptic darkness outside and no signal on my phone as we rode through the deserted countryside. He rested his leg against mine under the table. 'C'mon girly, *give it to me.*' I shifted uncomfortably in my chair.

'Yeah, fine.' I read him my number.

Thankfully the train began to pull into the next station and before I could attempt to gather myself, he stood up placing his hands on either side of my chair, his face inches from mine – I tried to move but his arms blocked me. I swallowed hard.

'You're not going to kiss me?' It was supposed to be a statement but instead it squeaked out of me like a half-hearted question. He stayed there for what felt like forever, his black, dilated pupils staring into my eyes, lingering at my lips. I felt completely unable to move, I wanted to, but I just didn't, couldn't.

The train stopped and a group of men got on laughing loudly. He glanced at them, then back at me, lightly touching my lips with his fingers, he put his mouth to my ear and whispered 'You got lucky Emma.' He swiftly took his hands away and disappeared through the train doors before they closed. I breathed a huge sigh of relief. He had been so close to my face that I felt like I could taste his breath. As the train began to pull away my phone beeped, it was him, 'Just a close-up look.' I felt sick. As soon as I got off the train I called Joe. He stayed on the phone to me until I got to my bedroom at my parents' house, all the time telling me if the man on the train had touched me he would have hunted him down and killed him. There was something in his voice, an anger so full of repressed violence, that made me believe that yes, he actually would have.

*

It was the next evening and Prue's wheezing down the phone was getting worse. 'You can breathe, honey, you're okay.' Her grandfather had died, and I'd been on the phone to her for about twenty minutes, my voice doing little to reassure or settle her. She kept trying to talk, but was barely audible through her sobs and gasps for air. Prue's grandparents had been her rock, her anchors in a violent sea of never-ending abuse. They brought her normality, and were the ones to offer her a place of solace on the rare occasions she managed to escape her abusers and stay with them. And now, in the wake of her grandfather's death, she was understandably heartbroken. I sat in the garden of the Caddick with the phone pressed against my ear, leaning against the glass doors of the community room. Joe appeared in front of me and pointed at the phone quizzically. I mouthed 'Prue.' He nodded and lit a cigarette, walking away to give me some privacy. In all honesty he needn't have bothered, I wasn't really saying anything, just telling her to breathe, telling her she was okay. But was she? Did I even believe what I was saying to her? Did it matter? She began to shout, as I knew she would once her breathing became slightly more under control.

'My childhood was robbed from me!' What could I say? 'They raped me!' What could I say? 'They killed my baby!' What could I say? 'My grandfather is dead!' *What could I fucking say?* Just listen. Just sit with it. Just be there and tolerate it, that was my role.

*

Of course I couldn't heal Prue's heartache, or even do very much to ease her pain, but I listened and I tried as best I could to be there. After an hour or so I left her drifting off to sleep with a couple of diazepam that I'd asked her to take whilst she had been on the phone to me. I walked back into the alcove where Joe sat reading. 'That was a long call.'

'Yeah, she's in bed now. That poor girl can't catch a break.' I flopped down next to him on the sofa.

'You can't fix her you know.' He closed his book and looked at me.

'I know that. She doesn't need me to fix her anyway, she's strong, Joe. Probably the strongest person I've ever met.'

He took my hand in his. 'I know she means a lot to you. I just worry sometimes that…' he trailed off not finishing his sentence.

'That what?' I asked. He sighed heavily. 'I worry that it's all quite manipulative…' I felt an instant surge of annoyance and cut him off.

'You leave Prue to me. She helped me plenty of times in this hospital and I'm not about to leave her to rot on her own when she needs me most.'

He gently traced his fingertips over the ridges of my skin, 'Okay, baby.'

*

'I think I am going to kill myself.' Bonnie drew a heart in her colouring book and started to colour it pink. 'Pink like your hair!' She smiled and leaned into me. I put my arm around her.

'I don't want you to kill yourself, I'd be really sad.'

She nodded in approval. 'Okay, well I won't… for today anyway.' She was nine. Her mother Josie had asked me to spend some time with her. Bonnie was all about shock value, she'd say anything to get attention but it's not like I was judging her for it – unlike a lot of the manipulative adults around me, at least she was honest when confronted. The family was in the hospital because Josie was borderline like the rest of us; her husband Solomon seemed like a nice man but was clearly at his wits' end. They had Bonnie threatening anything and everything she could every few hours to get a reaction, whilst everyone tiptoed around her younger brother Liam who was prone to violent

435

outbursts and had broken the youngest son's nose a couple of weeks before they came into the hospital.

The dining room was filling up for the lunchtime trough gathering. Josie came over to us. 'Bonnie, come on, we need to have lunch.'

'No. I'm not going to eat today. I want to be thin.'

Josie exhaled sharply – and suspecting Liam had learned his temper from his mother I quickly said, 'How about if I sit with you? We can have lunch together and chat some more?'

She squealed excitedly and threw her arms around me. 'Yes! Yes!' Chef Ken was now used to my two spoons of couscous bullshit but would still try to heap on a third spoonful before giving me a wry look as I snatched my plate away and smiled sweetly at him. I sat down opposite Liam as Bonnie ate her lunch.

'Why are you so ugly?' Liam pointed his spoon at me as he waited for an answer. I was starting to get used to him doing this. Whenever I spent time with one of his siblings he would be jealous of the attention they got, no matter how I tried to involve him. 'Hey, I'm talking to you. You're so ugly. And you wear the same clothes all the time.' He lowered his voice to a disgusted whisper. 'And they look awful.' He wanted a response from me.

'Don't be rude,' said Josie as she nudged him with her elbow.

'But Mummy, she is so ugly. She looks horrible.'

'Liam shut up,' said Bonnie as she grabbed my hand protectively. Josie had started talking to Solomon and had stopped listening.

'She's ugly!' he whispered at Bonnie.

'*Shut up!*' came her shrill cry back.

Solomon looked over. 'You're both going to go to bed if you carry on.' Liam stuck his tongue out at me. Josie and Solomon began to talk again.

'Her hair is disgusting and *she's fat*,' he whispered so his parents couldn't hear. Bonnie threw her burger at him, he threw his plate at her, it hit her hard in the chest and she began to wail.

'Oh for God's sake!' Solomon got up and dragged Liam away, pulling him by his arm as he continued to look back over his shoulder at me and jeer, 'Ugly, ugly!'

After I had calmed Bonnie down and got her another burger I made my exit, out into the garden, away from sight. I sat behind one of the huge oak trees, my head in my hands and cried. The crying went on for a long time and didn't seem to relieve any of the hurt inside me. I knew he was only six. A hurt, damaged six-year-old little boy, but it always surprised me that even though I never reacted to his jibes, he somehow seemed to know they would still affect me. I reached into my coat pocket and pulled out my bus pass where inside the holder, behind the card, I had a razor blade hiding. I only cut myself a couple of times, it was enough. I sat there watching as the blood soaked through my long-sleeved top and then my coat. I heard the sounds of someone walking nearby and saw Laura, her eyes red and swollen, blowing her nose into a tissue.

'Hi,' she said as she saw me, 'can I sit with you?'

I smiled up at her, 'Of course. What's wrong?'

She sat down and started to cry. 'I'm such a fucking failure, Emma... all of them on the family unit think I should be dead,' she began to sob even harder, '... and maybe I should be!' She wiped her eyes on her white cardigan sleeve.

'Has something happened?' I asked.

She nodded, looking around to make sure everyone was still inside eating. 'I... I used,' she glanced at me, then back at the ground, 'I know it was weak, but I just couldn't take it any more. I came back yesterday from my session and someone had written "paedo scum" on our bedroom door... I got it off before Ben saw... but it made me realise I'll never be able to escape this. Wherever I go, whatever I do, that's who people will see. I know what they think, and I know I am not the victim in this, but things happened to me too…things I've never talked about, they were bad Emma, really bad.' She looked down, closing her eyes for a second and exhaling… 'Those things,' she continued, looking back at me, 'made my head go funny for a long time. It's not an excuse, not at all, I know what I did was… disgusting. I know most people will automatically hate me for it. And I get it, I do. But I am trying…'

I thought back to the article I had read about her.

'I made a mistake last night. I shouldn't have turned to drugs. And I won't mess up again. No one knows, only you… Ben didn't suspect anything and I won't tell him, he'll just panic.'

'Have you thought about changing your name, Laura? Leaving London, or England, and starting again somewhere?'

She nodded 'Yeah, of course, but I can't… legally, not for a long time. It's part of the parole.' She looked at my arm 'You're bleeding.' I had forgotten. 'Do you need me to get someone? Or go get bandages?'

I shook my head. 'No, it's nothing.'

'Laura? Lunch!' We looked up to see Ben standing by the playground, Sam in his arms.

'Coming babe!' she called back. Quickly wiping her eyes again she said, 'I have to go… Sorry for going on at you, Emma. Please don't tell anyone; I'll lose Sam.'

I waved at Ben then looked at her. 'I won't, but you need to swear you won't do that again.'

She leaned over and hugged me, 'I swear, I won't.' She jumped up and ran over to Ben, taking Sam out of his arms and kissing him on his little head. I knew I should tell someone, I knew withholding this information was a bad idea. But if I told the staff they would more than likely take the baby away from her; he might end up in care, and what would become of her?

She'd probably be found dead with a needle with her arm in some bedsit in a year's time. It was so much responsibility; tell, don't tell, act, do nothing, hold your breath, hold in your secrets and hope for the fucking best.

'Baby?' I glanced up in time to see Joe appear behind the tree. The razor blade had long since been put away but he looked at the wet patch still seeping through my sleeve. 'What's going on?'

'Nothing, I'm okay.' Even I didn't believe myself. He sat down next to me on the grass.

'You've been crying. Haven't you? Please talk to me.'

'Liam was doing his "you're so ugly" routine again. I'm just tired and it got to me today.'

He put his hand on my knee then looked at the wet mark on my sleeve. 'And that?'

I nodded slowly. 'Yes, and that.'

He moved closer to me, putting his arm around my shoulder. 'Em, please ignore him. He's a fucked-up little kid – he's just saying anything he can to try and get attention, you're gorgeous.'

'Please, don't Joe, not right now.' When I felt like this, compliments sank into me like a knife to my gut. The voice in my head that dictated how I felt about myself was far too loud and powerful for anything to be heard over it and if its authority was challenged in any way it just grew louder and more angry – it was far easier to let it be. I pushed my hand through my hair, I so desperately did not want to be *this*. I wanted to be a smiley, fun, sexy girl for him. I wanted to make him happy, I wanted to give him a normal relationship (if that's what this was) but my depression was so abundant all the time. It was like walking around with hundred-pound chains shackled to both my ankles and no matter how much I wanted to break free I just couldn't escape my own misery or, more profoundly, the noise in my head telling me I was worthless. I was on a constant roller coaster of emotion that I didn't remember getting on… One loop and I was laughing and dizzy, high as a kite sailing up into an azure sky; the next loop and all I could see was black, lurid and heavy, gorging itself on me. Would it ever be full?

*

The blood on my coat had dried and stained the material a strange grey colour. I prodded it with my finger wondering how I'd get the stain out when Joe's voice broke through my thoughts. 'Why the actual fuck am I doing this?' He was visibly shaking as he took the next step along the two-metre-wide steel net walkway in the middle of Kew Gardens. We were on the treetop walk suspended twenty or so metres up, being supported by rusted steel columns that held everything in place.

'Because you wanted to cheer me up…' I began laughing, 'Bet you regret that one, hey?' I looked around me, it was a truly beautiful sight. I felt carefree and calm, high up above the trees looking over London town. Below me were the spectacular colours of the blooming spring flowers, the birds chirped, the sun shone and I felt happy again.

'I hope you appreciate this, young lady!' he said over his shoulder. 'Heights are my biggest phobia!'

'I do…' I sang back, smiling at him, '… I can show you how much later?'

'Promises, promises,' he said almost tripping over and having to steady himself on the handrails. I began to laugh again but tried to stifle it as he turned around and jokingly scowled at me. He kissed me as we stood overlooking the landscape, his arms wrapped around me, our bodies entwined. I felt so close to him, but it almost wasn't enough. I wanted to feel closer.

As we climbed down the (118) steps to the gardens we found a secluded spot surrounded by roses of every colour. I let go of his hand and turned to face him. 'Thank you. I love it here! It's so peaceful.' I bent down and smelled a plump yellow rose, looking up to catch him smiling back at me with those green-black eyes.

'It's okay, you needed it. I probably needed it too.' He lay down on the grass with his hands behind his head. I lay beside him and we simmered there for a while in the tranquil sounds around us. Although the scene we were in was perfect serenity there was a fire burning inside me, something untamed and almost uncomfortable. I began to kiss him again under the watchful eyes of the chestnut trees. The kissing felt different to how it usually did, more desperate, more intense; as close as he was I needed him to be closer and the closer he got, the more I needed him. My hands slid effortlessly under his shirt, my fingers exploring his chest, the ridges of his soft skin under a map of scars. I wanted to consume him, I wanted to devour him whole, I couldn't breathe and I didn't want to. He slowly moved on top of my body. I kissed him frantically like either one of us could disappear at any second. Between our lips I heard his words, 'Is this, okay?' I didn't need to answer. His hands moved quickly over my body, fumbling, trying to get it right, succeeding. The sweet smell of fresh cut grass and roses swirled around us as we forgot ourselves, forgot the rules, forgot the Caddick, and forgot the world right along with it.

47

FUNDING WARS

"These walls are funny. First you hate 'em. Then you get used to 'em. Enough time passes, you get so you depend on them. That's institutionalized."

— STEPHEN KING, *The Shawshank Redemption*

My funding was coming to an end, but I wasn't ready to go. Nora acknowledged there was still more work to do, as did my other therapists and the nurses, so they applied for six weeks' extra funding for me.

Applying for the extra time was, I'm sure, an arduous and intensive task and, despite my personal feelings for Dr Finstard, I can't deny he did me a huge service in petitioning for the extension. The NHS mental health services were starting to struggle; not outwardly massively at that point, but the cracks were beginning to show – obviously the Henshaw closing had been a big indicator of this, and I'd of course wager there were other hospitals and treatment facilities also being shut down around the same time. In order for me to stay at the hospital for an extra six weeks, the Caddick team would have to write a letter to the commissioners on my behalf and justify why I deserved funding.

Dear Mr Abraham,
Re: Miss ED d.o.b 22/04/85
Inpatient on the Caddick ESPD service

We have now had a further treatment review
in which we carefully looked at Miss ED's
development in treatment since her initial
treatment review and the plans for her future.

Please accept my apologies that I am not
sending you copies of reports or notes from
the review, as you requested. The reports
from the review and my notes on the review
discussion contain a lot of very intimate
details from her psychotherapy which would not
be appropriate to pass on. It is instead my
practice to summarise the developments in a
letter, as I am doing here now.

The various reports in the review, including
Miss D's own thoughtful contribution, showed a
promising development in the last few months.
She has moved from a position where her needs
have to be treated with contempt and denied,
to one in which they can be acknowledged
by her and she can even at times ask for
help; this is an important step towards being
able to make use of help offered to her as
an outpatient. She has moved from a more
withdrawn and frequently resistant place in
the therapeutic community to an active and
constructive engagement. She has not self-
harmed for a while. She has become more open
about her deep inner disturbance, for example
about the extent she can feel intruded upon
by people around her. However, having become
more open and engaged, she is also not so
protected by her old hard defences and is
much more vulnerable; this means that she can
easily and sometimes dramatically shut down.

443

There needs to be some further development before she can safely move on to outpatient treatment, without falling back into her old way of functioning.

The deep disturbance that we are beginning to see more openly now will very clearly need longer term treatment, in order for her to be able to form healthier social and intimate relationships and function in everyday life, all of which she has so far been unable to do.

An important aspect is that she has become stuck in her age appropriate development, reflected for example in her inability to separate properly from her mother. She has been wanting to move out for some time but has felt unable to do so. In this situation she is, rightly I think, worried that once discharged she would shut herself back into the same situation as she did after her discharge from the Henshaw hospital.

Considering these developments and difficulties, two things are extremely important in my view:

Firstly, that she continues at the Caddick's outreach treatment after discharge from inpatient treatment. You may be aware that it is the combination of residential and outreach treatment as a step down package that has convincing research results, much more than residential treatment alone. The residential treatment is laying the ground for the necessary longer term work on her severe disturbance to take place; she will need further intensive work, emotional and practical, to help her grow out of her entrenched relationship with her mother and enable her to take up work or training again.

Secondly, that the discharge from inpatient treatment is carefully planned and that she is sufficiently prepared to be able to step down into the outreach treatment, without falling back, as she did after treatment at the Henshaw hospital.

From our considerations at the review and subsequent CPA, I would therefore recommend that she has an additional six weeks' residential treatment.

The cost for the additional six weeks' residential treatment would be £11,634.00, and the cost for two years outreach treatment with twice weekly group psychotherapy and outreach nursing would be £24,636.00.

It is essential for the remaining work with Miss ED that we have clarity as soon as possible. I would therefore be grateful if you could come up with a decision and let us know as a matter of urgency.

Yours sincerely,
Dr Erik Finstard
Consultant Psychiatrist in Psychotherapy
Caddick ESPD service
(Emerging & Severe Personality Disorders)

*

Waiting for the funding to come through was a nerve-wracking time for me, not that I was going to admit that to anyone. Alison had tried to corner me in the community meeting – asking me how I felt – I was fairly nonchalant in response, but had told Nora and Johanna my concerns when I had been alone with them. Thankfully for me, but not so much for others in the meeting, there were more pressing matters.

Wendy had only been at the hospital for two weeks. She was a forty-something Scottish lady who was very quiet but seemed incredibly sweet and kind. Before coming into the hospital she had worked with special-needs children and was hoping to get back to her job once she was feeling better in herself and had gotten some therapy.

'Wendy, we've had some news.' Judy cleared her throat. 'Carrie is unwell. In fact she is terminally ill and they don't think she will make it more than a week or two.' Silence fell through the room, weaving its way through a sea of confused faces until it landed on Wendy who began to howl out like an animal in pain. Carrie, it turned out, was one of the children Wendy had worked with and was most close to. I was confused as to why they were choosing to tell her this painful news in the community meeting. It felt far too personal for us all to be listening in on.

While this was unfolding, people around the room looked upset, their own trauma and childhood ghosts seeping through the community rooms walls as they fed off Wendy's grief, other than Harriet, Crystal and Kiera, of course, who sat there with inane smiles on their faces prodding each other like three-year-olds. My eyes fell on Joe, who was a few seats away from Wendy, and he looked strangely agitated. After screaming at the staff, Wendy got up and ran out of the room in floods of tears, quickly followed by various patients saying the staff should have shown more sensitivity and told her privately. The staff's argument against this was that it was a community issue as Wendy would need our support. A quarrel about this broke out. All the while Joe's face was thunder as he stared at the floor; his usual gentle knee-bouncing had elevated to a violent pace and I could visibly see his hands shaking even from the other side of the room.

As the meeting ended and everyone left, I followed Joe who promptly went up to his bedroom. I couldn't go any further as it was early in the morning, and the staffroom, which was opposite his bedroom, would be awash with people. Instead I texted him. 'Are you all right?' After twenty or so minutes my phone beeped with a reply. 'Just not feeling good. Going to bed xx'. I'd never seen Joe like this, and it worried me. He was always so lively and happy. I decided to go out and buy him something I knew he would like.

I returned a couple of hours later with a copy of *Straw Dogs*, a big chocolate bar and a Banksy postcard which I wrote on, saying that I was around if he needed to talk. I went and sat in the alcove, texting him again to tell him there was something in the hallway for him. An hour or so later he walked through the door to the dining room and approached me. He cleared his throat.

'I've got a bone to pick with you.' A second of worry passed through me as he sat down. 'You've put me in a good mood… I had committed myself to being depressed but you've cheered me up.' I unapologetically apologised, and he took my hand into his and held it there.

'Did you go to your session whilst I was out?' I asked. He nodded. 'Helpful?'

'Yeah, it was…' he took a deep breath. 'This morning with Wendy… it reminded me of how I was told that my dad had died.' He paused, looking past me out of the window, 'It brought it all back… that anger at being told in front of a load of people.' He shook his head.

'I'm so sorry, Joe.' He drew my hand up to his lips and kissed it. 'How can I cheer you up?' I asked. A devious smile spread across his face and I laughed. 'Other that *that.*' He hesitated, shrugging his shoulders a little.

'I don't know, baby.' The door creaked open and I quickly whipped my hand away from him. It was Aaron; he looked upset. I called out, 'You all right?'

He stopped and looked at me, taking out his headphones. 'Yeah… sort of. Leah's got to go to A&E… she's been bloodletting.' He looked down at the floor then back up at me. 'Fifteen needles full. And I think Brooke is about to lose it too… Grace said she's hiding in her wardrobe screaming.' He looked like he might cry and began chewing on his black painted nails. I felt so bad for him.

'You can hang out with us if you like, Aaron?' I said, motioning to Joe, trying to make the offer seem as appealing as I could.

He shook his head. 'No, it's okay. I've got my one-to-one anyway.' He put his headphones back in and wandered off. We stayed quiet for moment until I broke the silence.

'Well, I'm guessing it's going to kick off here, and I'm also guessing you haven't eaten today… So shall we escape while we still can and get some dinner somewhere?'

He looked at me, bemused. 'You? *You* want to go and eat?'

I huffed jokingly. 'Well, not particularly! But I want *you* to eat, so I'll make an exception… this once.'

He nodded. 'I'd like that.'

*

We walked through central London hand in hand looking around the city and acting like a normal couple – and out there, away from the hospital, that's pretty much what we were. I cherished those moments, just me and him, free to kiss and touch and feel completely immersed in the blanket of safety he was able to wrap around me with just one look, even in his lowest moments. I had never felt this way about anyone before, and though I struggled to believe him, he had said the same thing. I never quite felt close enough though. I felt like I wanted to bury myself inside him and stay forever. There was always this feeling that he might slip away at any second, like waking from a perfect dream never to be able to fall back into it again, no matter how hard you try to go to sleep.

We sat in a little Moroccan restaurant near St Paul's, at a table surrounded by fairy lights and a waiter in a bow tie. I forced myself into eating a halloumi wrap, enjoying his company and ignoring the hisses about calories in my head. 'I have to get back for night meeting,' he said as he put twenty quid in the little silver dish on the table.

'Yeah, I know, that's okay.'

He did a little wave at the waiter, beckoning him over. 'I really don't want to though.'

I stood up and put on my coat. 'It's fine, we can head back.' As we walked across the Millennium Bridge I stopped and looked out at the Thames. The water was an ominous black, rippling hypnotically as it reflected the shimmering bright lights of the city. He came up behind me and wrapped his arms tight around my body. I lay my head back on his chest, listening to the quick thud, thud, thud of his heart.

'Emma, I feel like I'm alive when I'm with you.'

*

We got back to the hospital just in time for Joe to go into the night meeting. I sat with Ellie in our room while she chatted about Jack and how she couldn't wait for him to get out of hospital and be with her in the Caddick. 'You look tired, Em, are you sleeping?'

I shrugged. 'Yes and no.'

'Too busy up with Joe every night! Do you want some zopiclone?'

'Why? Do you have some spare?'

She shook her head. 'No, but you can have mine if you want, I don't need them at the moment, I'm tired enough going back and forth to the hospital to see Jack. Come on, we'll go now.' I got up and followed her to the dispensary where a few other people were queueing up for their night meds.

I sat on the floor next to Susie who laid her head on my shoulder and whispered, 'Did you have a nice time out with Joe? He looked much happier when he got back.'

'Yeah, it was lovely.'

'You were gone for a long time,' said Marie, who was standing up, leaning against the wall next to Susie.

'Yeah, we went for a bite to eat.' She didn't answer, just made a 'mhmm' noise.

'Ellie,' called Brian as he stood at the dispensary window. She got up and stood in front of him. 'Here's your zopiclone.' He passed her the tablet and in the quickest most fluid movement, she swapped it into her right hand and pretended to take it, knocking her head back for effect and opening her mouth afterwards to show him it was gone. She turned around and handed it to me, laughing her devilish little laugh as she did. I saw Slime's eyes flick to my hand. I'm sure she guessed we were up to something but she hadn't seen what had happened – she sat back against the wall looking miffed and carried on filing her nails.

*

I sat outside in the cool night air, waiting for Joe and thinking about the day. My phone started vibrating in my pocket. I lifted it out: Prue. I answered to the sounds of her gasping for breath. 'You can breathe, honey. Relax your shoulders. Nice slow breaths. Relax your back. Give your fingers a wiggle. Good. You're doing good. You're okay.'

She was distraught – the grief of her grandfather's death was still sucking the oxygen out of the air around her. She told me she'd cut and was bleeding badly. 'Do you need me to call an ambulance?' She said no, that she'd handle it; every time her voice reached an equilibrium she would begin to lose control again. I felt totally useless – I wanted so much to help, to stop the pain, but I knew I couldn't. She began to hyperventilate and as she did I took out the razor blade behind my bus pass and rolled up my sleeve.

'You're all right sweetheart.' Slash. 'You can get through this.' Slash. 'You're safe, honey.' Slash. I heard a door somewhere nearby creak open and quickly put the blade back under my bus pass on my lap and pulled my sleeve down. Joe appeared at my side; he bent down and kissed my head, and in a split second before I could react, he lifted up the bus pass, the blade falling off my knee onto the concrete with a clink, my hand diving to shield it just a second too late. I moved my palm over the speaker as he said, 'Come and find me when you get off the phone.'

Everyone had dispersed by the time I hung up from Prue; she had stayed on the phone to me until the ambulance I had insisted she call arrived to take her to A&E and stitch her wounds closed. I found Joe in the alcove and sat down with him – our bodies instantly entangled. I had swallowed the zopiclone and it was starting to take effect. I sat kissing him, his neck, his lips. The feel of him, the scars on his arms and chest, it was like music only I could hear. I was so tired, the drug was swirling in my brain, making everything feel odd and heavy. I couldn't keep my eyes open or my head up enough to kiss him. 'You need to go to sleep,' he said gently stroking my hair.

I shook my head. 'I'm fine.'

He laughed, 'Baby, you're losing a battle with my earlobe. It's definitely bedtime!' He stood up and helped me to my feet before wrapping his arms around me. As we broke away from our hug he kept a hold of my hand and tried to pull up my sleeve to look at what I'd done.

I resisted, pulling my arm away. 'I'll never be *that* tired, Joe.' He rolled his eyes, and I went up to bed.

48

GENTLEMEN, HIDE YOUR RABBITS

"Confession is not betrayal. What you say or do doesn't matter;
only feelings matter. If they could make me stop loving you –
that would be the real betrayal."

— GEORGE ORWELL, 1984

'Are you coming down?' Ellie was all too enthusiastically
spraying her sickly sweet body spray around the room. It made
me sneeze.

'No.'

'You'll get in trouble if you don't!'

'Just tell them I'm sick, El, I need to sleep.'

Leah jumped on my bed. 'C'mon, get up! I'll make you
breakfast.'

I scrunched up my face and sarcastically said, 'Oh, how well
you know me.'

She laughed and grabbed my hand, attempting to pull me
up. 'We'll send Judy to get you if you don't come to firm!'

I lay back down and closed my eyes. 'I fucking dare you!'

I rolled over in the bed and let unconsciousness wrap its comforting hands around me.

A few hours later I walked down the staircase to the alcove, make-up on, hair washed. As I pushed open the doors I took a seat next to Marie, Susie and Brooke. Aaron and Leah sat at one of the dining tables and, as I waved hello, Leah darted her eyes away so fast it made her blush. Something was off; she'd been playful and happy just a couple of hours earlier.

'How is everyone?' I asked, my voice curling up at the edges.

'Yep, fine thank you.' Marie shot me a strange look as she answered. I sat there for a few moments trying to work out what could have happened. Had someone tried to kill themselves? No, they'd be sadder; this felt more... hostile. The door to the kitchen creaked open, Joe stood there and quietly gestured for me to come to him. I got up and followed him out of the room.

'What's up with everyone?' He put his coffee mug down on the table and, ignoring my question, responded, 'Do you want to get out of here?'

I glanced up at the clock, it was ten thirty. 'Okay, I have to be back at three for Nora but I'd only miss dance which I'm not going to anyway.' I grabbed an apple out of the fridge, hesitated and then put it back. Even Joe seemed off, jittery, wound up.

'Cool, I'll meet you at the bus stop in ten, okay?' he said walking off to get his coat.

I called after him, 'Joe what's going on?'

He shook his head slightly too vehemently. 'Nothing, baby girl, I just want to go out.'

*

We walked along the Southbank hand in hand under London's grey, petulant sky, stopping to sit on a bench outside the Tate. I playfully poked him, 'So, what's wrong?' He lit a cigarette.

'It's going to piss you off massively. That's why I wanted to get away, so you wouldn't be around all of them when I told you.'

I felt my heart pace quicken, what was this? 'Is this about us?'

He nodded. Panic. 'What? You're regretting it? You want it to stop?' The 'it' being the relationship that I was too frightened to give a name to. He took my hands in his and turned to face me.

'No! No. Nothing like that. My feelings are still the same, in fact I think I feel even more crazy about you. But we, well, you, were brought up in firm today.'

'Okay, what was said?' He glanced over my shoulder at the river then back at me. 'They said I should be careful of getting involved with you. They said you latched onto Dan, and Katie, that this is something you "do".'

I felt my eyes growing larger. 'Are you joking?'

'No baby. It was Marie mainly, but Adaline too, and Judy. They said I should stop spending time with you alone, and that if you approached me to go out I should get one of them to come.'

The anger inside me was overwhelming. I stammered and stumbled over my words. How could they? 'This is what I "*do*"? Are they fucking kidding? Dan had feelings for me, it was mutual.'

'I know, I told them that.'

'And Katie? Latched on to Katie? We were friends! And it was mainly her asking me to go out anyway!' I felt like screaming, how could I make him understand that I was in fact *not* Glenn Close in *Fatal Attraction*; small furry creatures were not in danger of meeting a watery end at my hands. I stood up, facing him. 'Joe, I don't know what the fuck their problems are, well no actually I do, Adaline is a narcissistic miserable conniving headcase and Marie, Marie is just a headcase!' My voice was a little too loud for the tourists who swarmed around us en route to see what London's modern art had in store for them. Joe grabbed my hand and pulled me down onto his lap like a toddler that needed pacifying.

'Em, I know. I know they're wrong. It may have only been a few months but I know you, maybe I don't know everything but I certainly know more than that lot.'

I rested my head in my hands. 'It's just so frustrating. So unfair.'

'If it helps I stood up for you. I told them it was me who follows you everywhere, who asks you out all the time.'

I looked up. 'Thanks.' I paused. 'But what does this mean, for us?'

He sighed. 'It means we have to be a bit more careful, that's all. My feelings for you are very real and none of those lot are going to ruin this for us. I'm already pretty clear in my mind I've found someone I could be happy with long term.'

*

Spending the day with Prue was easy and familiar. She was slowly coming to terms with her grandfather's death, but her pain was coming out in other ways. She had spent most of the day obsessing about her weight, which had only added to my own neurosis. I was feeling huge. Something about all the positive attention from Joe was feeding the demons inside my head, making them restless, angry. And then there were his hands, constantly wandering my body, pawing at my fat. It was so strange to spend time with Prue feeling that I had to censor myself and not tell her honestly about my feelings for him. I swerved topics that would give me away, I was cautious and dishonest and desperate for her not to find out the depths of my helplessness. She was my friend – not being able to share my relationship with her was excruciating. I wanted her advice, her input... but I couldn't stand the idea that I had somehow betrayed her with my feelings for him and more than that, I couldn't bear her turning her back on me.

*

Lying in my bed listening to Leah and Ellie chatter to each other my thoughts flew me far away. I should have been happy. I was at my lowest weight; I had a man in my life who was making me feel like I was awake for the first time in years; I was seeing a therapist twice a week who could see into my soul and was slowly but surely helping to fix me. But I was scared. Of everything. Of him. Of myself and my flailing, hopeless feelings. I wanted to run so badly from him and yet I found myself constantly running into his arms. The fat. The fat I could focus on. Tangible. Real. I could see it. On my thighs, my arms, my stomach. The fat I could believe in. The fat I could do something about. I would binge in secret and then berate myself for my 'piggery', which in reality consisted of a couple of crackers and fruit. I felt like all I was doing was consuming. Consuming without thought, consuming without consciousness... Everything was so distorted, confused. I loathed myself for the thoughts, all of them.

Joe had said the day before that he wanted to take me out to dinner and a film at the weekend. That's what normal couples do, isn't it? Go out to dinner and the cinema. But then why did I feel like a horse refusing to wade into the water? Stomping my hooves at the bank. I didn't want to go but I was worried if I told him that, it would just be one more thing. One more negative attribute. One more ugly scar. One more reason for him to snap out of it and see me for the car crash that I felt I was. It was a deeply strange feeling, to want someone to be vile to you, for them to turn around and say, '*Yes*, actually, you *are* disgusting. You are hideous. *You make me sick*,' and then equally want them to promise they will never, ever turn away from you. My phone beeping to say I had a text broke my train of thought. It was him. 'I miss you x.'

*

'You're getting nervous. You know your treatment here will be coming to an end soon.' I exhaled loudly as Nora continued. 'You are very aware that many people here do not agree with your relationship with Joe and I think a part of you worries they're right, and that your therapy is being jeopardised.'

I sat back. 'Is that what you think?'

She paused and seemed to really contemplate my question. 'Why does it matter what I think?'

'Because it does, you know it does, Nora. We've come too far over the last nine months for this back and forth bullshit.'

She smiled knowingly at me. 'I think that this relationship has been very developmentally important for you. I think it is a good thing.' I never expected such a straight answer. I eyed her suspiciously and she laughed. 'You asked, Emma! I'm giving you my answer.'

I came out of my session feeling confused, and wanting to get away. The high I had felt when I had received what I deemed to be Nora's approval dissipated fast, and I wanted to cut. But low and behold, my knight in shining armour was waiting. He tilted his head to the side. 'What's wrong?'

'Nothing, just a long session.' Joe took my hand and led me out into the garden, past the playground where the family unit children screeched happily as they chased each other. Bonnie waved from the slide, skipping and pirouetting as she jumped off, Liam glaring at me from beside her.

'Where are you two off to then?' shouted Laura smirking at us from the swings as she cradled Sam in her arms.

'Going for a chat!' I called back.

She giggled, 'Sure you are!' I stuck my middle finger up at her which made her laugh even more.

We walked to the back of the garden to our usual spot and I sat down on the grass next to Joe. We talked for a long time, and then he took a piece of paper out of his pocket and unfolded it, handing it to me.

'What's this?' I said turning it over in my hands.

'My review summary, read it.'

The first thing to be brought up in it was his 'disordered eating'. They had used the word 'anorexia' several times, which surprised me a bit. Joe was thin, for sure, but he was toned. They were the experts, though, if they said he was anorexic I guess he was.

'There has been a significant lack of a secure male role model, leading to huge difficulties in childhood and early adulthood. This is prevalent in certain behaviours Joe exhibits such as his self-injurious behaviour, intense insecurities, disordered eating and chronic depressive symptoms.'

It felt strange and satisfying to read his review. Like I was getting to see into a part of him that no one else was. 'Do you agree with it?' I asked handing it back to him.

He folded the paper back up again and shrugged. 'Yeah, I wish I didn't but I can't really argue with it.'

I lay back on the grass. 'You don't really ever talk about your dad.'

Joe looked a little defensive. 'Well, why would I? He died when I was a kid. I didn't know him.'

'But, he didn't want to leave you… he didn't take his own life; he got ill. I'm sure given the choice he'd have stayed.'

He lay down next to me. 'I know. But I'm still angry with him. I still feel like he left when I needed him. That might sound stupid, I know it wasn't his choice, but maybe if he'd been around things would have turned out differently.' I held his hand and listened to him talk until eventually the sun began to set and dusk rolled in around us.

49

GONE BABY, GONE

"Nothing is more dangerous, than a man who thinks he's in charge. He will sabotage everyone and everything for the sake of his own ego."

— SASHA SCARR

Landon was finally out of hospital after months of being on section. He had texted me asking me to meet him. I left the hospital and made my way to the new flat he was now sharing with Andy, Cara's boyfriend.

I knocked on the door to be met with a bleary-eyed Andy.

'Dave!' (his rather annoying, yet endearing, pet name for me). The whoosh of skunk smell hit me as he moved aside to let me in. Cara was half dressed lying on the sofa.

'Em!' I walked over and kissed her on the cheek. We sat and chatted for a while. I hadn't seen them in a long time and it was nice to catch up. Landon appeared in the doorway smiling at me.

'Hey, Em.' I jumped up and gave him a hug.

'I've missed you!' I whispered into his ear before he let me go.

'I need your help with something,' he said as he took my hand walking me into his bedroom.

I sat on his bed, him at his desk. He began shuffling some paperwork around then handed it to me. As I took it I asked, 'What's this?' There was a nervous expression on his face.

'My CV... I just wanted you to check it before I start giving it out.'

I looked down at the pieces of paper. 'Yeah, of course... But Lan... you *just* got out of hospital. You've been in there for so long... don't you think you could use a break... take things slowly?'

He smiled that beautiful smile of his. 'Em, I stopped taking my meds before, that's why all this happened. I didn't take them for a long time and things just spiralled out of control. I'm okay now, better than okay, I'm great!'

I ran my fingers along the edge of the paper. 'I just don't want you to overdo it.'

He got up and came and sat next to me on the bed. 'Stop worrying about me, I'll be fine. You're the one still in hospital!'

He nudged me gently, pushing his shoulder against mine. 'Okay, fair enough.' I read his CV as he rolled a joint. 'It's good, Lan, the only thing is, I'd take out all the mental health stuff.'

He reached for a lighter. 'What do you mean?'

'You don't need to give them full disclosure unless they ask for it... and people can be wankers... They could judge you, and you don't deserve that, you're a wonderful person.' I pointed at the paper. 'Take this out here, about being in hospital and your diagnosis.'

He looked upset. 'But I want to be honest.'

I put my hand on his. 'And you can be! But get a gauge of the situation first, get a job, get to know your boss, and then you can be more open.' He was adamant he wanted to keep it all in, so I stopped trying to dissuade him. He was such an honest person, perhaps being true to himself was the best option?

I hugged Landon before I left and told him to message me if he felt 'wobbly' again. 'And babe, take your meds!'

He chuckled. 'I will!'

'To both?'

He kissed my cheek. 'To both, Em. I've missed you so much.'

I hugged him again. 'Same.'

*

I had been ordered into a management meeting with Finstard and Judy. They were concerned about my relationship with Joe; they felt it was affecting both our treatments. I had been waiting for this 'chat' ever since my funding extension had been approved a few weeks earlier; I was expecting it and had wondered why it had taken so long. I was convinced that if the funding was approved they would use the extra time to berate me for my feelings for Joe and use the added weeks to convince him that I was trouble, something that had already begun to happen in the firm meeting that I hadn't been present for.

The atmosphere in the room was frosty from the second I walked in. I sat opposite Finstard, noticing that Judy had rather markedly sat behind me out of view. *Ah, so Daddy was driving today was he?* Finstard's eyes were black, like a shark, and he seemed to take some joy in swimming around me for a moment before launching his attack. And what an attack it was.

'I honestly don't know why I *bothered* to give you the extension. Please tell me, Emma, what was the point? What exactly are you using this six weeks for? Your presence in the community is virtually non-existent.'

I felt like I needed to try and defend myself but I just couldn't find the words. I knew he didn't like me but I was still taken aback by the way he was speaking to me now, like I'd done something to personally and purposefully offend him. Every word was brimming with a slow, constructed, controlled aggression. My eyes flicked onto his desk behind him, where his oversized mug sat facing me, the word 'Boss' printed on it in large black lettering. I wondered for a second if it was placed there deliberately. I wanted to cry, I wanted to run out of there as fast as I could, but I didn't want to give him the satisfaction. So I sat and listened with a blank face and just let the feelings inside me snowball. Judy didn't say a word, just let him go on and on. There wasn't really a conclusive or constructive end to the meeting. I honestly felt like he only took me in there to belittle me, and I wasn't able to defend myself.

As Judy followed me out she said, 'It's your group time now. I suggest you go, Emma.' I didn't answer her, just walked up the three flights of stairs to the group room.

I sat opposite Brooke, in between Leah and Aaron. To my relief Harriet wasn't there; she was probably down at the family unit around a cauldron with Crystal and Kiera. As Johanna looked at me I could tell she knew something was wrong; her perception when it came to me often felt like both a blessing and a curse. I sat there feeling like I was in a compression chamber, like the air was slowly being sucked out of the room. I looked at Leah. She was wearing a vest top with her arms uncovered. Row after row of jagged cuts and red keloid scars. There were so many of them, from her wrist up to her shoulder on both arms. I couldn't not look. I felt enticed and triggered and furious all at the same time. How could she just sit there like that? With it all on display? Did she not feel embarrassed? Did she not feel ashamed? Did she not think it might be triggering for other people? I didn't understand why everyone else in the room could tolerate it and just not look – what was wrong with me? I couldn't concentrate on anything anyone was saying; I kept trying to listen but my eyes would just keep darting straight back to her arms. Before I knew it the words were rising up out of my throat.

'Leah, I'm sorry, but you're arms are triggering me really badly right now.' I didn't even mean to say it, it just fell out of my mouth. She looked at me, mortified. *Oh dear, what had I done? I was the CEO's drunk wife at the Christmas party unable to handle my alcohol – trying to look elegant while swaying with my crystal champagne flute in my hand.* I tried to make it better. 'I'm sorry, I'm really sorry, it's just making me want to self-harm.' *Oh no, stop Emma, just stop talking.* I started up again. 'I can't help it if it's triggering me, I can't, I'm sorry...' *Shut up, shut up! There goes the Swarovski glass slipping out of my hand smashing on to the varnished beechwood floor... Any second I'll be telling them all I think hubby's having an affair.* I cringed back in my seat as her cheeks went bright red and she stood up.

'I'm going to get a jacket.'

'No, Leah, I'm sorry.' Too late, off she went, slamming the door as she left. *I'm pretty sure he's fucking his secretary.*

Cue the tears, because what was left really?

'What's wrong, Emma?' Johanna looked at me.

'I'm just a fucking cunt aren't I?'

'Why?' she asked, seeming confused.

I felt my eyes narrow. 'Really? I didn't need to say that, I should have just shut up, I should have left or just tried harder not to look... I've upset her, I really didn't mean to... I wanted to stay in here and I couldn't if I'd just been staring at her arms the whole time.' I was basically wailing now. I could feel the mascara drying on my cheeks, staining my face.

Brooke cleared her throat, peeking out from behind her red baseball cap. 'I think it's okay that you said something. It was triggering... There's nothing wrong with what you said... You didn't do it in a horrible way.'

Aaron moved his black hair out of his eyes. 'Yeah, I think it's fair enough. It's better you tell her instead of walking out.'

I wiped the tears away. 'But *she* walked out.'

'Maybe that's okay, Emma?' said Johanna. 'You were honest and spoke up about your feelings. People *do* get triggered by other people, and sometimes it's okay to let them know if they've affected you. You weren't being critical, and we are all here to support Leah and talk to her when she comes back.'

Brooke spoke again, 'You didn't really seem okay when you came in, before Leah.' I looked at the floor. It was so hard to open up but I needed to talk to someone. I told them about the management meeting and how abrasive I'd found Dr Finstard.

'It felt personal, it felt like he was attacking me.'

'That was your experience, Emma and you're entitled to feel upset.'

Mr Newman had been fairly quiet so far through the session. I dabbed my face again with the tissue Johanna had passed me. 'But *bothered*, he doesn't know why *he bothered* to give me the extension... Would you have used that word?'

Mr Newman paused. 'No, I wouldn't have used that word.' Validation. Finally.

Speaking about the meeting definitely did help, and they were all so much more supportive than I had imagined they would be. But it still left me with a feeling of raw exposure that was completely overwhelming. I left the group room and scurried down the hallway to the nearest bathroom and plied my face with foundation and eyeliner. By the time I walked out no one would have ever known I'd been upset. I found Joe standing outside the hospital smoking with a few of the others, it took everything I had in me not to run into his arms and kiss him. One by one the other patients went back inside, until finally we were alone. I grabbed his hand, 'Can we get out of here?'

He smiled. 'Of course we can.'

We sat opposite the Thames in the sun, his arm around me, our fingers entwined. I told him about what Finstard had said, how bad it had made me feel. It was feeling easier and easier to talk to him, to feel vulnerable with him. He allowed me to speak without interrupting, he let the thoughts (as tangled and upsetting as they were) spill out of my mouth and didn't panic as they hit the floor. He was leaving for the weekend and I desperately didn't want him to go. He was going to stay with his sister and would only be gone for a day and a half, but it felt like too long. Joe was giving me a sense of self-worth, he was grounding me, and while I was standing in his sunlight I basked in it, content and fulfilled, but I could never hang onto it once he left. Whenever he went, so did my reason to not hurt myself. It never occurred to me how much my self-harming could and did affect him – as soon as he was out of sight I almost lost touch with reality. I genuinely thought he wouldn't find out if I cut; I made myself believe it would somehow not get back to him. Of course, it always would. It was the elephant in the room that we both knew was there.

I said goodbye to Joe at the train station, watching as he got on and headed to his sister's house. As I walked back towards the hospital feeling hollow and alone I saw Ellie walking towards me. She had her thigh-high boots on and a strange swagger in her walk.

'Oi oi,' she called out as we approached each other.

I deliberately looked her up and down. 'Mhmm. And where are *you* going?'

She smiled. 'Just for a walk.'

'You're lying, El.'

She reached out and touched my hair, began twirling it around her long fingers. 'Okay fine. I want to buy drink. I want to get off my face. I miss Jack.'

I sighed. 'I feel like crap too.'

She poked me affectionately. 'You're not going to end up in the bathroom are you?'

I looked down. 'I don't know. But I can't deal with you drinking tonight – I'll have to tell the staff.'

'Then I'll tell them you're going to cut!' She stuck her tongue out like a naughty three-year-old. We were at a stalemate. If I let her drink, I could cut. If I told the staff, so would she and they would stop us both.

'So what do we do then?' I heavily sat down on the bench that was next to us. She slumped next to me.

'I suppose we could watch a film. Have some popcorn or something? Do normal, boring shit?'

I nodded, defeated. We walked back to the Caddick, her arm linked through mine, and spent the night lying on the sofa next to each other watching crap TV and throwing popcorn into each other's mouths. Our evening was only interrupted by Ellie breaking away to call the general hospital to check on Jack and Joe calling me to tell me he missed me.

*

Saturday morning in the hospital and an emergency community meeting was called. Judy was chairing it, and mostly everyone was there. As I stared around the room I noticed there were a lot of staff, more than usual. I instantly felt worried; they must have called everyone in to make sure it was contained. So what, then, were they going to tell us? What news would warrant twenty-odd staff in the meeting? Judy adjusted herself in her chair, smoothed down her long dress and began.

'We have called you all in to this meeting today because there has been a serious safety concern raised. Crystal's daughter was taken to hospital two days ago.' I quickly looked at Harriet and Kiera. I had just assumed Crystal was sandwiched in between them, but she was nowhere to be seen. 'Crystal's daughter, Casey, ingested an illegal substance she found in Crystal's room and had to be taken to the emergency room. She's lucky to be alive. It's not the first time something like this has happened. Last month there was an issue with Casey being found chewing on electricals; again, she could have been terribly injured.'

Susie raised her hand and began to speak. 'Where was Crystal when this was happening? Casey's only two, she wasn't on her own surely?'

Claire took over from Judy. 'Crystal was drunk. On both occasions. She wasn't watching the baby.'

'Everyone makes mistakes!' shouted Kiera.

'Mistakes are one thing…' said Judy, 'a child dying in our care is quite another.'

'Crystal is a good mum,' quipped Harriet, 'she'd never hurt Casey on purpose!'

Claire nodded. 'But she did, Harriet, she hurt Casey by putting alcohol before her. Casey could have died.' Claire paused, looking slowly and purposefully around the room at everyone. 'Can we all stop to think, really, really think about what that would have been like, if a two-year-old child had died in our hospital?' There was a long silence in the room.

'So, what's going to happen?' asked Adaline, looking at the staff.

Judy inhaled slowly. 'We have decided that Casey is going to be removed from Crystal and placed in foster care.'

Kiera jumped to her feet. 'You can't do that!' she screamed pointing at them. 'What the fuck? You can't take away a little baby like that!'

Judy stared resolutely back at her, 'Yes, we can. The child is in danger.'

Kiera's face turned bright red. 'You're monsters!'

Harriet grabbed Kiera's arm trying to pull her back down in her seat; she shook Harriet off and carried on. 'Where is Crystal?' she demanded, eyes wide, her whole body shaking with rage.

'You need to calm down, Kiera,' said Judy.

'Don't you tell me to calm down, you fucking babysnatcher!'

Alison who had been silent so far throughout the meeting spoke. 'If you don't sit down, Kiera, we will have to remove you, and give you something to *ensure* you calm down.'

'You're evil! You're all evil!' Kiera ran out of the room with Harriet quickly following behind her.

'We know this is very difficult,' said Judy, looking genuinely upset. 'It's a last resort. And everyone reacting badly, screaming and shouting, will only make it more upsetting for Casey. Crystal is spending today under supervision with her, and Casey will be leaving this afternoon. Crystal will need the community's support going forward.'

The meeting came to an end, and people slowly meandered out of the room. I stood up, walking over to Susie who was sitting in an armchair staring at the floor. 'Are you coming, Susie?' I held out my hand; she took it and stood up.

'Yes, Em. It's just so sad. That poor little girl.'

*

I went power walking for three hours attempting to rid myself from the guilt of the popcorn the night before, then spent the afternoon visiting Jack in the premature baby ward with Ellie. He was so small, still only slightly bigger than my palm, but now he had grown eyelashes and nails. I stuck my little finger into his hand and he managed to clench it with all of his might. He was beautiful, even with his pink translucent skin. He'd survived so much already in his tiny life – I couldn't help but love him.

*

Ellie and I arrived back to the Caddick just as social services had arrived to take Casey. 'I can't watch this, it's too awful,' said Ellie, rushing up to our bedroom. I went into the kitchen and stood at the window. Two women, dressed informally, both with name badges on, stood in the car park next to a blue volvo; one of the back doors was open to reveal an empty baby seat inside it. Judy, Claire and a few other nurses came out of the front door, Crystal following, Casey in her arms. Trailing behind them were Harriet, Kiera and a couple of the other parents from the family unit. I felt deeply uncomfortable watching this, like I was viewing something incredibly private, something that I had no right to be seeing, but I couldn't peel my eyes away. Claire said something to Crystal who was crying as she clung onto the baby. The social services women spoke one by one, slowly moving in closer. Crystal shook her head and started to shout at them, a look of panic spreading across Casey's chubby face. Judy put her hand on Crystal's back, seeming like she was trying to comfort her, but Crystal was hysterical now, sobbing and gasping for air. She fell to her knees in the gravel clutching the baby close to her chest. The two women approached quickly at his point, one of them attempting to pry Casey away from her. Crystal tried to fight it, but her efforts were futile, she was outnumbered, and in a matter of seconds Casey was in the social worker's arms being carried towards the car, her little face crumpled, screaming and reaching out for her mum. They strapped her into the baby seat, said something to Judy who nodded, and got in the car. As they drove out of the gates Crystal let out a scream, a noise so thick with pain that it pierced my ears, even through the glass.

50

THE FINAL REVIEW

"I look at the world and I see absurdity all around me. People do strange things constantly, to the point that, for the most part, we manage not to see it."

— DAVID LYNCH

As my discharge date loomed I began to feel increasingly mixed about what it was that I actually needed. I wanted to leave the structures, the regime, being forced to feel and to talk – but I was going to miss my sessions with Nora, and also Mr Newman and Johanna. I'd miss Susie and Ellie and Leah… and then of course there was Joe. Someone had turned on the taps to my feelings and they were gushing. I felt unsettled and anxious and I hated it; I didn't know how to contain it or make it stop. Cutting felt like the most logical answer. I had new unopened blades hidden in my room and the means to clean up and dress my own arm without anyone knowing a thing, yet I felt a disturbing pang of responsibility. I was leaving in a month, shouldn't I be fixed? Why was I still running back to self-harm at every available opportunity? When was I going to put my foot down and finally snap out of this? Did I really, truly believe that putting a razor blade to my arm was going to help me? *Why couldn't I just go and talk to someone? Just ask for fucking help.*

I lay on my back looking up at the moody navy-blue sky with its crescent moon and stars shining through the trees, their leaves rustling in the breeze. I held Joe's hand and didn't say a word. If I had opened my mouth the three words I had been holding back would have tumbled out. *I love you. I think I love you. I think I fucking love you.* Instead, I bit my tongue and despite the hissing somewhere in the back of my ears that I was *disgusting and fat...* it was peaceful.

'Joe...?'

'Yes baby?'

I could, if I wanted to. I could make the ultimate leap into vulnerability. But what if this was all in my head? What if it all fell apart in a month? What if he didn't feel the same?

I closed my eyes, 'It's beautiful here.'

'It really is.'

*

'Everyone freaks out before they leave!' Jess handed me the joint. 'Seriously Em! It's completely normal. I think the therapists expect you to lose your shit a bit.'

'But I'm not losing my shit.' I took a drag then handed the joint back. 'I'm just not better. I'm supposed to be fixed! I'm not supposed to be still self-harming, or doing any of the food stuff.' I couldn't bring myself to use the words 'eating disorder' or 'bulimia'. Jess's cat came and sat down next to me.

'It's not a broken leg – it can't be fixed just like that.' I stroked Sidney as he purred softly. I knew she was right, I knew there was no quick fix for this – but I didn't understand what I was supposed to do next? Leave, get a job? Move out? Wait for Joe to be discharged? Live happily ever after? Getting through each hour was still a very real struggle for me; how on earth was I going to manage back out there in the real world? What would I do when my mother said that I needed to get a job? Would I go out and get one? Or would I just take a massive overdose and end up back in a hospital because the thought of it was just too overwhelming? I didn't feel ready to leave. I didn't feel able to cope. I didn't know what I was going to do and I didn't know how to tell anyone.

*

'How long has this been going on, Brooke?' I sat in firm picking pink nail varnish off my jeans. The room was an uncomfortable sort of quiet. Judy readjusted her position and continued. 'Brooke, you're going to have to speak to us. We are here to help. When did you start eating dog food?' Brooke picked at her face and from under her cap came the soft sound of her voice.

'I… I do it when I need to be punished.'

'So it's like self-harming?' asked Wendy from the other side of the room.

Brooke cleared her throat. 'Kind of. I just need to be punished.'

'Brooke can you stop doing that please?' Judy pointed to her face, which was now bleeding.

'Why do you feel like you need to be punished?' asked Aaron.

'Because I'm evil. So I make myself eat it. Because it's disgusting, but I deserve it.'

'You don't deserve it, Brooke,' said Grace who was sitting next to Judy. I felt like I was walking along the edge of a double-edged sword… On the one hand I was finding this funny – yes I know the reasons behind her eating the dog food were not in the slightest bit funny, but I was getting bombarded with images of Pedigree Chum and my ridiculous inquisitive nature was assaulting me with suggestions... Would you use a spoon? Or actually just eat it like a dog? With tripe or without? On the other edge of the sword was the very distressing reality of this girl feeling so bad that she forced herself to eat what was ultimately shit to punish herself for some heinous childhood horror show that got inflicted upon her.

'If you feel like you are going to eat dog food, or do anything self-damaging you need to make the effort to ask for help Brooke, alright?' Judy pressed her lips together waiting for a response. Brooke nodded slowly. 'That's not a "yes" Brooke!' Judy was obviously getting irritated with the lack of eye contact. Brooke looked up, a forlorn expression on her face, 'Okay, yes. I'll ask for help.' She put her head down again and went back to picking at her skin. I actually liked Brooke a lot, but I found her distress too uncontrollable most of the time – I would try to help but she would disassociate so badly that there was no getting through to her and it was frustrating. I was also envious of the help that rushed around her when she self-harmed – the staff, the other patients, everyone was so sympathetic and caring whereas in contrast I felt like a lot of the time I got a telling off – like they thought I could help it and stop if I wanted to, but she couldn't. Brooke was a big neon flashing sign that read 'HELP ME' and people flocked to it... Whilst I stood invisible in the background whispering that I was falling apart.

'I would like to welcome Lyle at this point,' said Judy. Lyle tried to smile, but instead just opted to raise his hand in a semi-wave. 'Lyle, would you like to introduce yourself to everyone?' Of course it wasn't a question. I never knew why Judy bothered with that upward inflection. He took one of those long, drawn-out breaths that I hadn't heard for so many months and slowly began to speak.

'Hello. I'm Lyle. I was at the Henshaw before but, I... left there.' Susie and I exchanged knowing looks but said nothing. It was so good to see him – I certainly wasn't going to tell any of them what had happened to force him out of the Henshaw. I wondered if the Caddick had waited to admit Lyle until Esther had left to avoid any of the same old patterns repeating themselves; surely they would have been told what had happened? 'Since leaving the Henshaw my drinking and eating has got out of hand,' he continued, 'and with it my depression. I want to work on getting better, becoming in control of myself and my problems, I want to get it right this time.' Bless him.

I gave Lyle a big hug after firm and told him how glad I was to see him despite the fact that as he was coming, I was going. He had gained some more weight since I'd last seen him, but even more noticeably had two thick long scars down the entire side of his left cheek. I'm sure he'd have told me if I'd asked but I chose not to, some questions are best left unanswered.

*

Later that day I had my final review. Something which I had been dreading. I felt a lot of the staff were in disagreement with how I had spent the last couple of months of my treatment – namely preoccupied with Joe. It didn't go badly, but when, a couple of days later, Len informed me that I had a letter waiting at reception from Dr Finstard I felt the dread swell inside like me a tidal wave. I knew it would be a write-up of the review and I was less than enthused to hear his summary of the whole thing.

Dear Emma,

I am writing to you following your final review.
    You brought a very thoughtful contribution to the review, in which you spoke about your difficulties and your development in treatment. You described some of the ways in which you

feel you have begun to change. As a concrete sign, your self-harm has decreased a lot. But you also spoke of more internal changes, like the sense recently of reconnecting to your feelings from which you had been shut off so massively. You felt that you have been able to be more open in your therapy and are gaining from it. You conveyed that you have built important and trusting relationships and are more in touch with the need for others, which also makes you more vulnerable. You thought you could have benefited from more time, particularly in relation to your difficulties in moving out from home.

I think a change in you was very noticeable in your own contribution and in the way you took part in the review. Whereas you had been quite distant and cut off, appearing somewhat superior, in the first review, you were now more engaged with us, emotionally alive and thoughtful. There has also been a clear change recently in the way you have engaged in the community, reflected for example in you taking on the role of firm chair.

In looking back at your treatment since the first review, you had seemed rather stuck for quite a while. Your individual therapist felt that you had used the therapy for some time more as a retreat than as a help for change and your group therapist described the kind of 'nothing can get to me' posture you adopted. You yourself expressed a regret that you had not made more of your time here. However, it was clear that you have done work in your therapy and that your hard shell has gradually softened. You have become more able to access your own thoughts, feelings and fantasies, some of them very painful and disturbing ones,

475

and to be more open about them. Experiencing these feelings and being more in touch with your own emotional needs has made you feel much more vulnerable.

It was noted how, when you have opened up, you can then close down again. You seemed aware of that yourself when you voiced your concern that you might shut yourself off again when discharged from the Caddick, in the same way that you did after leaving the Henshaw.

You have started to work, particularly in your individual therapy, on some of the disturbing experiences of feeling invaded and intruded upon. You have also begun to think more about moving out from your parental home, but you have also realised that this is more than a practical task and involves facing major emotional conflicts and anxieties.

It is clear from all of that how much work there is to do for you in therapy in the future, while you are still at the Caddick, as well as afterwards in outreach. You were concerned about the group therapy in outreach, partly because you have experienced a very unstable and often changing young persons group, but maybe also because you often treated the group very dismissively. You will have more of an experience of stability in the outreach group and that will give you the space to do the necessary work and I hope you will use it better that you have often used the group here.

Some of the practical tasks before discharge involve reducing your medication, considering work or training opportunities and potentially arranging something and working towards your own accommodation, even though this may only become a reality some time in the future.

```
Best wishes,
Yours sincerely,
DR ERIK FINSTARD
Consultant Psychiatrist in Psychotherapy
Caddick ESPD service for adults & young people
```

I sat back against the headboard of my bed. 'I hope you will use it better that you have often used the group here.' Ugh, fuck off. The write-up could have been much, much worse, but I did feel like it was Finstard's last-ditch attempt to dig his elbow in and just remind me that I had not lived up to (his) expectations.

*

'We will look forward to seeing you once you've left the Caddick, Emma.' Charles Rogers shook my hand. His deep, slow American voice had been putting me to sleep for the last hour. He was the psychiatrist who ran the outpatient psychotherapy group I would be transitioning into once I left the Caddick. I left his office and snapped back awake as I walked down the hallway towards the lift. I stood aside as a group of ten or so inpatients headed past me on their way to what I assumed was some sort of music therapy, banging tambourines loudly and singing. 'Stranger danger!' shouted a short woman with an eye patch on as she walked behind me, holding the hand of what I assumed was a nurse. 'Dirty stupid dyke!' she yelled again, hitting herself hard on the side of her face and pointing at me as I pressed myself against the wall to let them past. 'Come on Nina, that's not how we speak to people, is it?' the nurse smiled graciously at me as she pulled the woman along the corridor. 'Your hair is bloody amazing!' said an incredibly flamboyant man with a thick Indian accent following behind the rest of the troop, as he floated past me in an oversized fur coat, pink Stetson and sunglasses.

I smiled, 'Thank you.'

'No! Thank you, darling! Thank you!' Compliments aside, these people were nuts. Really nuts. Batshit fucking crazy. And I was going to be spending two days a week here, being buzzed in and out of my therapy. At least Prue was in my group – something which, unlike me, Nora had not been pleased with. She had petitioned to be allowed to carry on with me in one-to-one sessions as part of my outreach programme, but because I was now twenty-four I was deemed 'too old' to spend the NHS's money on individual therapy – and she was told that she was not allowed to be my therapist once I left. I was incredibly upset, but what could I do? She'd tried, they'd said no, so Charles Rogers and the crazies it was.

I only had a week left with Nora and I was terrified. I felt like we were really starting to get somewhere. I was allowing us to talk more fluidly about my issues with intimacy – Joe obviously being the springboard for this: the forbidden affair. But regardless of what they said, the whispers or the sniggers, I had officially stopped caring – I had seven days left, they all knew we were together and I might as well talk about it in therapy while I could.

In my last session with Nora, I had never seen the woman work so hard to try and help me, and I had never been so open. We were Thelma and Louise, hands clasped, minutes to go before our Ford Thunderbird flew off that cliff – these were to be our final words, the last bit of wisdom she could impart.

Nora had never held back with me; she had many times called me out and wasn't afraid to tell me when she thought I wasn't pushing myself to my full potential within our therapy, and just because it was our last session it didn't mean she wasn't going to keep dropping her psychological truth bombs on me.

'I feel like there was a stalemate in our work for some time, Emma, but I believe it was down to that voice inside you, which severely undermines and tries to inhibit your development. Sometimes I've felt as though you want to be so close to me that you want to be within the same skin, but then just as quickly you feel like you have to distance yourself and be as far away as possible, from me or the entire hospital.'

I let her words settle for a moment before answering. 'That sounds like a fair observation... I have wanted to have an honest relationship with you, but sometimes it felt too much, too exposing.' She nodded her head in agreement looking like she wanted me to say more. I went on, 'I get that with a lot of people, though, in a lot of situations... I want to be close and open, but then all of a sudden it just feels like too much and I want to run away.'

'You get stuck!' she said with wide eyes like it was something that should have been patently obvious to me. 'You feel vulnerable! Riddled with anxiety about me ejecting you in a highly humiliating way, because I believe you fear that I can't stand you or even begin to manage and understand your distress and *that's* what keeps you stuck! And what you need to keep working on. You seem to have this fantasy of me penetrating intrusively into your body...' *Oh God, we're back to the big penis comment,* I thought as I continued to listen. 'You feel like I am going to overtake you. But these are fantasies, paranoid delusions that you have to challenge.'

I nodded. 'I know...' I let my voice trail off before going on. 'So do you feel like I've made no progress here, that I've just wasted my time?' I had to ask, I didn't want to, but I needed to know the answer. Finstard had made me feel like this was the general consensus amongst the rest of the staff and I wanted to know if Nora felt the same.

'The question is, do *you* feel you've made progress?'

'Nora! Please!' I rolled my eyes and threw my hands onto my lap in a mock fashion which made her laugh out loud.

'I think you have engaged with me, and in your treatment, and yes, Emma,' she paused, 'I do think there have been significant shifts. You've gone from a place where you couldn't even fathom asking for help or letting anyone see even a trace of vulnerability in you, to letting people in, and that's what you need to keep doing; no matter how frightening or painful it might seem at times, it's the only way you'll be able to progress.'

Before I left the room I handed her a present. It was a canvas print I had found and for some reason felt like the perfect leaving gift for her. It was the image of a rotund man looking out over the sea as he stood in the pouring rain with his equally rotund dog sitting next to him. The man was holding an umbrella over himself and another umbrella over his dog as they both stared out into the distance. It was called 'She Who Must Be Kept Dry'. I tried not to cry as she smiled at the image.

'I really love it, Emma, thank you.'

'It's okay.'

We stood up. 'Keep in touch, write to me?' I nodded through my tears, fighting the urge to throw my arms around her. Instead we shook hands (oh those boundaries) and I rushed out and cried for hours on my bed about losing undoubtedly the best therapist I would ever have.

51

SAYING GOODBYE

"Nothing behind me, everything ahead of me,
as is ever so on the road."

— *JACK KEROUAC, On The Road*

People rallied around me during those last few days. I was told by staff and patients that they would miss me. I did my rounds saying goodbye to all the children – Bonnie cried hysterically, Liam ignored me and baby Sam pulled on my hair. I had 'goodbye teas' where everyone ate cakes and gave me cards wishing me good luck.

I told Laura to keep strong, that she was creating a new life and she had to keep going. Those pretty eyes of hers filled to the brim and ran over her cheeks. 'I'll miss you so much... You've been so kind to me.'

I leaned over and hugged her. 'But you don't deserve any less, Laura, not when you're working so hard to right the wrongs of the past.'

'Will you come and visit us, when we get out of here and go back to the coast?'

'Of course I will!'

I sat with Brooke and told her to keep fighting her demons and that in a couple of months I'd see her in the outreach group (she was on the cusp of twenty-four too, so would also be cast out of individual therapy when she was discharged). I gave Grace a hug, high-fived Aaron and told Leah to keep going, that amazing things were on the horizon for her and that her young life was just beginning.

'Well, this is our second goodbye, Em...' said Susie as she held my hand, '... and I'm going to miss you.'

I felt a lump rise in my throat. 'I'll miss you too, we've been through an awful lot together these last two years.'

She wiped a tear from her cheek and nodded, 'We really have.'

Adaline wandered over and handed me a card. 'I know we haven't always seen eye to eye, but I really do wish you luck out there.' Sure you do. I wasn't going to miss Adaline in the slightest, but I did appreciate that she had made the effort to give me a card – she certainly didn't have to – so I hugged her and wished her all the best.

Lyle held out his hand for me to shake. I took it but moved in and wrapped my arms around him. 'It's better here, Lyle. The groups, the therapists – it will help.'

He nodded solemnly. 'Yes, I hope so. I hope everything goes well out there for you, and don't be a stranger.' He smiled at me – something he rarely did and a big gesture in itself.

I had made my way around all the patients but saved Ellie for last. She squeezed the life out of me and cried on my shoulder as she mumbled through her sniffles, 'You won't forget about me will you? Or Jack? You'll still keep in touch?' Saying goodbye to her was probably the hardest for me; Ellie was technically a woman – she had a baby, she was beginning a new life – and yet when I looked at her I saw a little girl who still needed so much help. It was hard to think about leaving her. And added to that, there was also a very real part of me, a polarising part (perhaps the jealous little girl part, Nora?) who felt annoyed that Adaline and Ellie were getting to stay. They had both been given well over a year's worth of funding and I felt put out that I couldn't have more time – but then would I have used it to its full advantage? Would I have wasted the extra months just as Finstard already thought I had? Or would it merely have been an excuse to spend more time with Joe? And if it had, would that have necessarily been a bad thing?

*

The staff, one by one, took me aside and talked to me about their experience of me and my time at the Caddick.

'We've had a right old laugh, haven't we Judy?' She made her disproving librarian 'Mhmm' noise as I grinned at her. 'Just admit it, you'll miss me.'

She paused. 'I shall miss you actually, Emma, despite what you might think.' Of course Judy's summary of my time there was laced with 'you could have done more' innuendos, but I knew that, and more to the point *she knew* I knew that. I hugged Mena, Kirk, Claire, Max, Brian and said goodbye to Alison. I even managed to thank Derron for (trying) to put up with me. I skimmed through the staff goodbyes like they were white noise, never once admitting my fears about the future. Though, as I sat in the alcove with Johanna, my pretence began to fall away and I told her I was worried. She spoke a lot about Joe and me.

'I just really don't want you to get hurt, Emma. I know how much you care about him; it's very obvious. I just don't want it to end in disaster.'

'Johanna I've never felt like this before... I trust him. I think we're going to be together for a long time.'

She looked as though she was holding back massively but instead laid her hand on my arm. 'And I'm pleased for you, both of you, but I want you to be careful… That's all I'm saying, okay?'

I nodded and she gave me a hug, holding me tight. When we let go she said, 'I'll really miss you. It won't be the same here without you and Prue, especially after everything we went through together that night at the hospital. You can call me to chat whenever you want or need to.' Tears welled in her eyes as she embraced me again. I watched her walk away with a small ache growing in my heart. This wasn't fair, why did I have to leave her? Or Nora? Or Ellie? Or any of them? I wasn't ready. But no amount of kicking or screaming or promises of working harder could help me now; that was it, funding gone, time up.

*

It was a tradition that Dr Finstard had a meeting with every patient to say goodbye, I had watched it happen with everyone who had left prior to me: Kane, Prue, Katie, Angela, Dan. And I waited quietly to be summoned to his office – I was going to use it as an opportunity to thank him, sincerely, for giving me the chance to be there and to apologise for not using my time as perhaps he would have wanted me to. I needed to address the fact that maybe we just didn't 'get' each other, maybe neither of us were the 'baddie'? Perhaps it was just a clash of personalities where no one was to blame? Maybe he was just the Narcan to my heroin? I constructed what I was going to say over a few days and waited for my presence to be requested, but it didn't happen. He never met with me. The first patient in history not to get a goodbye. I took it as a sign that I had been right all along, that he was glad to see the back of me and, more than that, he must have really disliked me to not even bring himself to say goodbye.

I was lying on my bed thinking about Dr Finstard, ruminating over all the mistakes I had made inside my interactions with him – whether I would do it all differently a second time around, whether I could have tried harder to let him in – when my phone beeped. I looked down at it.

'A little birdie tells me you'll be getting out soon.'

It was Landon. 'Yeah, just a couple days now!' I typed back.

'How are you feeling about it?' Landon was one of the few people I didn't have to lie to.

'Really worried. I'm trying to be positive, but I don't know how well I'll cope, and if I'll just plummet again.'

'I'll be here, you won't be alone.' I smiled and put my phone down only for him to beep through again a few moments later. 'You're beautiful, Emma. And you have every right to be here, just as much as the trees, stars and whole universe.'

*

The TV room was dark, the glow of the muted television creating a candlelit effect throughout. My arms were around Joe's neck as I straddled him, kissing like we would never kiss again. Touching each other with a desperate ferocity. I heard a floorboard creak outside the door and leapt off him and onto a nearby armchair. It was Petrice. 'I thought I'd find you two in here!' she said, almost wanting to sound disapproving but not quite managing it. She looked at me, and sighed softly, gently clasping her hands in front of her, 'Emma, it's your last night, you need to get some rest.'

I held out my hand for her to take, 'Are you going to miss me, Petrice?' She reached out and took it, leaning down next to me in the armchair, putting her arm around me. 'I am going to miss you so much, my sweetie! Who will I chat to at night now?'

'What about me!' I gasped. 'Who will give me advice? And cheer me up in the early hours of the morning?'

I hugged her back and felt a pang of loss as she stood up again. 'But it's late, and you need to go to bed, okay?'

Joe batted his eyelashes at her. 'One more smoke first?'

She turned back to the door rolling her eyes. 'One. And then bed.'

'Goodnight, Petrice,' I called out as she began to disappear through the wooden frame; she looked back at me, her warm smile lighting up her face.

'Good night, sweetheart. And good luck.'

*

Joe dragged hard on his cigarette as he put his hand on my thigh; letting out a long plume of smoke he said, 'I'll come and visit you… as much as I can! And you can visit me! We'll see each other just as much, if not more.'

'And what about your therapy, Joe?'

'Therapy will be fine. This place ticks over, no one will notice me not being here.'

I half laughed, 'Oh and of course you'll have the blue-eyed girl to play with. I'm sure you'll be just fine!' Those sapphire eyes of Madison's were still loitering in the forefront of my mind.

'Oh stop it, she's got nothing on you.' I moved into him and rested my head on the crook of his neck.

'I just wish we could have met somewhere else, when things were more settled for both of us.'

He kissed my forehead. 'I would have liked you wherever we had met, Em. Here, out there. It's you I care about, not where I met you.' He held my body close against his and God it felt so good, so safe, so contained.

*

Lying in my bed for the last time that night was a sobering experience. I ached. I ached because as much as I was saying 'It'll be fine, I'll come and see you all, I'll call Johanna and chat, I'll go on dates with Joe, I'll write to Nora, nothing will change!' I knew everything was about to change. As much as I wanted to deny it, there was something very holding about a place like the Caddick, even if you do have those you don't get on with. Yes, you have to step over or bypass the people who are challenging you on a daily basis, you have mirrors constantly held up to your behaviour (both bad and good), and you have to repeatedly take accountability and foist it on others. You have the gossip, the bitchiness, the sadness and of course the awful, raw distress of so many people living under the same roof all in varying degrees of severe emotional pain, and it does spread; it spreads like a wild fire. It gets into you and overwhelms you from time to time; it triggers you and infects you and causes you to question everything you ever knew. But then there are the good parts, the wonderful parts, like, no matter how alone you feel, you're never actually alone, or knowing that regardless of how badly you lose your shit, or cut yourself, or freak out, there will be people there to comfort you, bandage your arms and tell you that tomorrow will be better. There was no need to hide the pain in there – if you were having a terrible day, you could unapologetically have one and no one would tell you to 'snap out of it' or 'cheer up' or look on the fucking 'bright side'. And finally, above all else, there was him. At the end of every day his body around me was like a glimpse into heaven, pure, unadulterated solace. How was I going to survive out there without being wrapped up in his arms every night? Could I? Did I even want to?

*

'Diet Coke?' The waitress smiled as she put the glass down in front of me. I waited for her to walk away and then turned back to Joe. 'So what happens then, after today? That's it, I'll be gone.' I was sitting in a café with him overlooking the river. We'd spent the afternoon walking hand in hand wandering through London.

He cleared his throat, 'Nothing happens. We go on like this, as we are.' I wasn't convinced.

'But how will we see each other?' When I said it, I hoped the true meaning of my words wouldn't show on my face (*But how will I see if you're carrying on with Madison?*).

'Emma,' he said taking a deep breath, 'I'm in love with you. It's only been five months, but I know it. I know I want to be with you, only you.'

BANG! He'd said it. He loves me! Love! Love! Love! My heart pounded in my chest. So this was it, was it? My climactic moment? What the last couple of years, the last two decades, had all been leading up to? Finally I had arrived where I needed to be, where I was always destined. All the bullshit, the self-abuse, the self-hatred and suffering had been worth it; the pain, the misery, the feelings I never thought would end, they were all working to lead me here, to him. He looked embarrassed for a second then continued, 'I know I shouldn't say it! I know that. But I don't care! I love you, I'm in love with you.'

I wrapped my arms around him. 'I love you too.' He smiled as he pulled me towards him and kissed my lips. I moved away after a few seconds. 'And nothing will change?' Those eyes, green dilated pools – I could swim in them for days.

'Baby girl, you have me. I'm yours.' He paused, clutched my hands in his then carried on. 'I love you more than I ever thought I could, more than I thought possible. I've never felt this way before. Nothing will change, Emma, I promise.'